AF809175

NECTARY BIOLOGY
Structure, Function and Utilization

NECTARY BIOLOGY
Structure, Function and Utilization

Editor
BIR BAHADUR
C. Biol., F.I. Biol. (London)

DATTSONS
J.L. NEHRU MARG, SADAR, NAGPUR, INDIA

First Published : 1998

© Publisher

ISBN : 81-7192-030-6

Published by :
Vinod Kumar
DATTSONS
J.L. Nehru Marg
Sadar, Nagpur, India.

Laser Composed by :
ENEN GRAFIKS
CB-178/1, Ring Road,
Naraina, New Delhi.

Printed By: Chetna Printers, Maujpur, Delhi-110053

This Volume is respectfully dedicated to

Prof. B.M. Johri
and
Prof. V. Puri

for their outstanding contributions to Botany and for continued inspiration and encouragement to the author.

PREFACE

This book is primarily meant to provide an integrated, unifying and utilitarian perspective of the basic and applied aspects of plant nectaries. Their diversity, application in systematics and phylogency is indispensible and has wide ramifications in various related applied sciences making nectaries, nectar and honey as the most researched objects. Therefore, the book is essentially multi-disciplinary in approach and meant for students and researchers in Botany, Ecology, Plant Physiology and Entomology. It is also relevant to pollination and evolutionary biologists, agriculturists, apiculturists and melisso-palynogists.

Experts in the field with deep and extensive knowledge were involved in unravelling the myriad and fascinating aspects of nectaries, through their thoughtful, original, stimulating and up-to-date reviews.

I wish to acknowledge my deep gratitude to all the contributors who evinced keen interest in the book by promptly responding to my request; but for their cooperation and support this book would not have seen the light of the day.

My most grateful thanks to Prof. B.M. Johri, Delhi University for kindly going through the prescript of the book with keen interest and for making invaluable suggestions and to Prof. V. Puri who from the beginning has been source of strength and encouragement. Finally my special thanks to Mr. Vinod Nangia, Dattsons Publishers, Nagpur, India, for bringing out the volume in readable and elegant get up. I hope this book will be received with enthusiasm by all those interested in the subject. I am aware of the deficiencies but with more research still to come, nectaries will continue to attract greater attention of botanists, agriculturists, apiculturists/melissopalynogists and others in the years to come.

Editor
(Dr. BIR BAHADUR)

Warangal, India.

FOREWORD

Nearly 50% of the global population will soon be urban. Diversification of dietary habits and increasing demand for health foods invariably accompany urbanisation. The demand for honey is hence likely to increase in the new millenium. The present book is therefore a timely contribution.

The book covers a broad spectrum of topics starting from the structure of nectaries and ending with the role of nectaries in agriculture. The authors are eminent scientists in the respective areas. Prof. Bir Bahadur deserves our gratitude for bringing together so many active researchers to contribute informative papers.

All interested in the further development of horticulture, plantation crops like oil palm and agriculture as well as those interested in human nutrition will derive benefit from this book.

19th June, 1996
3rd Cross Street
Taramani. Institutional Area
Madras 600 113, India.

(M.S. SWAMINATHAN)
UNESCO Chair in Ecotechnology
M.S. Swaminathan Research Foundation

CONTENTS

CONTRIBUTORS

1. **Abraham Fahn**, Botany Department, The Hebrew University, Jerusalem, Israel 91904.
2. **Aluri, J.S. Raju**, Departmnt of Environmental Sciences, Andhra University, Visakhapatnam 530003, India.
3. **Ananthakrishnan, T.N.**, Entomology Research Institute, Loyola College, Madras 600034, India.
4. **Bir Bahadur**, Botany Department, Kakatiya University, Warangal 506009, India.
5. **Bory, G.**, Botany Department, University of Paris, Paris 7, France.
6. **Burquez, Alberto,** Department of Ecology, Institute of Biology, National University of Mexico, Mexico 04510, Mexico.
7. **Chaubal, P.D.**, Botany Department, Shivaji University, Kolhapur 416004, Maharashtra, India.
8. **Clair-Maczulajtys, M**, Botany Department, University of Paris, Paris 7, France.
9. **Chaturvedi Mithilesh**, National Botanical Research Institute, Lucknow 226001, India.
10. **Corbet Sarah, A**, Department of Applied Biology, University of Cambridge, Cambridge CB2 3DX, England.
11. **Gopinathan, K**, Entomology Research Institute, Loyola College, Madras 600034, India.
12. **Gulyas, S**, Institute of Botany, Josef Attila University, Szeged, Hungary.
13. **Inamdar, J.A**, Botany Department, Sardar Patel University, Vallabh Vidya Nagar, Gujarat 388120, India.
14. **Jain, H.K**, Department of Zoology, Haryana Agricultural University, Hissar, Haryana 141004, India.
15. **Kalpna, T.P**, Botany Department, College of Science, Saifabad, Hyderabad 500004, India.

16. **Khatija, F**, Botany Department, College of Science, Saifabad, Hyderabad 500004, India.

17. **Manure, A.R**, Botany Department, Karnatak University, Dharwad 580003, India.

18. **Peny, J.H.J,** Cambridge University, Cambridge CB2 3EQ, England.

19. **Ramanujam, C.G.K**, Botany Department, College of Science, Saifabad, Hyderabad 500004, India.

20. **Ramayya, N**, Botany Department, Osmania University, Hyderabad 500007, India.

21. **Rudramuniappa, C.K,** Botany Department, Karnatak University, Dharwad 580003, India.

22. **Shanmukha Rao, S.R**, Botany Deparment, Sardar Patel College, Padmaraonagar, Secundrabad 500025, India.

23. **Subba Reddi, C**, Department of Environmental Sciences, Andhra University, Visakhapatnam 530003, India.

24. **Subramanian, R.B**, Botany Department, Sardar Patel University, Vallabh Vidya Nagar, Gujarat 388120, India.

25. **Suryanarayana, M.C**, Central Bee Research Institute, Khadi & Village Industries Commission, Pune 410016, India.

26. **Swamy, N.R**, Botany Department, Kakatiya University, Warangal 506009, India.

NECTARIES STRUCTURE AND NECTAR SECRETION

ABRAHAM FAHN
Department of Botany
The Hebrew University of Jerusalem, Jerusalem 91904, Israel.

ABSTRACT

Nectaries which occur within the flowers and are directly associated with pollination are termed *floral nectaries*. Nectaries, which occur on the outside of the floral parts and on vegetative organs and are not directly associated with pollination are termed *extrafloral nectaries*. The view that extrafloral nectaries attract ants, which protect the plants from herbivore damage is now widely accepted. These nectaries tend to be more common in tropical environments than in temperate ones.

Flower nectaries are found on different flower parts. It has been suggested that there is a phylogenetic trend of shifting of the nectary in a centri-acropetal direction, i.e. from the outer flower parts towards the inner ones and to the upper region of the gynoecium.

Nectaries occur on plant surfaces. They may be at the level of the ordinary epidermis, may form outgrowths or be sunken; in some cases even deeply in the organs, as in *septal nectaries*. The nectariferous cells are relatively small, contain dense granular cytoplasm and relatively large nuclei. Some nectaries contain special vascular bundles, which are connected to the regular bundles of the organ on which they occur.

Nectar is exuded from the nectary by epidermal cells, by trichomes or by nectariferous parenchyma *via* modified stomata or lysigenous cavities. The cells from which the nectar is secreted to their outside are called *secretory cells*. The nectar consists of sugars and small amounts of other substances. The most common sugars are sucrose, glucose and fructose. The ratio between the different sugars is generally constant. Substances other than sugars usually occur in small amounts. Studies on the occurrence of amino acids in nectar, suggested that the level of their concentration affects significantly the flower-visiting behaviour of potential pollinators. The origin of the secreted nectar is in the phloem sap. The composition of the pre-nectar may become modified in the nectariferous tissue.

Electron microscopical studies of nectaries revealed several interesting characteristics which add much to the understanding of the process of secretion. In many nectaries protuberances on the inner side of the cell walls, which are lined by a highly convoluted plasmalemma, are present. In the nectaries, which secret through trichomes, Casparian-like bands occur at the trichome base. The cells of the nectariferous tissue are interconnected by numerous plasmodesmata. In most nectaries the ER is much developed, in many also numerous dictyosomes are present. At the state of secretion nectary cells contain numerous mitochondria. Plastids varying in number occur in the nectariferous cells. In nectaries of some species, preceding secretion, numerous plastids with large starch grains are present. The contribution of the ultrastructural studies to the understanding of the process of nectar secretion is discussed.

Key words : Nectaries; structure, nectar secretion.

INTRODUCTION

During the course of evolution, the plants living today have acquired various adaptive properties, which contributed to their ability to survive in the surrounding environment. The nectaries which secrete a sugar-rich solution play an important role in attracting pollinators as well as in attracting defense insects, mainly ants, which protect the plant from herbivores. Darwin (1876) in his work "*The Effects of Cross and Self Fertilization in the Vegetable Kingdom*" wrote : "Many years ago I suggested that primarily the saccharine matter in nectar was excreted as a waste product of chemical changes in the sap; and that when the excretion happened to occur within the envelopes of a flower, it was utilised for the important object of cross-fertilization, being subsequently much increased in quantity and stored in various ways."

The *nectary (nectarium)*, which secretes the nectar, was termed so by Linne (1735). Caspary (1848) distinguished between *floral* and *extrafloral nectaries*; the former occurring in flowers and the latter on vegetative organs.

Delpino (1868-75) who considered the function of the nectaries, proposed the term *nuptial nectary* for nectaries occurring within the flowers and which are directly associated with pollination, and the term *extranuptial nectary* for nectaries appearing on the outside of the outer floral parts and on vegetative organs and which are not directly associated with pollination. The terms floral and extrafloral nectaries are now commonly used in the same sense as Delpino used the terms nuptial and extranuptial nectaries (Elias and Gelband, 1976; Fahn, 1979a, b).

Delpino (1868-75) expressed the view that the extrafloral nectaries of all plants function in attracting ants and wasps which defend the plants against herbivores. Darwin (1876) doubted whether this was true in all cases. He mentioned, for instance, the *Pteridium aquilinum* is rarely attacked by enemies and yet, as discovered by his son Francis, at the base of the fronds of this fern there are large nectary glands. However, Darwin agreed that in some cases, such as in *Passiflora* and *Acacia* secretion by the extrafloral nectaries "serves to attract insects as defenders of the plant"

Recently much attention has been paid to the function of the extrafloral nectaries, and more and more evidence has been obtained in support of the view that they attract ants which protect the plants from herbivore damage (Bentley, 1977; Schemske, 1980; Keller and Kaul, 1984). Extrafloral nectaries tend to be more common in tropical environments than in temperate environments, where ant foraging is less intense, thus increasing the potential selective advantage of extrafloral nectaries in tropical communities relative to temperate ones (Morellato and Oliveira, 1991). A view on the physiological aspect of extrafloral nectaries has been expressed by Bory and Clair-Maczulajtys (1990). On the basis of their study on the foliar nectaries of *Ailanthus glandulosa*, they concluded that these nectaries which enable the elimination of excess of sugars play an appreciable role in the regulation of photosynthesis.

Localization of the nectaries in the flower

The problem of the localization of the nectary in the plant is of interest from the phylogenetic point of view. Extrafloral nectaries occur not only in the angiosperms. They were also found in species of some ferns (*Angiopteris, Cyathea, Hemitelia, Platycerium, Pteridium*) (Bonnier, 1879; Darwin, 1877; Dummer, 1911; Figdor, 1891). Frey-Wyssling (1933) expressed the view that in the course of evolution the extrafloral nectaries preceded the floral nectaries.

Sugar-containing droplets exuded by the micropyle of Gnetophyta flowers were suggested to play a role in pollination (cf. Meeuse, 1978).

The floral nectaries of the Angiospermae are found on the different flower parts (Fahn, 1953, 1979a). They may be present on the sepals, petals, stamens, receptacle, ovary and style. On these organs they may be situated in different places. Ovarial nectaries occur, for instance, in some plants on the surface of the ovary (e.g. in *Limnocharis*), in others they are sunken deep in the ovary (septal nectaries of many monocotyledons). Stylar nectaries may occur at the base of the style (e.g. in species of Umbelliferae and Compositae), or at the stigma (e.g. in *Arum* and *Asclepias*). Staminal nectaries may be present on the filaments (e.g. in *Laurus* and *Dianthus*), or on the anthers (e.g. in species of some Mimosaceae, Myrtaceae and Pedaliaceae) (Chaturvedi and Bahadur, 1985).

When examining the position of the nectaries in the flowers of the various families it appears that there exists a phylogenetic trend of the shifting of the nectary in a centri-acropetal direction, i.e. from the outer flower parts towards the inner ones, and the the upper region of the gynoecium (Brown, 1938; Fahn, 1953). Support for this view can be found in a number of works on floral nectaries (Daumann, 1930, 1970; Kartashova, 1965). Deviations from the above mentioned trend may exist in particular groups of plants. Rose Decraene and Smets (1991), for instance, expressed the view that in the Polygonaceae a centrifugal evolutionary trend has occured. Magin (1983) suggested that in the Umbelliferae there exist two main phylogenetic trends of nectary shifting in the flower : 1. A centrifugal shift to the axial part of the peripheral phyllomes and/or to the axial parts of the gamophyllous pedestal. 2. An acrocentrical shift to the upper dorsal parts of the style.

Anatomy of the nectaries

Nectaries occur on plant surfaces. They may be at the level of the surface of the plant part on which they occur, may form an outgrowth, or be sunken, in some cases even deeply in an organ, as for instance are the *septal nectaries* of many monocotyledons. The term *nectariferous tissue* refers to the tissue of which the nectary consists; an epidermis with or without trichomes substanded by a specialized parenchyma. The parenchyma is usually composed of relatively small cells containing dense granular cytoplasm and relatively large nuclei (Caspary, 1848; Behrens, 1879; Bonnier, 1879; Fahn, 1952)

The nectaries either abut the regular vascular bundles of the organs on which they occur, or contain special bundles which are connected with the regular ones. The special vascular bundles may consist of phloem and xylem or of phloem only (Frei, 1955; Kartashova, 1965; Fahn, 1979a; Said, 1982; Davis et al. 1986; Dafni *et al.*, 1987). Nectar is exuded from the nectary by epidermal cells, by trichomes, or by nectariferous parenchyma cells (Figs. 4-7). The latter secrete the nectar into intercellular spaces and from them to the outside of the nectary via modified stomata (Figs. 1-3 & 6) or *via* lysogenous cavities (Fig. 7) as for instance in the extrafloral nectaries of *Sambucus* (Fahn, 1987). Recently a comprehensive study on the development and structure of the modified stomata of *Vicia faba* floral nectaries, and the causes for the inability to close the pore by these stomata, has been carried out by Davis and Gunning (1992). The cells from which the nectar is secreted to the outside are called the *secretory cells* of the nectary (Fahn, 1979a).

In closely related plants, with nectaries of similar structure, a correlation appears to exist between the volume of the nectariferous tissue and the amount of secreted nectar (Fahn, 1949; Dafni *et al.*, 1988).

Extrafloral nectaries, which secrete nectar, may lack morphological and anatomical characteristics typical of nectaries. Such nectaries were termed *non-structural nectaries* (Zimmermann, 1932; Frey-Wyssling and Häusermann, 1960; Galetto and Bernardello, 1992).

The nectar

The secreted nectar consists of sugars and small amounts of other substances. The most common sugars are sucrose, glucose and fructose. Apart from these sugars small amounts of other sugars, such as maltose, raffinose, galactose and melibiose may occur. Based on the quantitative relation between sucrose and glucose-fructose, three main types of nectar are distinguished : 1. sucrose dominant, 2. glucose-fructose dominant, 3. equal ratio of sucrose/glucose-fructose (Fahn, 1949; Percival, 1961; Bahadur *et al.*, 1986). The ratio between the different sugars is generally constant within a species, but may differ markedly between species, sometimes even between closely related species (Baker and Baker, 1983a, b). Percival (1961) mentioned that there exists a correlation between tubular flowers and sucrose richness, and a tendency for open-bowl flowers to have hexose rich nectar.

In addition to sugars other substances are reported to occur, usually in small amounts, in the nectar of various plants. These are, polysaccharid mucilage, proteins (Figs. 1 & 2) (mainly enzymes, among them transglucosidase and transfructosidase), amino acids, lipids, organic acids, ascorbic acid (functioning apparently as an antioxidant), mineral ions, phosphates and in some plants toxic glycosides and alkaloids (cf. Lüttge, 1961; Baker and Baker, 1975, 1983a; Fahn, 1979a). Baker and Baker (1973a, b) found amino acids in minor but significant amounts in 260 of 266 plant nectars examined. These authors concluded that the amino acids affect significantly the flower-visiting behaviour of potential pollinators; so for instance, butterfly-pollinated flowers appear to produce nectar containing high concentrations of amino acids more consistently than bee flowers. This difference may be related to the fact that bees have an alternative source of amino acids in pollen.

Source of the nectar

The origin of the secreted nectar is the phloem sap (Frey- Wyssling and Agthe, 1950; Zimmermann, 1953; Frey-Wyssling, 1955; Matile, 1956). The pre-nectar moves from the sieve elements to the cells of the nectariferous tissue. The composition of the pre-nectar may become modified in the nectariferous tissue by enzymatic activity and by the process of reabsorption (see Ziegler and Lüttge, 1959; Lüttge, 1961;

Shuel, 1961; Ziegler, 1965). The differences in composition of the phloem sap and of the secreted nectar of the extrafloral nectaries of *Ricinus communis*, as shown by Baker *et al.*, (1978), may serve as an example of changes occurring in the pre-nectar (Table 1). Bieleski and Redgwell (1980) suggest that there is a bi-directional movement of sugars from the nectary to the outside and from the secreted nectar back into the nectary. According to these authors, the two-way transfer of sugars plays a significant part in the final sugar composition of the nectar.

TABLE 1 : The composition of phloem exudate and of nectar secreted by the extrafloral nectaries of *Ricinus communis* plants. The concentrations are expressed in mg/ml. (Data from Baker *et al.*, 1978).

	Phloem exudate	*Secreted nectar*
Dry matter	100–125	900
Sucrose	80–106	280
Glucose α	0	107
Glucose β	0	190
Fructose α and β	0	295
Galactose	0	1.0
Protein	1.45–2.2	0.12–0.20
Amino acids (as glutamic acid)	5.2	1.7
Organic acids (as malic acid)	2.0–3.2	Trace
Nitrate	0	0.04
Phosphate	0.35–0.55	0.17
Potassium	2.3–4.4	7.0–9.4
Sodium	0.05–0.28	0.092–0.21
Calcium	0.02–0.09	0.48–0.80
Magnesium	0.11–0.12	0.15–0.22
pH	8–8.2	6.8–7.2

The factors governing the preferential movement of the pre-nectar towards the secretory cells rather than to neighbouring cells are not yet clear. It has been suggested that hydrolyzation of sucrose into its monomers might play a role in forming a sink for sugars in the nectariferous cells. As a result of hydrolyzation, a sucrose concentration gradient could be maintained, which would cause a passive flow of sucrose from the sieve elements to the nectariferous cells (Lüttge and

Schnepf, 1979; Lüttge (1977) considers an active transmembrane transport to play the main role in the sugar movement. However, exocytosis and endocytosis or a pumping force resulting from the elimination of the nectar by the secretory cells, may also take place. The elimination of the nectar from the secretory nectariferous cells may occur either via a granulocrine process of secretion or an ecrine one (see later).

Ultrastructure of the nectariferous tissue

The electron microscopical studies of nectaries opend new ways toward a better understanding of the processes of nectar secretion. The main ultrastructural characteristics of the nectariferous tissues are the following.

Cell wall

The outer wall of the cells of the secretory epithel or papillae are usually covered by a cuticle. The cuticle may be thin, as in the septal nectaries of the banana (Fahn and Benouaiche, 1979) and in the nectaries lining the stigmatic chambers of *Asclepias* (Schnepf and Christ, 1980); or thick, as in receptacular nectaries of *Vinca rosea* (Fig. 6) (Rachmilevitz and Fahn, 1973) and in the trichome nectaries of *Abutilon* (Kronestedt *et al.*, 1986); or with thick ridges, as on the papillae of the corolla nectaries of *Lonicera japonica* (Fig. 8) (Fahn and Rachmilevitz, 1970). During the process of secretion the cuticle becomes detached from the pectinocellulosic cell wall. No cuticle was found on the epithelial cells of *Cynanchum vincetoxicum* (Christ and Schnepf, 1985). In *Abutilon*, pores were observed to occur in the cuticle above the secretory cell (Kronestedt *et al.*, 1986).

In many secretory cells protuberances develop from the inner side of the cell wall (Figs. 8 & 9). These may develop to different extents. They may be very small and inconspicuous, as in the epithelial cells of the septal nectaries of *Tillandsia* (Cecci Fiordi and Palandri, 1982); somewhat larger, as in the septal nectaries of the banana (Fahn and Benouaiche, 1979); or they may form a thick labyrinthain layer, such as in the septal nectaries of *Gasteria trigona* (Schnepf 1969), in the corolla nectaries of *Lonicera japonica* (Figs. 8 & 9) (Fahn and Rachmilevitz, 1970) and in the secretory trichomes of the extrafloral and floral nectaries of *Vicia faba* (Tarkowska *et al.*, 1981; Davis *et al.*, 1988).

In the wall of the apical side of the epithelial cells of the *Cynanchum* nectary, Christ and Schnepf (1985) found channel-like structure of low electron density.

In nectaries which secrete through papillae or multicellular trichomes, the side walls of the lower part of the papillae or the side walls of the cells at the base of the multicellular trichomes, are impregnated with fatty material, similarly to the Casparian strips of endodermal cells (Fahn, 1979b; Eleftheriou and Hall, 1983). This phenomenon is characteristic not only of nectaries, but of all secretory trichomes (Fahn, 1979a, 1988).

Numerous plasmodesmata were found to travers the neighbouring walls of the nectariferous cells (Fahn and Rachmilevitz, 1970; Fahn, 1979b; Findley and Mercer, 1971; Wergin *et al.*, 1975; Zandonella and Piolat, 1982; Eleftheriou and Hall, 1983; Marginson *et al.*, 1985a, b; Figueiredo and Pais, 1992). Eleftheriou and Hall, (1983) have observed, in the extrafloral nectaries of cotton, ER cisternae close to or oriented towards the plamodesmata.

The cytoplasm

The volume of the cytoplasm in the nectariferous cells is relatively large. With the growth of the cells toward the stage of secretion, the volume of the vacuoles may increase. The cytoplasm is usually dense, rich in ribosomes.

The plasmalemma is often highly convoluted, and in many cases multivesicular structures are present between the cell wall and the infolded regions of the plasmalemma (Eyme, 1967; Fahn and Rachmilevitz, 1970; Rachmilevitz and Fahn, 1973; Kalman and Gulyas, 1974; Belin-Depoux and Clair Maczulajtys, 1975; Fahn and Benouaiche, 1979; Mohan and Inamdar, 1986). In many plants, vesicles occurring in the cytoplasm, were seen to be in contact with the plasmalemma (Fig. 9) (Fahn and Rachmilevitz, 1970; Rachmilevitz and Fahn, 1973; Eleftheriou and Hall, 1983).

In most nectaries the endoplasmic reticulum (ER) was found to be much developed, and its cisternae were often seen to be arranged in stacks (Fig. 8). The ER is mainly rough, but at the stage of secretion it may become partly smooth. At this stage the ER cisternae are dilated and vesicles occur in association with them (Figs. 9 & 11) (Fahn and Rachmilevitz, 1970; Fahn and Benouaiche, 1979; Schnepf and Christ, 1980; Eleftheriou and Hall, 1983; Mohan and Inamdar, 1986).

In *Vinca rosea* ER cisternae were seen in contact with the plasmalemma (Fig. 10) (Rachmilevitz and Fahn, 1973).

In many nectary cells, in addition to the ER the Golgi apparatus is also well developed (Fig. 12) (Eyme, 1966; Figier, 1968, 1971; Tacina, 1973; Benner and Schnepf, 1975; Fahn and Benouaiche, 1979; Christ and Schnepf, 1985; Marginson *et al.*, 1985a, b).

At the stage of secretion the nectary cells contain numerous mitochondria (Fig. 6), the cristae of which are usually well developed (Fahn and Rachmilevitz, 1970; Eriksson, 1977; Fahn, 1979a, b; Schnepf and Christ, 1980; Mohan and Inamdar, 1986). In *Cynanchum vincetoxicum*, Christ and Schnepf (1985) have observed that most of the mitochondria are aggregated in complexes.

Plastids varying in number occur in the nectariferous cells. They contain very few inner membranes and most of them contain starch grains. In some plants e.g. *Passiflora* (Durkee, 1982; Durkee *et al.*, 1981) and in *Rosmarinus* (Zer and Fahn, 1992), the amount of starch is very large, at the stage preceding secretion.

Free osmiophilic droplets or globuli are often present in the cytoplasm of nectariferous cells (Fahn and Benouaiche, 1979; Mohan and Inamdar, 1986).

The contribution of the ultrastructural studies to the understanding of the process of nectar secretion

Transport of the pre-nectar. Several possible pathways by which the pre-nectar flows from the phloem endings, through the nectariferous cells, to the secretory cells, which exude the nectar to the outside, were suggested. These are : 1. Via the apoplast (Vassilyev, 1969, 1971). 2. Via exocytosis and endocytosis (tentatively suggested by Eyme, 1966, and by Findley and Mercer, 1971). In this pathway multivesicular structures may be involved (Kalman and Gulyas, 1974). 3. Molecular transport across the plasmalemmas of the successive cells and passage through cell walls. 4. Via plasmodesmata.

The first possible pathway can be discarded, at least in the case of nectaries that secrete from trichomes, because at the base of the latter there are endodermal cells which prevent the passage of solutions through their apoplastic regions. The second possible pathway would involve repeated secretion and absorption of pre-nectar as it passes from cell through the cell wall.

Several studies of nectaries lead to the deduction that the transport of the pre-nectar is mainly in the symplast. Numerous plasmodesmata have in fact been observed connecting the protoplasts of cells of nectariferous tissues (Fahn and Rachmilevitz, 1970, 1975; Findley and Mercer, 1971; Wergin *et al.*, 1975; Eleftheriou and Hall, 1983; Kronestedt *et al.*, 1986). Gunning and Hughes (1976) studied the nectary trichomes of *Abutilon* and found a high frequency of plasmodesmata in the periclinal cell walls. These authors have calculated that the required sugar flux through the endodermal stalk cell of the trichome is 3-4 orders of magnitude greater than quoted in the literature for flux through cell membranes; on the other hand the number and dimensions of the plasmodesmata in the distal periclinal wall of the stalk cell provides a low resistance pathway for bulk flow of a sugar solution. Their study thus supports the view that the pre-nectar flows through the plasmodesmatal pathway.

Transport of the nectar outward of the secretory cells. Various manners of transport of nectar to the outside of the protoplast of the secretory cells of the nectary have been suggested. There are theories of active molecular transport through membranes (*eccrine secretion*, see Lüttge and Schnepf, 1976) and of transport *via* vesicles whose membranes fuse with the plasmalemma (*granulocrine secretion*).

In 1964, Schnepf expressed the view that in the septal nectaries of *Gasteria* and some other Liliaceae, nectar transport is based on molecular processes at the plasmalemma. He found the evidence for his view in the very great enlargement of the plasmalemma, resulting from the occurrence of wall protuberances that develop as nectar secretion approaches. The possibility of molecular transport of sugars within the nectary of *Abutilon* was discussed by Reed *et al.* (1971).

Fahn and Rachmilevitz (1970, 1975) and Rachmilevitz and Fahn (1973) studied the changes in the ultrastructure of the secretory cells of the nectaries of *Lonicera*, *Vinca*, and *Citrus* at various developmental stages. Their approach was that by studying the changes in the ultrastructure occurring toward the stage of secretion it would be possible to establish which cell compartments are involved in the process of secretion. It was found that towards the phase of secretion there is a pronounced increase in the amount of the ER; the cisternae of the ER become dilated, and many vesicles which seem to originate from them, occur in continuation to their edges (Figs. 9 & 10). In some nectaries ER cisternae were seen approaching the plasmalemma (Rachmilevitz and Fahn, 1973). On the basis of the presence of vesicles close to the plasmalemma along with its invaginations it was suggested that the vesicle membranes fuse with the plasmalemma. It was thus assumed that the nectar accumulates in the ER and is transported to the plasmalemma by vesicles which bud off from the ER cisternae. The membranes of these vesicles fuse with the plasmalemma and release the nectar by reverse pinocytosis. This view was supported by authors who worked on nectaries of some other plants (Belin-Depoux and Clair-Maczulajtys, 1975; Eleftheriou and Hall, 1983).

Suggestions that Golgi vesicles rather than vesicles of ER origin are involved in outward transport of the nectar were made by Eyme (1966), who studied the floral nectaries of *Diplotaxis* and *Hellebores*; by Tacina (1973), who studied the floral nectaries of *Cynoglossum officinale*; by Figier (1968, 1971) who studied the extrafloral nectaries of *Vicia faba*; and by Benner and Schnepf (1975), who studied the septal nectaries of some Bromeliaceae.

In the nectary occurring in the calyx spur of *Tropaeolum majus* (Rachmilevitz and Fahn, 1975) and in the septal nectary of *Musa paradisiaca* var. *sapientum* (Fahn and Benouaiche, 1979), numerous dictyosomes were found to be budding off vesicles at the stage of secretion (Fig. 12). Dilated ER cisternae (Fig. 11) and ER vesicles were also numerous. It was thus suggested that in the nectaries of these plants both the ER and the Golgi apparatus are involved in nectar secretion. A similar suggestion was made by Marginson *et al.*, (1985a), who observed in the extrafloral nectaries of *Acacia terminalis* both Golgi vesicles and ER vesicles associated with the plasmalemma. Schnepf and Christ (1980) and Christ and Schnepf (1985), who studied the floral nectaries of *Asclepias currasavica* and *Cynanchum vincetoxicum*, also suggested that the Golgi apparatus and the ER may be involved in the process of nectar secretion.

Some nectaries, as for example those of *Musa paradisiaca* var. *sapientum*, secrete a nectar which contains in addition to sugar, polysaccharides and protein. It was suggested that in these nectaries the ER and the Golgi apparatus are involved not only in the process of the sugar secretion, but also in that of the polysaccharide secretion (Fahn and Benouaiche, 1979).

In addition to the study of the ultrastructural changes occurring in the secretory cells during their differentiation, some investigations based on labelling and histochemical techniques, were carried out. With the aid of the Gomori test and other techniques, Heinrich (1975a) studied the localisation of phosphatases in the secretory epithelial cells of the septal nectaries of *Aloë*. He found a high activity of ATPase, nucleoside diphosphatase, and glucos-6-phosphatase in the ER, and generally, and absence of activity of these phosphatases in the plasmalemma. Heinrich thus assumed that the ER plays an important role in nectar transport.

Figier (1972), who tried to localise acid phosphatase in petiolar nectaries of *Impatiens*, also observed only limited reactions on the plasmalemma and the cell walls, except for the region of sieve tubes and transfer cells, where he found heavy deposits of lead phosphate.

Attempts to follow the path of sugar in the nectary by means of autoradiography were made by Fahn and Rachmilevitz (1975) and by Heinrich (1975b). After feeding floral nectaries of *Lonicera* with tritiated sucrose, Fahn and Rachmilevitz found, in the autoradiograms of the secretory cells, labelling in the ER cisternae and vesicles. In the nectariferous tissue below the secretory cells, labelling was frequently observed in the plasmodesmata. Heinrich, on the basis of labeling septal nectaries of *Aloe* with tritiated glucose, concluded that the nectar is secreted by vesicles, but he could not decide whether they originated from the ER or from the dictyosomes.

While summerising the various ultrastructural studies on nectaries the following conclusions can be drawn.

1. The passage of the pre-nectar from cell to cell in the nectariferous tissue is mainly *via* plasmodesmata, although in some cases additional transport by exocytosis and endocytosis may perhaps also take place.

2. The endoplasmic reticulum is involved in transport of the pre-nectar in all nectariferous cells and in the accumulation of nectar in the secretory cells from which it is exuded to the outside. In these cells the nectar may also accumulate in the Golgi apparatus.

3. Many authors suggested that the outward transport of the nectar from the secretory cells is carried out by granulocrine secretion (Fahn and Rachmilevitz, 1970, 1975; Benner and Schnepf, 1975; Fahn and Benouaiche, 1979; Cecchi Fiordi and Palandri, 1982; Eleftheriou and Hall, 1983; Mohan and Inamdar, 1986). The possibility that both granulocrine and eccrine secrétion takes place has been suggested by Schnepf and Christ (1980), Christ and Schnepf (1985) and Margimson et al. (1985a, b). Elimination of the nectar *via* eccrine secretion only, has been suggested by Eriksson (1977) to occur in *Trifolium*, by Meyberg and Kristen in *Aptenia* and by Durkee *et al.*, (1981) in *Passiflora*.

4. The outer wall of the secretory cells is adapted for passage of the nectar solution, in many cases by possessing an inner layer of protuberances. In trichome nectaries a back flow of the secreted nectar through the apoplast is blocked by Casparian-like strips. A cuticle, if present may be thin and permeable, or when thick it may become thin as a result of the pressure of the nectar accumulating below it. As a result of pressure the cuticle may also rupture. In some secretory cells, thick cuticles may have pores.

Explanation of Figures

Fig. 1—3. Scanning electron micrographs of a floral nectary of *Rosmarinus officinalis* (From Zer and Fahn, 1992). Fig. 1. General view of the nectary (N) subtanding four lobes of the ovary (O). Modified stomata occur only on the large nectary lobe (on right), which faces the lower corolla lip. x 80. Fig. 2. Upper part of the large lobe, showing numerous open modified stomata. x 300. Fig. 3. Wide open modified stomata. x 1800.

Figs. 4—7. Fig. 4. A portion of a cross-section of a septal nectary of a male flower of *Musa paradiasica* var. *sapintum*, stained with Coommassie Brilliant Blue. The material (apparently protein, p) in the furrows of the nectary absorbed the stain. The rest of the material in the furrows consists of polysaccharides. x 250. (From Fahn and Benouaiche, 1979). Fig. 5. Scanning electron micrograph of a portion of a floral nectary of *Abutilon*, showing the secretory trichomes. x 300. Fig. 6. Longitudinal section of the upper part of a floral nectary of *Vinca rosea*, showing stomata (s) and a thick cuticle (c). x 500. (From Rachmilevitz and Fahn, 1973). Fig. 7. Upper portion of an extrafloral nectary

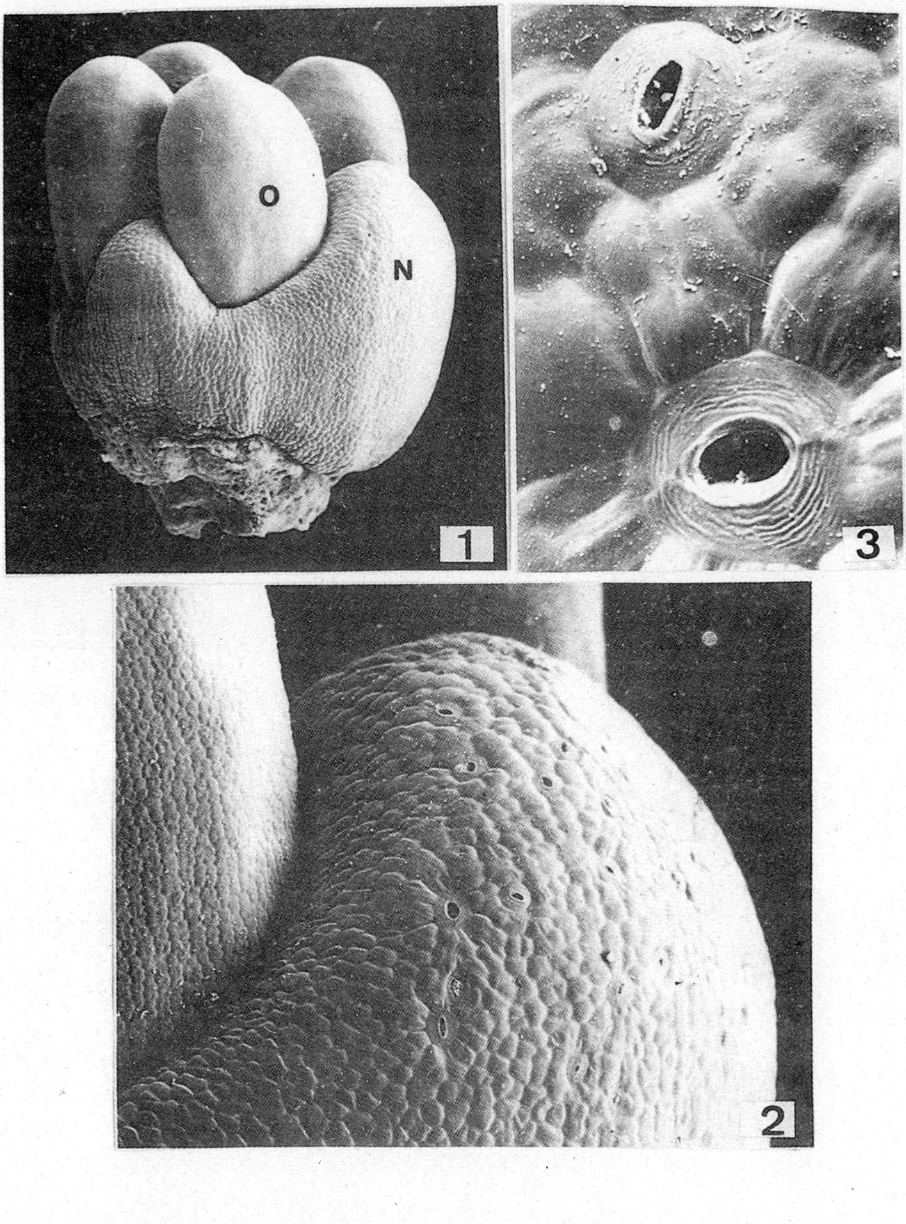
O
N
1
3
2

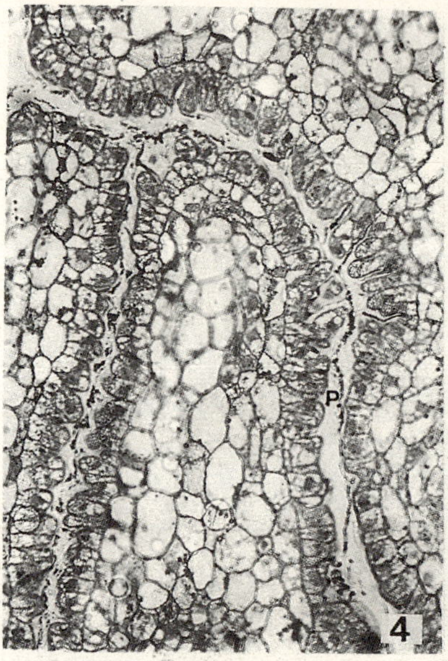
P
4

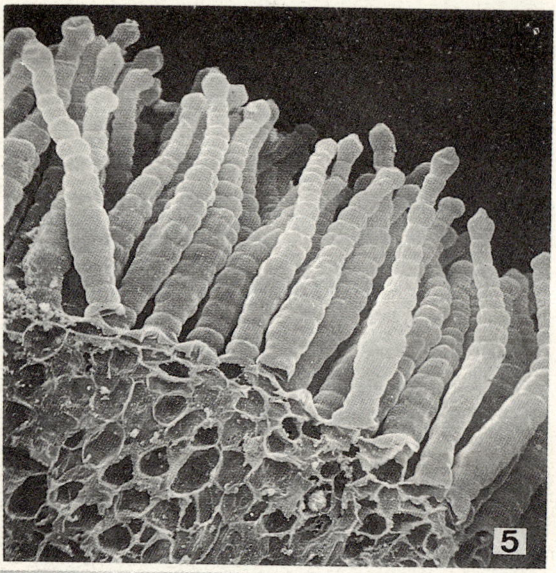
5

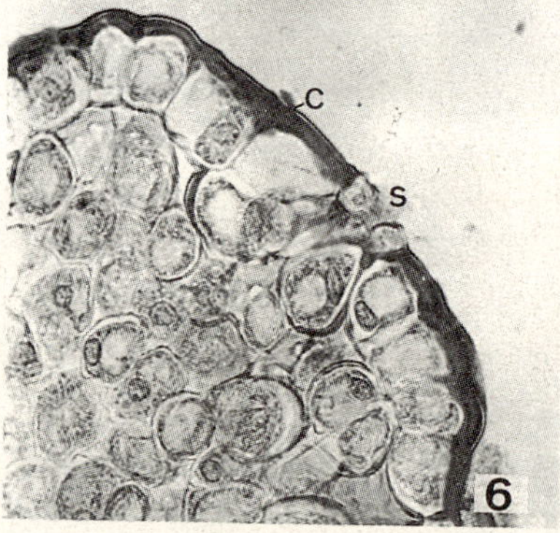
c
s
6

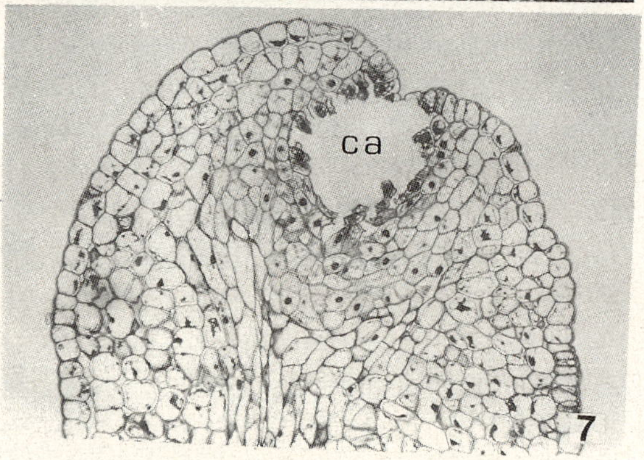
ca
7

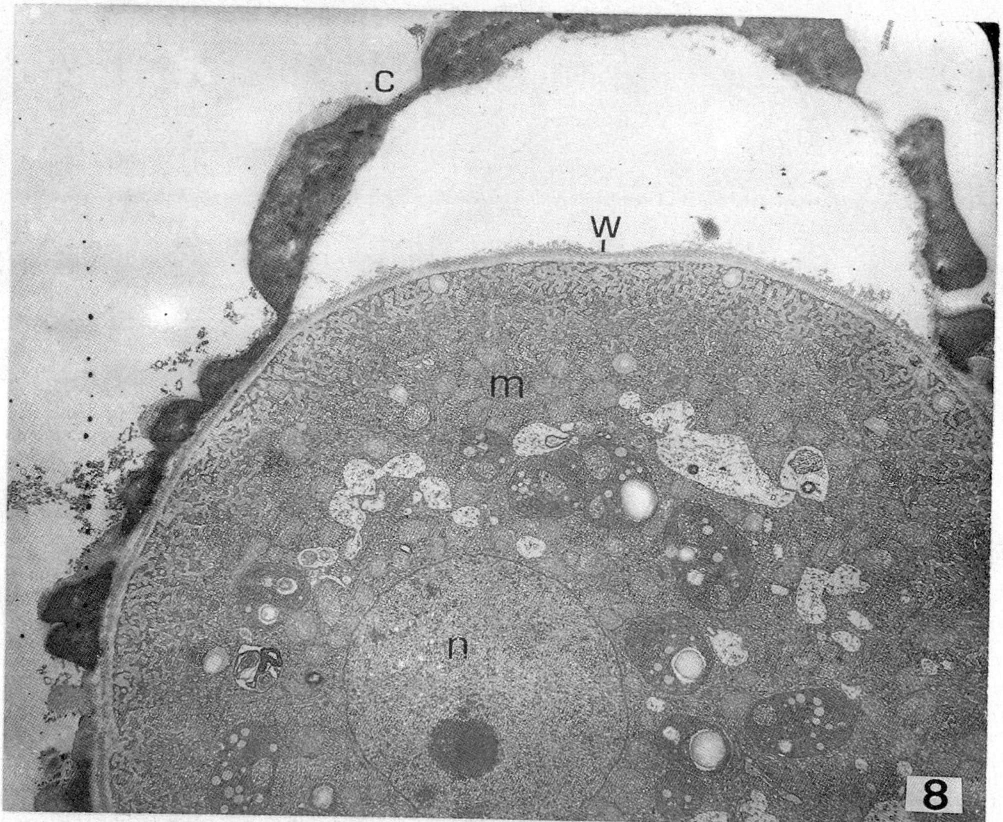

8

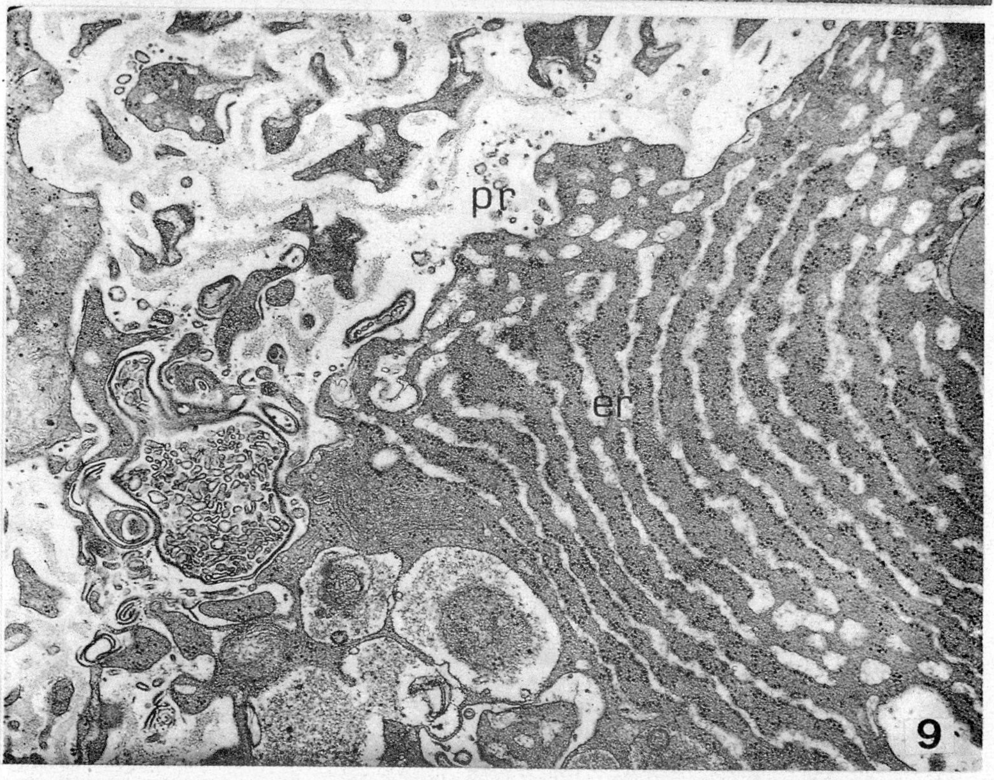

9

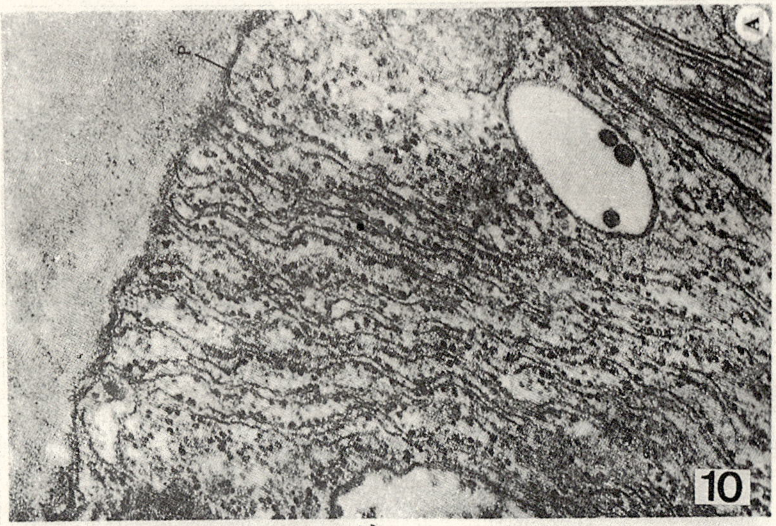
A
p
10

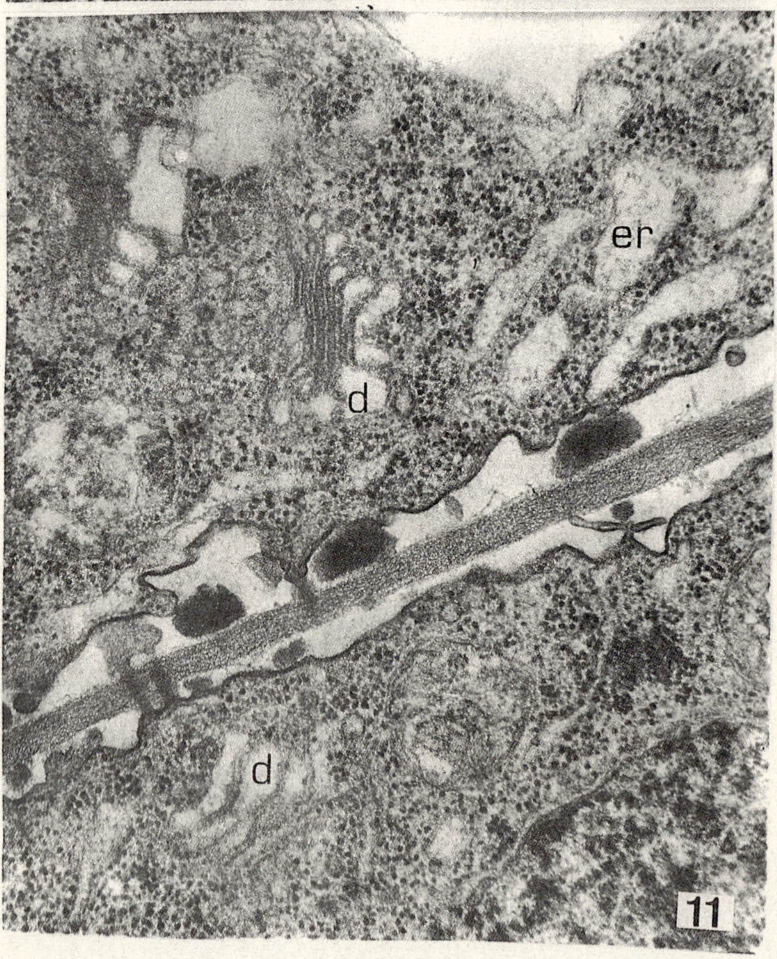
er
d
d
11

of *Sambucus nigra*, showing a cavity (ca) which developed as a result of disintegration of cells of the nectary (n). x 300. (From Fahn, 1987).

Figs. 8—9. Fig. 8. Electron micrograph of a papilla of a floral nectary of *Lonicera japonica*, in which a subcuticular space started to develop. c, cuticle; n, nucleus; m, mitochondria; pl, plastid; pr, layer of wall protuberances; w, pecto-cellulosic wall. x 3,000. Fig. 9. Portion of a secretory papilla of a nectary of *Lonicera japonica*, in which cisternae of the endoplasmic reticulum (er) are seen approaching the wall protuberances (pr). At the edges, the ER cisternae are swollen and vesicles are seen close to them. x 25,000. (From Fahn and Rachmilevitz, 1970.)

Figs. 10—11. Fig. 10. Epidermal cell of a nectary of *Vinca rosea*, at the stage of secretion. Rough ER cisternae are apparently continuous with the plasmalemma. x 34,000. (From Rachmilevitz and Fahn, 1973). Fig. 11 Epithelial cells of a septal nectary of a male banana flower. The ER cisternae (er) are much dilated. Dictyosomes x 44,000. (From Fahn and Benouaiche, 1979.)

Literature Cited

Bahadur, B., Chaturvedi A. and Swamy, N.R. 1986. Nectar types in Indian plants. *Proc. Indian Acad. Sci. (Plant Sci.). 96* : 41-48.

Baker, H.G. and Baker, I. 1973a. Amino-acids in nectar and their evolutionary significance. *Nature*, London. *241* : 543-545.

------- and ------- 1973b. Some anthecological aspects of the evolution of nectar producing flowers, particularly amino· acid production in nectar. In: (ed.) Heywood, V.H., *Taxonomy and Ecology*, p. 243-264. Academic Press. London.

------- and ------- 1975. Studies of nectar-constitution and pollinator-plant coevolution. In: (eds) Gilbert, L.E. and Raven, P.H. *Coevolution of animals and plants*, p. 100-140. University of Texas Press. Austin.

------- and ------- 1983a. A brief historical review of the chemistry of floral nectar. In: (ed.) Bentley, B. and Elias, T., *Biology of Nectaries*, p. 126-152. Columbia University Press. New York.

------- and ------- 1983b. Floral nectar sugar constituents in relation to pollinator type. In: (eds.) Jones, C.E. and Little, R.J., *Handbook of Experimental Pollination Biology*, p. 117-141. Scientific and Academic Edition, Van Nostrand Reinhold Co. New York.

Baker, D.A., Hall, J.L. and Throp, J.R. 1978. A study of the extrafloral nectaries of *Ricinus communis. New Phytol., 81* : 129-137.

Behrens, W.J. 1879, Die Nectarien der Blüten. *Flora, 62* : 2-11, 17-27, 49-54, 113-123, 145-153, 233-240, 241-247, 305-314, 369-375, 433-457.

Belin-Depoux, M. and Clair-Maczulajtys, D. 1975. Introduction à liétude des glandes foliaires de l. *Aleurites moluccana* Willd. II. Aspects histologiques de la glande pétiolaire fonctionnelle. *Rev. Gén. Bot., 82* : 119-155.

Benner, U. and Schnepf, E. 1975. Die Morphologie der Nectarausscheidung bei Bromeliaceen : Beteiligung des Golgi Apparates. *Protoplasma, 85* : 337-349.

Bentley, B.L. 1977. Extrafloral nectaries and protection by pugnacious bodyguards. *Annu. Rev. Ecol. Syst., 8* : 407-427.

Bieleski, R.L. and Redgwell, R.J. 1980. Sorbitol metabolism in nectaries from flowers of Rosaceae. *Aust. J. Plant Physiol., 7* : 15-25.

Bonnier, G. 1879. *Les nectaires*. Theses Fac. Sci. Paris.

Bory, G. and Clair-Maczulajtys, D. 1990. Importance of foliar nectaries in the physiology of tree of heaven (*Ailanthus glandulosa* Desf., Simarubaceae). *Bull. Soc. bot. Fr., 137* : 139-155.

Brown, W.H. 1938. The bearing of nectaries on the phylogeny of flowering plants. *Proc. Amer. Phil. Soc., 79* : 549-595.

Caspary, R. de 1848. De nectariis. Elberfeld.

Cecchi Fiordi, A. and Palandri, M.R. 1982. Anatomic and ultrastructural study of the septal nectary in some *Tillandsia* (Bromeliaceae) species. *Caryologia, 35* : 477-489.

Chaturvedi, A. and Bahadur, B. 1985. Gland crested anthers in some angiosperms. *J. Swamy Bot. Cl., 2 : 79-86.*

Christ, P. and Schnepf, E. 1985. The nectaries of *Cynanchum vincetoxicum* (Asclepiadaceae). *Isr. J. Bot., 34* : 79-90.

Dafni, H., Lenski, J. and Fahn, A. 1987. Flower and nectar characteristics and their influence on the honeybee visit in nine species of the Labiatae. (In preparation).

Darwin, Ch. 1876. *The Effects of Cross and Self Fertilization in the Vegetable Kingdom.* John Murray, London.

Darwin, Fr. 1877. On the nectar glands of the common brakenfern. *J. Linn. Soc. Bot., 15* : 407-409.

Davis, A.R., Petersom, R.L. and Shuel, R.W. 1986. Anatomy and vasculature of floral nectaries of *Brassica napus* (Brassicaceae). *Can. J. Bot., 64* : 2508-2516.

Davis, A.R. and Gunning, B.E.S. 1992. The modified stomata of the floral nectary of *Vicia faba* L. 1. Development, anatomy and ultrastructure. *Protoplasma, 166* : 134-152.

Davis, A.R., Peteson, R.L. and Shuel, R.W. 1988. Vasculature and ultrastructure of the floral and stipular nectaries of *Vicia faba* (Leguminosae). *Can. J. Bot., 66* : 1435-1448.

Dauman, E. 1930. Das Blütennektarium von *Magnolia* and Futterkörper in der Blüte von *Calycanthus*. *Planta, 11* : 108-116.

------- 1970. Das Blütennektarium der Monocotyledonen unter besonderer berücksichtigung seiner systematischen and phylogenetischen Bedeutung. *Feddes Reperatorium, 80* : 463-590.

Delpino, F. 1868-75. Ulteriori osservazioni sulla dicogamia nel regno vegetale. I and II. *Atti Soc. Ital. Sci. Nat. XI. XII.*

Dümmer, R. 1911. Grape sugar as a secretion in *Platicerium*. *Ann. Bot., 25* : 1205-1206.

Durkee, L.T. 1982. The floral and extra-floral nectaries of *Passiflora*. II. The extra-floral nectary. *Amer. J. Bot., 69* : 1420-1428.

-------, Gaal, D.J. and Reisner, W.H. 1981. The floral and extra floral nectaries of *Passiflora*. I. The floral nectary. *Amer. J. Bot., 68* : 453-462.

Elias T.S. and Gelband, H. 1976. Morphology and anatomy of floral and extrafloral nectaries in *Campsis* (Bignoniaceae). *Amer. J. Bot., 63* : 1349-1353.

Eleftheriou, E.P. and Hall, J.L. 1983. The extrafloral nectaries of cotton. I. Fine structure of the secretory papillae. *J. Exp. Bot., 34* : 103-119.

Eriksson, M. 1977. The ultrastructure of the nectary of red clower (*Trifolium pratense*). *J. Apic. Res., 16* : 184-193.

Eymé, J. 1966. Infrastructure des cellules nectarigenes de *Diplotaxis erucoides* D.C., *Helleborus niger*, L. et *H. foetidus* L. *C.R. Acad. Sci. (Paris) Ser., D. 262* : 1629-1632.

------- 1967. Nouvelles observations sur l infrastructure de tissues nectarigénes floraux. *Botaniste, 50* : 169-183.

Fahn, A. 1949. Studies in the ecology of nectar secretion. *Palest. J. Bot. Jerusalem Ser., 4* : 207-224.

------- 1952. On the structure of floral nectaries. *Bot. Gaz., 113* : 464-470.

------- 1953. The topography of the nectary in the flower and its phylogenetical trend. *Phytomorphology, 3* : 424-426.

------- 1979a. *Secretory tissues in plants*. Academic Press. London.

------- 1979b. Ultrastructure of nectaries in relation to nectar secretion. *Amer. J. Bot., 66* : 977-985.

------- 1987. Extrafloral nectaries of *Sambucus niger* L. *Ann. Bot., 60*.

------- and Benouaiche, P.1979. Ultrastructure, development and secretion in the nectary of of banana flowers. *Ann. Bot., 44* : 85-93

------- 1988. Secretory tissues in plants. *New Phytol., 108* : 229-257.

------- and Rachmilevitz, T. 1970. Ultrastructure and nectar secretion in *Lonicera japonica*. In: (eds.) Robson N.K.B., Cutler, D.F. & Gregory, M. *New Research in Plant Anatomy. Bot. J. Linn. Soc., 63 : Supl.* 1. 51-56. Academic Press. London.

------- and ------- 1975. An autoradiological study of nectar secretion in *Lonicera japonica* Thumb. *Ann. Bot., 39* : 975-976.

Figdor, W. 1891. Über die extranuptialen Nektarien von *Pteridium aquilinum*. *Osterr. bot. Ztschr., 41* : 293-295.

Figier, J. 1968. Localisation infrastructurale de la phosphomonoestérase acide dans la stipule de *Vicia faba* L. au niveau du nectaire. Rôles possibles de cet enzyme dans les mechanismes de la sécrétion. *Planta*, 83 : 60-79.

------- 1971. Etude infrastructurale de la stipule de *Vicia faba* L. au niveau du nectaire. *Planta, 98* : 31-49.

------- 1972. Localisation infrastructurale de la phosphatase acide dans les glandes pétiolaires *Impatiensd' holstii*. Rôles possibles de cette enzyme au cours des processus sécrétoires. *Planta, 108* : 215-226.

Figueiredo, A.C.S. and Pais, M.S. 1992. Ultrastructural aspects of the nectary of *Limodorum abortivum (L) Sw. (Orchidaceae). Ann. Bot., 70* : 325-331.

Findlay, N., and Mercer, F.V. 1971. Nectar production in *Abutilon*. II. Submicroscopic structure of the nectary. *Aust. J. Biol. Sci., 24* : 657-664.

Frei, E. 1955. Die Innervierung der floralen Nektarien dikotyler Pflanzenfamilien. *Ber. schweiz. bot. Ges., 65* : 60-114.

Frey-Wyssling, A. 1933. Über die extrafloralen Nektarien von *Hevea brasiliensis* Muell. *Ber. schweiz. bot. Ges., 42* : 109-122.

------- 1955. The phloem supply to the nectaries. *Acta bot. neerl., 4* : 358-368.

------- and Agthe, C. 1950. Nektar ist ausgeschiedener Phloemsaft. *Verh. schweiz. Naturforsch. Ges., 130* . 175-176.

Frey-Wyssling, A. and Häusermann, E. 1960. Deutung der gestaltlosen Nektarien. *Ber. schweiz. bot. Ges., 70* : 150-162.

Galetto, L. and Bernardello, L.M. 1992. Extrafloral nectaries that attract ants in Bromeliaceae : structure and nectar composition. *Can. J. Bot., 70* : 1101-1106.

Günning, B.E.S. and Hughes, J.E. 1976. Quantitative assessment of symplastic transport of pre-nectar into the trichomes of *Abutilon* nectaries. *Aust. J. Plant Physiol., 3* : 619-637.

Heinrich, G. 1975a. Über die Localisation verschiedener Phosphatase in Nektarium von *Aloë. Cytobiologie, 11* : 247-263.

------- 1975b, Über den Glucose-Metabolismus in Nektarien zweier *Aloë-Arten and über den Mechanisms der Pronektar-Sekretion. Protoplasma, 85* : 351-371.

Kalman. F. and Gulyàs, S. 1974. Ultrastructure and mechanism of secretion in extrafloral nectaries of *Ricinus communis* L. *Acta biol. Szeged, 20* : 57-67.

Kartashova, N.N. 1965. Stroeniei funktsiya nektarnikov tsvetka dvudol nykh rastenii. *Izdatel stvo Tomskogo Universiteta. Tomsk.*

Keeler, K.H. and Kaul, R.B. 1984. Distribution of defense nectaries in *Ipomoea* (Convolvulaceae). *Amer. J. Bot., 71* : 1364-1372.

Kronestedt, E.C., Robards, A.W., Stark, M. and Olsen, P. 1986. Development of trichomes in the *Abutilon* nectary gland. *Nord. J. Bot., 6* : 627-639.

Linné, C. von 1735. *Systema naturae, sive regna tria naturae systematicae proposita per classes, ordines, genera et species* Leiden.

Lüttge, U. 1961. Über die Zusammensetzung des Nektars und den Mechanisms seiner Sekretion. I. *Planta, 56* : 189-212.

------- 1977. Nectar composition and membrane transport of sugars and amino acids : A review on the present state of nectar research. *Apidologie, 8* : 305-320.

------- and Schnepf, E. 1976. Elimination processes by glands. Organic substances. In: (eds.) Lüttge, U. and Pitman, M.G., *Transport in Plants*. II. *Encyclopedia of Plant Physiology. N. S. 2* : part B, p. 244-277. Springer-Verlag. Berlin.

Magin, N. 1983. Die Nektarien der Apiaceae. *Flora, 173* : 233-254.

Marginson, R., Sedgley, M. and Knox, R.B. 1985a. Structure and histochemistry of the extrafloral nectary of *Acacia terminalis* (Salisb.) MacBride (Leguminosae, Mimosoideae). *Protoplasma, 127* : 21-30.

-------, -------, Douglas, T.J. and Knox, R.B. 1985. Structure and secretion of the extrafloral nectaries of Australian acacias. *Isr. J. Bot., 34* : 91-102.

Matile, Ph. 1956. Über den Stofwechsel und die Auxinabhängigkeit der Nektarsekretion. *Ber. schweiz. bot. Ges., 66* : 237-266.

Meeuse, A.D.J. 1978. Nectarial secretion, floral evolution, and pollination syndrome in early angiosperms. *Proc. Koninklijke Nederlanse Akademie van Wetenschappen, Amsterdam*, S.C., *81* : 300-326.

Meyberg, M. and Kristen, U. 1981. The nectaries of *Aptenia cordifolia*. Ultrastructure, translocation of ^{14}C–labelled sugars, and a possible pathway of secretion. *Z. Pflanzenphysiol, 104* : 139-147.

Mohan, J.S.S. and Inamdar, J.A. 1986. Ultrastructure and secretion of extrafloral nectaries of *Plumeria rubra* L. *Ann. Bot., 57* : 389-401.

Morellato, L.P.C. and Oliveira P.S. 1991. Distribution of extrafloral nectaries in different vegetation types of Amazonian Brazil. *Flora, 185* : 33-38.

Percival, M.S. 1961. Types of nectar in angiosperms. *New Phytol., 60* : 235-281.

Rabinovitch, H.D., Fahn, A., Meir T. and Lensky Y. 1993. Flower and nectar attributes of pepper (*Capsicum annuum* L.). *Ann. appl. Biol., 123.*

Rachmilevitz, T. and Fahn, A. 1973. Ultrastructure of nectaries of *Vinca rosea* L. *Vinca major* L. and *Citrus sinensis* Osbeck cv. *Valencia* and its relation to the mechanism of nectar secretion. *Ann. Bot., 37* : 1-9.

------- and ------- 1975. The floral nectary of *Tropaeolum majus* L. — The nature of the secretory cells and the manner of nectar secretion. *Ann. Bot., 39* : 721-728.

Reed, M.L. Findlay, N. and Mercer, F.V. 1971. Nectar production in *Abutilon*. IV. Water and solute relations. *Aust. J. Biol. Sci., 214* : 677-688.

Ronse Decraene, L. P.R. and Smets E. 1991. The floral nectaries of *Polygonum* s.l. and related genera (Persicarieae and Polygoneae) : Position, morphological nature and semophylesis. *Flora, 185* : 165-185.

Said, C. 1982. Les nectaire floraux des Crassulacees. Etude morphologique, histologique et anatomique. *Bull. Soc. bot. Fr., 129* : 231-240.

Schemske, D.W. 1980. The evolutionary significance of extrafloral nectar production by *Costus woodsonii* (Zingiberaceae) : an experimental analysis of ant protection. *J. Ecol., 68* : 959-967.

Schnepf, E. 1964. Zur Cytologie und Physiologie pflanzlicher Drüsen. 4. Teil. Licht-und elektronenmikroskopische Untersuchungen an Septalnektarien. *Protoplasma, 58* : 137-171.

------- 1969. Sekretion und Exkretion bei Pflanzen. *Protoplasmatologie* VIII/8. Springer. Wien.

Schnepf, E. and Christ, P. 1980. Unusual transfer cells in the epithelium of the nectaries of *Asclepias curassavica* L. *Protoplasma, 105* : 135-148.

Shuel, R.W. 1961. Influence of reproductive organs on secretion of sugar in flowers of *Streptosolen jamesonii*. *Plant Physiol., 36* : 265-271.

Täcinä, F. 1973. La structure optique et électronmicroscopique de la glande nectarifere chez *Cynoglossum officinale Rev. roum.* Biol. sér. *Bot., 18* : 201-209.

Tarkowska, J.A., Zobel, A.M. and Maciak, M. 1981. Development and transfer character of secretory glands in the broad bean (*Vicia faba* L.). *Acta Soc. Bot. Polon., 50* : 391-398. Vassilyev, A,E.

------- 1969. Submicroscopic morphology of nectary cells and problems of nectar secretion. *Bot. Zv. SSSR, 54* : 1015-1031. (In Russian.)

------- 1971. New data on the ultrastructure of the cells of flower nectary. *Bot. Zh. SSSR, 56* : 1292-1306.

Wergin, P.W., Elmore, C.D., Hanny, B.W. and Ingber, B. 1975. ultrastructure of the subglandular cells from the foliar nectaries of cotton in relation to the distribution of plasmodesmata and symplastic transport of nectar. *Amer. J. Bot., 62* : 842-849.

Zandonella, P. and Piolat, C. 1982. Nectaires et sécrétion du nectar chez *Thunbergia laurifoiia* Lindl. (Acanthacees). *Bull. soc. bot. Fr. 129*, Actual. bot. : 109-117.

Zer, H. and Fahn, A. 1992. Floral nectaries of *Rosmarinus officinalis* L. Structure, ultrastructure and nectar secretion. *Ann. Bot., 70* : 391-397.

Ziegler, H. 1965. Die Physiologie pflanzlicher Drüsen. *Ber. dt. bot. Ges., 78* : 466-477.

------- and Lüttge, U. 1959. Über die Resorption von C^{14}– Glutaminsäure durch sezernierende Nektarien. *Naturwissenschaften, 46* : 176-177.

Zimmermann, M. 1953. Papierchromatographische Untersuchungen über die pflanzliche Zuckersekretion. *Ber. schweiz. bot. Ges., 63* : 402-429.

------- 1954. Über die Sekretion saccharosespltender Transglukosidasen im pflanzlichen Nektar. *Experientia, 10* : 145-146.

Zimmermann, J.G. 1932. Über die extrafloralen Nektarien der Angiospermen. *Beih. bot. Zbl., 49A* : 99-169.

NECTAR CHEMISTRY

BIR BAHADUR[1], C. SUBBA REDDI[2], J.S. ALURI RAJU[2], H.K. JAIN[3] and N. RAMA SWAMY[1]

[1]Department of Botany, Kakatiya University
Warangal 506 009, India.

[2]Department of Environmental Sciences
Andhra University, Visakhapatnam 530 003, India.

[3]Department of Zoology, Haryana Agricultural University
Hissar 141 004, Haryana, India.

ABSTRACT

Nectar Chemistry is very complex. It contains various chemicals consisting of sugars, amino acids, lipids, alkaloids, toxic substances, phenolics, proteins, organic acids, vitamins, inorganic compounds, resins, melanin content, ant-repellents, etc. Of these, sugars are the major constituents. Within sugars, glucose, fructose and sucrose commonly occur, while the other sugars are rare, and if present, are in minute quantities. Amino acids are also common but only some of them are usually found. Lipids occur in some floral nectars only. All other chemicals when present, have been shown to be available in minute quantities.

Among the different chemical constituents of nectar, sugars provide instant energy to the flower-visitors. Amino acids, lipids, proteins are valuable in the nutrition of flower-visitors. The nectars containing toxic substances show detrimental effects on flower-visitors. Floral nectars and their pollinators have developed a tight relationship with reference to nectar constituents. The details of chemicals of nectar and their influence on flower visitors and pollinators and in phylogeny have been reviewed in this paper.

Key Words : Nectar Chemistry, Sugars, Amino acids, lipids, alkaloids, pollinators, relationship, phylogeny.

INTRODUCTION

Nectar is a major primary attractant and reward of flowers to their pollinators. Its secretion is a consequence of different complex physiological processes of special glands called 'nectaries'. It is a derivative of phloem sap (Günning and Steer, 1975) through a number of modifications along the route from the sieve elements to the secretory cells. The secretion and concentration of nectar relate to the physiological and nutritional state of the plant and autonomous rhythms within the plant.

The chemistry of nectar is very complex. Analysis of nectar in a number of plant species shows that the sugars are the major constituents. Other chemical compounds are amino acids, vitamins, lipids, ascorbic acid, alkaloid, etc. In some nectars, proteins are present as enzymes. The sugars and lipids have been shown to be the major nutrients, while all other constituents of nectar are the micro-nutrients (Baker and Baker, 1975; 1982; 1983a, b; Baker, 1978).

Nectar is an important source of energy for the flower-visitors. Although the major sugar components of nectar are found important in this respect, the volume and concentration of nectar are also equally important. The concentration of nectar normally refers to the percentage of all types of sugars present. The quality and quantity of nectar influence the flower-visitor species which have been shown to have certain preferences for particular nectar types.

This paper is an attempt to review all the relevant scattered information on nectar chemistry and the influence of different chemical compounds on flower-visitors which have a definite role in pollination and in phylogency.

SUGARS

Nectars of many species of flowering plants have been analysed for their chemical constituents by several workers. Percival (1961) provided nectar types present in 900 angiospermic species belonging to 101 families. Baker and Baker (1982) analysed nectars of over 1,000 species of flowering plants. Other investigators have also analysed nectars of various plant species (Watt *et al.*, 1974; Hainsworth and Wolf, 1976; Macior, 1978; Gottsberger *et al.*, 1984). Bahadur *et al.*, (1986) analysed the nectars of one hundred Indian plant species belonging to various families. All these studies unequivocally established that the common sugars present in nectar are the hexose monosaccharides, glucose and fructose and the disaccharide sucrose. These three sugars occur in combination or separately. Baker and Baker (1982) called these common sugars as "big-three sugars". Based on their own work, these authors have listed out the occurrence of big-three sugars in detectable amounts in 765 species (Table 1). Other sugars are also found in the floral nectar. They occur in small amounts and include mono-, di-, tri- and tetra-saccharide sugars (Table 2). Among the mono-saccharides, arabinose and galactose are frequent (Gottsberger *et al.*, 1973; Watt *et al.*, 1974) while mannose is rarely

TABLE 1 : Numbers of nectars with detectable sugar-combinations (Baker and Baker, 1982)

Sucrose	7
Glucose	2
Fructose	0
Sucrose + glucose	29
Sucrose + fructose	0
Glucose + fructose	78
Sucrose + glucose + fructose	649
Total :	765

TABLE 2 : Minor sugars reported from nectar (Baker, H.G. and I. Baker, 1981)

Monosaccharides :
- arabinose
- galactose
- mannose

Disaccharides :
- gentiobiose
- lactose
- maltose
- melibiose
- trehalose

Trisaccharides :
- melezitose
- raffinose

Tetrasaccharides :
- stachyose

found in the floral nectar. Crane (1977) reports that mannose is secreted in *Tilia* species under drought stress conditions. The disaccharide sugars occur occasionally (Percival, 1961; Baker and Baker, 1982). The trisaccharide sugars occur more frequently (Mauritzio, 1959; 1962; Percival, 1961; Baker and Baker, 1982). Bahadur *et al.* (1986) from India reported the present of the big-three sugars and also the xylose in the floral nectar of heterostylous *Turnera subulata* and homostylous *T. ulmifolia*; melezitose sugar is additionally present in the latter.

While analysing the composition of sugars in floral nectars in various species, Wykes (1952) found that the relative proportions of sugars in nectar in any of the species he studied tended to remain constant, while their occurrence was characteristic of certain families. Percival (1961) in an elaborative study on the common sugars in nectars found distinct differences in the quantities of different types of sugars between species and such differences are divided into three broad groups as sucrose-dominant (*Berberis, Helleborus*); all three-sugars in about equal amounts (*Abutilon*) and glucose and fructose dominant (Crucifers, Umbellifers and some Asteraceae members). She concludes that some families of flowering plants may be characterised by sucrose-rich nectars (Ranunculaceae and Lamiaceae) and some by predominantly or entirely hexose-rich nectar (Brassicaceae and Asteraceae).

Harborne (1982) analysed nectars of different species of the genus *Rhododendron*. He found the common sugars in all species. According to the proportion of the three common sugars and presence/ absence of an oligosaccharide sugar, he divided the species into five nectar classes (Table 3). The quantitative variations in nectar sugars are consistent with the species and are not subject to divisional or seasonal variations. Since sucrose is readily converted to glucose and fructose *via* the enzymic invertase, one might expect some changes with age of the flower although invertase was detected in these nectars, it was not present in quantity at the right time to change the patterns. Baker and Baker (1983a) designated nectar types which they found in their study into different categories. The nectars with sucrose/hexose ratio of more than 0.999 have been shown as sucrose-dominated, while those with ratios between 0.5 and 0.999 as sucrose-rich. Nectars with ratios between 0.1 and 0.499 are hexose-rich and those with ratios of less than 0.1 are hexose-dominated.

TABLE 3 : Nectar classes within the genus *Rhododendron* (Harborne, 1982)

*Nectar class**	*No. species present in*	*% total*	*Example of species contain in this nectar*
Glu : Fru : Suc in (1 : 1 : 1) ratio	12	22	*R. phaeochrysum*
Suc with traces of Glu and Fru	8	15	*R. augustinii*
Glu : Fru : Suc (1 : 1 : 1) with oligosaccharide	3	5	*R. jasminiflorum*
Suc only	15	27	*R. camphylocarpum*
Glu and Fru only	17	31	*R. campanulatum*

****Abbreviations*** : Glu. = glucose; Fru. = fructose; Suc. = sucrose.

The relative proportions of common sugars and their concentration in nectar are equally important in the context of pollinator. In general, the total mean of sugar concentration is higher for nectar from insect-pollinated flowers than vertebrate-pollinated ones. However, there are individual cases where especially humming bird-pollinated flowers nearly equal the highest values of bee-flowers (Gottsberger *et al*., 1984). Higher sugar concentrations might not limit humming bird feeding since humming bird flowers show more variations in their sugar concentration than that for bee-flowers (Gottsberger *et al*., 1973, 1984). Similarly, sunbird-flowers in the paleotropics also show variations in sugar concentrations as the sunbirds tend to visit both dilute and concentrated floral nectars (Aluri and Subba Reddi, 1994).

Nectar production and concentration can be subject to considerable fluctuations even within individual flowers as a result of some subtle changes in the environment, such as wind, temperature, relative humidity, cloudiness, soil moisture, the position of the flower on the plant, shading, age of the plant, seed, pollinator activity and/or reabsorbtion (Shuel, 1955, 1957; Wood, 1961; Lüttge, 1961; Percival, 1965; Massengale *et al*., 1968; Kugler, 1970; Free, 1970; Cruden, 1976; Corbet, 1978; Corbet *et al*., 1979a, b; Baker, 1978). Therefore, sugar concentration can also fluctuate to some extent under the influence of the prevailing environmental conditions. Environmentally-induced variations amount and concentration of nectar, however, do not bring change in the sugar ratio and remains constant.

The sugar ratio is consistent between individuals even in obligately out-crossed species (Baker, 1978). This consistency may have a key role in giving the nectar a uniform ''taste'' recognizable by legitimate pollinators.

The sugar concentrations are lower in nectars of narrow-tubed flowers than in nectars of short-tubed or open flowers. the tubular shape of the flowers has been considered to be important as an evaporation-reducing device and also important in hiding nectar from unwanted visitors or from short-tongued nectar thieves. The nectar in open or bowl-shaped flowers is exposed to the air and has the tendency to evaporate, which reduces the sugar concentration in accordance with the prevailing climatic conditions (Subba Reddi and Aluri, 1993). Simpson and Neff (1983) suggest that caution must be exercised in interpreting nectar characteristics strictly in terms of pollinator selection based on Percival's (1961) results. Percival (1961) noted the dominance of hexose-sugars in shallow, exposed nectaries, whereas sucrose tended to dominate in deep, hidden nectaries. Corbet *et al.* (1979) and Plowright (1981) stressed on the importance of humidity in controlling nectar concentrations. At a given relative humidity, a nectar containing only sucrose must have a higher concentration than a nectar consisting of hexoses in order to maintain an equilibrium with the air. The simple physical relationship is probably a principal factor influencing the dominance of hexose-sugars in shallow, exposed nectaries. Baker and Baker (1982) explained that the sugar concentrations are much higher in the trees and wines which flower in dry region in low land tropical forest than in the flowers that occur in highly humid, cool conditions of the cold forest. The flowers of alpine forests contain high sugar concentrations which are essential for foraging by potential pollinators.

Baker and Baker (1983) report that the flowers with sucrose-rich nectars are pollinated by long-tongued bees, whereas those with hexose-rich or hexose-dominant nectar by short-tongues prefer balanced nectar with roughly equal presentation of the three common sugars mentioned earlier. Percival (1961) suggests that such balanced nectars are not common. Waller (1972) from his experiments shows that honey bees prefer a sucrose-rich nectar, but they do not necessarily depend on its availability. The flowers that are exclusively visited by butterflies are sucrose-rich and those visited both by bees and butterflies are hexose-rich. Interestingly, *Colias* butterflies have the enzymatic capability to inter-contest the common sugars and make use of nectars with any combination of these sugars (Baker and Baker, 1983). Baker and Baker (1973) reported that butterfly nectars are not very viscous. However, a wide range exists in the concentration of nectar used by butterflies as reported by various investigators : 15-25% (Watt *et al.*, 1974), 13-44% (Baker, 1975), 16-40% (Baker, 1978) and 20-25% (Kingsolver and Daniel, 1979). Kevan and Baker (1983) stated that butterflies can also use viscous nectars, diluting them by secreting a type of saliva. Pivnick and McNiel (1985) observed *Thymelicus lineola* feeding on concentrated nectars varying from 40 to 65% sucrose in a variety of flower species. Subba Reddi (unpublished data) examined nectars of various plant species and the concentrations of those nectars fall into two ranges, 12-48% and 53-62%. The former range of concentration being more common in flowers receiving frequent visits from butterflies and thereby indicating that butterfly nectars are less viscous. The latter concentration range is found in flowers less often visited by butterflies. This finding suggests that the highest sugar concentration in nectar might not deter butterflies from feeding. Flowers visited by hawkmoths and settling moths are predominantly sucrose-rich, in strong contrast with bat-flowers which contain hexose-rich nectars although the flowers of both open at night (Baker and Baker, 1983). Thus sucrose-richness in nectar appears to be a characteristic of Lepidoptera-adapted flowers (Percival, 1961).

AMINO ACIDS

Ziegler (1956) seems to have been the first to locate amino acids in detectable quantities in floral nectar. Later, Lüttge (1961; 1962) found amino acids in floral nectars. Since then, several investigators have analysed floral nectar for amino acids in a number of plant species (Cruden and Toledo, 1977; Cruden and Hermann-Parker, 1977; Rust, 1977; Keeler, 1977; 1980; Scogin, 1980; Voss *et al.*, 1980; Bahadur *et al.*, 1984; Baker and Baker, 1983; 1976). Their analysis of floral nectars indicate that it is common to find amino acids either in traces or in measurable quantities in nectar. The production of amino acids in higher concentrations in nectar is quite often associated with flowers that simulate carrion-or dung and attract the female flies for egg-laying.

The mere presence or absence of amino acids in nectar can not be taken to indicate their role in nutrition of flower visiting animals. The composition of amino acids has to be thoroughly worked out so as to relate the presence of amino acids to the pollinators. The phloem sap which seems to have a concentration of ninhydrin-positive substances is the source for both sugars and amino acids. The substances contain amino acids as a major fraction (Lüttge 1961). Lüttge and Higinbotham (1979) show that anatomically more primitive nectaries filter these ninhydrin-positive substances less than the anatomically more advanced ones. This is the reason to see more concentrated amino acids in the more primitive nectaries and highly reduced amino acid concentration in the more elaborated nectaries which are found in more advanced plant species. This is in contradiction to the conclusion of Baker and Baker (1973; 1975). Gottsberger *et al.* (1984) report that the more advanced morphological characters nearly always connected with nectar of lower amino acid concentrations; the concentrations vary widely between individual plant species, however. They suggest that more amino acid concentration in the flowers of advanced plant species may be due to the contamination of nectar with pollen containing more proline. Proline is generally present in the pollen, but rare in nectar. The amino acid proline is always prevalent in pollen and plays a metabolic role in pollen-tube growth (Linskens and Schrauwen, 1969; Stanley and Linskens, 1974). The proline from the pollen grains when mixed with nectar, increase the amino acid amount through rapid diffusion. Regardless, nectar amino acids indeed may have some importance in nutrition to flower-visiting animals but their role in evolutionary advancement or direct connection with the pollination system is doubtful (Gottsberger *et al.*, 1984).

Baker and Baker (1976) show that all essential amino acids are present in floral nectar, but the number varies from nectar to nectar. Generally, arginine, histidine, lysine, tryptophan, phenylalanine, methionine, thrionine, leucine, isoleucine, valine, glutamic acid, aspartic acid-all or some are essential for insect nutrition, and even proline (Baker and Baker, 1976).

The open bowl-like or short-tubed flowers pollinated by syrphids, bombyliids, muscids and less specialized flies produce low levels of amino acids. The flowers pollinated by butterflies, settling moths and wasps produce nectars of high amino acid concentration (Baker and

Baker, 1982). Baker and Baker (1975) and Willmer (1980) show that in the Lepidoptera-pollinated flowers with narrow corolla-tube containing introrsely dehiscing anthers, the probability is that the amino acid concentration in the nectar will be significantly higher when pollen is dislodged by an active pollinator and falls in the floral tube. But flowers in the new world tropics and sub-tropics are usually poor in the amino acids as bats primarily feed on pollen and fruit juices for protein source (Howell, 1974; Voss *et al.*, 1980). Passerine bird flowers in the old World produce nectars of low amino acid concentration. On the contrary, the tropical *Erythrina* in the New World when adapted to passerine birds contain nectar of high amino acid concentration (Cruden and Toledo, 1977; Baker and Baker, 1982). Such dual concentrations may be due to a slow-down in insect catching and fruit taking by the passerines at a time when the said trees are in massive bloom and the birds defending territories of trees (Baker and Baker, 1982; Cruden and Toledo, 1977; Cruden and Hermann- Parker, 1977). An *Erythrina* hybrid produced from a cross between *E. herbaceae* with sucrose-rich nectar and *E. crystagalli* with hexose-dominant nectar indicates a quantitive intermediacy and qualitative additiveness in amino acids compared to its parents, and intermediacy in sugars and other compounds is also evident (Baker and Baker, 1982). The composition and concentration in floral nectar varies strongly and in general appear scanty to be of nutritive value to most pollinators (see Gottsberger, 1986). The relationship between nutritional requirements of pollinating animals and dependence on floral nectars has to be thoroughly studied before any definitive conclusion is made.

The composition of amino acids usually differs between floral and extrafloral nectars even on the same plant, because the two kinds of nectar are aimed at serving different purposes for the pollinators (Baker *et al.*, 1978). The amino acids present in the floral nectar are not always related to protein making. There may also be non-protein amino acids (Baker, 1975; Baker and Baker, 1982). It is not yet known the usefulness of non-protein amino acids in nectar. But it should be mentioned that the function of nectar is the reward of pollinators and not their poisoning (Rhoadès and Bergdahl, 1981; Baker and Baker, 1982). Non-protein amino acids are present in seeds and have been regarded as chemical defenses against seed-predators (Rehr *et al.*, 1973). Therefore, the functional aspects of non-protein amino acids have to be explored as to its value in nutrition of the pollinators.

The floral nectars contain various chemicals other than sugars and amino acids. They include lipids, alkaloids and toxic chemicals, phenolics, proteins, organic acids, inorganic compounds, vitamins, nectar pH, resins, black nectar and ant-repellents (Baker, 1975; Lüttge, 1977; Baker and Baker, 1982; 1983a & b; Harborne, 1982). The functional aspects of these minor chemical compounds have been described separately as under :

Lipids

Vogel (1969) was the first to report the presence of lipids in floral nectar as liquid reward to pollinators. He has provided more information about lipids in subsequent papers (Vogel, 1971; 1974; 1976). The production of lipids is a function of glands which he named "elaiophores" and regarded them as an alternative to the production of aqueous nectar. Simpson and Neff (1981) report that the lipids are nothing but floral oils which are a group of florally secreted chemicals from glandular structures present in nectaries. The oils are also produced in different floral parts such as corolla, stamens and ovary bases. The lipids and their complement fatty acids have an advantage over nectar in that they contain more energy per unit than even pure sugar (oil 9 cal/g; sugar 4 cal/g). These compounds are nutritionally more attractive to the pollinators. Harborne (1982) shows that lipids serve as a good substitute for sugars. However, lipid production must be energetically more expensive for the plant than to make nectar.

Baker (1978) suggests that oil flower-oil collection syndrome arose from a nectar production-nectar feeding system. His suggestion is based on the finding that lipids are found, sometimes in large quantities, in many plant nectars. Oil collection requires that use of specialised structures formed by modified setae in the pollinators (Neff and Simpson, 1981). Oil production/oil collection is a fairly tight system acquiring specializations on the part of both plant and pollinator (Simpson and Neff, 1983). Many genera of six unrelated families (Iridaceae, Orchidaceae, Malphgiaceae, Krameriaceae, Scrophulariaceae, Solanaceae) and possibly, a seventh one, Melastomataceae in the New World tropics may exhibit an oil-flower syndrome. The oils from the floral nectar of these plant species is collected by female Anthophorine bees which have the morphological specialisations necessary for collection of these oils. These bees mix the oils obtained from floral nectars with pollen and use the pollen-oil (lipid) mixture as food for the larvae. This indicates that the lipids play a dual role in the evolution of plants and pollinators.

Alkaloids and toxic substances

Alkaloids are group of heterogenous substances found in floral nectar. These substances show detrimental effects on flower-visitors. They can be identified by spot tests with Iodoplatinate and Dragendroff reagents on dried nectar samples (Baker and Baker, 1982). Baker (1977; 1978, 1983b) reported that the alkaloids occur frequently in floral nectars. The alkaloid substances are very rich in tropical flowers and low in alpine-tundra.

Alkaloids act as poison in plant tissues and may also be temporary storage substances for nitrogen (Robinson, 1968). The exact function of alkaloids in nectar in relation to pollination is not known. However, it is suggested that the alkaloids have a selective value in killing unwanted visitors so that the visits of the real pollinators are fully justified with the floral rewards.

Toxic substances are found in some nectars. The function of these substances on the flower visitors is observed in some species. The hawkmoth, *Manduca quinquemaculata* after being fed with nectar of *Datura meteloides* behaves in an intoxicated manner. Nectar thieves also show erratic behaviour and other behavioural abnormalities. Such behaviours have been observed when nectar thieves obtained nectar from the flowers of *Catalpa speciosa*. Gottsberger (1986) shows that the role of toxic substances in nectar as well as pollen of *Zigadenus paniculatus* is probably to reduce the number of potential pollinator species and increase the flower constancy of those species capable of using the floral reward. Cruden (1977) reports that the nectar of *Tilia* is toxic to bees. Madel (1977) indicates that a couple of flowers of *Tilia* produce enough toxic nectar to kill *Bombus* spp. due to presence of monosaccharide mannose in the few hours. Schulz-Langer (1967) found that the nectar of *Aesculus hippocastanum* contains saponins which are toxic to bees. Deodikar *et al.* (1958) reports that the nectar of *Euphorbia geniculata* may be poisonous to honey-bees. They have found an instance of large-scale paralysis and deaths of honey-bees due to their foraging on the floral nectar of *E. geniculata*. Further, Deodikar (1961) remarks that the flowers of this plant may be visited when the honey-bees are in acute hunger and starvation particularly in times of acute shortage of normal forage during floral gap periods. Subba Reddi (unpublished) noted that *E. geniculata* flowers are very rarely visited by honey-bees and this substantiates Deodikar's findings. Toxic nectars which cause erratic or narcotic behaviour have also been found in several other plant species. Vogel (1978) shows that the cause of toxicity to insects comes from mannose sugar in nectar. According to Crane (1978) various less known sugars are also toxic. The insects lacking mannose phosphate isomerase enzyme cannot completely digest mannose. When such insects consume nectars having mannose, the mannose-6-phosphate gets accumulated, and becomes toxic to bees. Toxic nectar is hazardous not only to insect but also to man, because man consumes honey which is produced by honey-bees. The honey-bees in making the honey may also gather toxic nectars from different flowers. In this context, it is important for apiarist to avoid the growth of plant species which produce toxic nectars in the areas where honey-bees gather nectar.

Phenolics

Phenolics are a group of diverse chemicals and their occurrence in nectar can be detected by colour testing with p-nitraniline. Baker (1978) found phenols in a number of tropical flowers. He extended studies in this direction and reported in 1982 that phenolic chemicals occur more in tropical flowers than in temperate and alpine-tundra ones. He concludes that phenolic chemicals need further examination and closer identification in relation to pollination syndromes.

Proteins

It is common to find proteins in nectar. Protein presence is easily detected by bromo-phenol blue test. The proteins in nectar are largely enzymatic in occurrence and function. The common proteins are invertase, transglucosidase, phosphotase, oxidase, tyrosinase, etc. Scogin (1979) found the presence of esterase and malate-dehydrogenase in nectar of *Fremontia* (Sterculiaceae). It is unclear how frequently the interconvertion of sucrose and hexose sugars takes place in nectar under the influence of enzymatic proteins. Baker and Baker (1983a) urges that identification and distribution of all proteins occurring as enzymes must precede any conclusion as to their function.

Organic acids

Nectars that contain lipids, quite often contain anti-oxidant organic acids (Baker and Baker, 1975). The presence of organic acids in honey was first found by Kask (1938). His finding led to search for ascorbic acid in floral nectars. Griebel and Hess (1940) were the first to report organic acids in floral nectar of Lamiaceae members. The acids are also found in nectars of *Fritillaria* and *Impatiens* (Weber, 1942; 1951). Later on, a number of organic acids has been found in different nectars. Baker and Baker (1983) suggest that the presence of organic acids, particularly ascorbic acid, may play a *rancidity*-preventing role. So also Harborne (1982) suggests by reporting that organic acids prevent rancidity in standing nectar.

Other substances

Floral nectar has also been found to contain vitamins. The vitamins are water-soluble and provide nourishment to the flower- visitors (Ziegler *et al.*, 1964). In organic chemicals like potassium are also found in nectar. Walker (1972) states that the potassium and its content in *Allium cepa* nectar varies from 3800 to 13,000 ppm an amount much higher than the nectar present in adjoining plants and concluded low potassium content is responsible for more attractiveness nectar to bees in amphidiploid *Allium* species.

Most Nectars show pH ranging from 5.6 to 5.9. Some are acidic as in *Oxalis* spp. (Oxalidaceae) (pH 1.6) and *Silena alba* (Caryophyllaceae) (pH 3.0). In the former species, oxalic acid contributes to the extreme acidity of nectar (Baker, 1985). Alkaline nectar (pH 10) is found in *Viburnum costaricum*. Baker and Baker (1982) express the possibility of organic substances contributing to the pH picture. The pH parameter is taxonomically and phylogenetically important. The relationship between nectar pH and pollinator type is yet to be understood.

Resinous nectars are found in a few plants. The nectars of *Dalechampia* (Euphorhiaceae) and *Clusia rosa* (Guttiferae) produce resins in good amount (Armbruster, 1984). The resins are viscous and transluscent in nature, and are water repellent. Anthophorine female bees collect the resins and use them in nest-lining.

Scott-Elliot (1890) found that *Melianthus* spp. (Melianthaceae) produce nectar with melanin as one of the ingredients. The nectar is collected by sunbirds in South Africa. As the nectar contains melanin, it looks black. Why the nectar is black and what is its adaptive value are still a mystery even after a century?

Ant repellents

Some nectars may contain ant-repellants, so that nectar may be chemically protected from ant-foraging. *Hippobroma longiflora* has an ant-repellent chemical (Feinsinger and Swarm, 1978). Guerrant and Fiedler (1981) explain that in this species, the toxic substance is in the petals and is released into the nectar when the corolla-tube is damaged by the probing mouth-parts of insects. This enables the flowers to keep the ants out of reach. Nevertheless, the morphology of flowers appears to be important than chemical defenses to keep the ants away from foraging. In general, ant-pollination systems are rare. Several characters have been proposed for the rarity of ant-pollination (see Subba Reddi and Aluri, 1993). The chemical components of floral nectar characterising the ant-pollination system are not yet known.

Pesticides

With increase dependence on pesticides in modern agriculture, traces of pesticides have been detected as component of nectar in several species (Lord *et al*.,. 1968; Shuel, 1970; Fielder and Drescher, 1984). Revathi (1982) reported pesticides in Indian honeys.

From the foregoing it is obvious that nectar until recently considered as "sugar-water" shot into scientific prominance in view of its richness in variety of chemicals and as stated by Baker and Baker (1983b). "We have only began to find and appreciate its biological significance."

Literature Cited

Aluri, R.J.S. and Subba Reddi, C. 1984. Pollination ecology and mating system of the weedy mint *Leonotis nepetaefolia* R.Br. in India. *Proc. Indian Nat. Sci. Acad., B60* : 255-268.

Armbruster, W.S. 1984. The role of resin in angiosperm pollination : Ecological and chemical considerations. *Am. J. Bot., 71* : 1149-1160.

Bahadur, B., Rama Swamy, N. and Farooqui, S.M. 1985. Floral nectaries in two species of *Turnera* L. *New Botanist, 12* : 117-127.

Bahadur, B., Chaturvedi, A. and Swamy, N.R. 1986. Nectar types in Indian plants. *Proc. Indian Acad. Sci.* (Plant Sci.), *9* : 41-48.

Bahadur, B., Arthi, C. and Rama Swamy, N. 1987. Floral Biology in *Hybanthes ennaespermus* (L.) F. Muell. (Violaceae) *New Botanist, 14* : 29-45.

Bahadur, B., Chaturvedi, A. and Rama Swamy, N. 1986. Nectar types in Indian plants. *Proc. Indian Acad. Sci.* (Plant Sci.), *96* : 41-48.

Bahadur, B. and Rama Swamy, N. 1984. Pollination biology of heterostylous *Turnera subulata* J.E. Smith. *J. Palynol., 20* : 198-209.

Baker, H.G. 1975. Sugar concentrations in nectar from hummingbird flowers. *Biotropica, 7* : 37-41.

Baker, H.G. 1977. Non-sugar components of nectar. *Apidologie, 8* : 349-356.

Baker, H.G. 1978. Chemical aspects of the pollination biology of woody plants in the tropics. In: (eds.) P.B. Tomlinson and M.H. Zimmerman. *Tropical Trees as Living Systems.* pp. 57-82. Cambridge University Press, New York.

Baker, H.G. 1985. Trends in pollination biology. *Aliso, 11* : 213-229.

Baker, H.G., and Baker, I. 1973. Some anthecological aspects of the evolution of the nectar producing flowers, particularly amino acid production. In: (ed.) V.H. Heywood. *Taxonomy and Ecology*, Academic Press, London.

Baker, H.G. and Baker, I. 1976. Analysis of amino acids in nectar. *Phytochem. Bull., 9* : 4-7.

Baker, H.G. and Baker, I. 1975. Studies of nectar constitution and pollinator-plant coevolution. In: (eds.) L.E. Gilbert and P.H. Raven. *Co-evolution of animals and plants.* University of Texas Press, Austin.

Baker, H.G. and Baker, I. 1982. Some chemical constituents of floral nectars of *Erythrina* in relation to pollinators and systematics. *Allertonia, 3* : 25-36.

Baker. H.G. and Baker, I. 1982. Chemical constituents of nectar in relation to pollination mechanisms and phylogeny. In: (ed.) M.H. Nitecki. *Biochemical Aspects of Evolutionary Biology.* pp. 131-171. University of Chicago Press, Chicago.

Baker, H.G. and Baker, I. 1983a. Floral nectar sugar constituents in relation to pollinator type. In: (eds.) C.E. Jones and R.J. Little. *Handbook of Experimental Pollination Biology.* pp. 117-141. Scientific and Academic Editions, New York.

Baker, H.G. and Baker, I. 1983b. A brief historical review of the chemistry of floral nectar. In: (eds) Bentley B. and Elias, T. *The Biology of Nectaries.* Columbia University Press, NewYork.

Baker, H.G., Opler, P.A. and Baker, I. 1978. A comparison of the amino acid compliments of floral and extra-floral nectars. *Bot. Gaz., 131* : 322-332.

Corbet. S.A. 1978. Bees and the nectar of *Echium vulgare.* In: (ed.) A.J. Richards. *The Pollination of Flowers of Insects.* pp. 1-30. Academic Press, London.

Corbet. S.A., Unwin. D.M. and Prys-Jones, O.E. 1979a. Humidity. nectar and insect visits to flowers. with special reference to *Crataegus, Tilia* and *Echium. Ecol. Entomol, 4* : 9-22.

Corbet, S.A., Willmer, P.G. Beament, J.W.L., Unwin, D.M. and Prys-Jones, O.E. 1979b. Post-secretory determinants of sugar concentration in nectar. *Pl. Cell Environm., 2* : 293-308.

Crane, E. 1978. Sugars poisonous to bees. *Bee Wld, 59* : 37-38.

Cruden, R.W., 1976. Fecundity as a function of nectar production and pollen-ovule ratios. In: (eds.) J. Burley and B.T. Styles. *Tropical Trees, Variation, Breeding and Conservation*. pp. 171-178. Academic Press, London.

Cruden, R.W. 1977. Pollen-ovule ratios : A conservative indicator of breeding systems in flowering plants. *Evolution, 31* : 32-46.

Cruden, R.W. and Hermannparker, S. 1977. Defense of feeding site by Orioles and hepatic tanagers in Mexico. *The Auk., 94* : 594-596.

Cruden, R.W. and Toledo, V.M. 1977. Oriole pollination of *Eryithrina breviflora* (Leguminosae) : Evidence for a polytopic view of Ornithophily. *Pl. Syst. Evol., 126* : 393-403.

Deodikar, G.B. 1961. Some aspects of bee-botany. In: (ed.) T.S. Mahabale. *Prof. S.P. Agarkar Commemoration Volume*, pp. 61-78 Published by Mahabale, T.S. Pune.

Deodikar, G.B., Shah, P.N., Thakar, C.V. and Salvi, S.R. 1958. Poisoning of honey-bees foraging on *Euphorbia geniculata*. *Bee Wld., 39* : 118-120.

Fielder, L. and Drescher, W. 1984. Residue analysis of *insecticides* in nectar : possible contamination after pre-blossom *Proc. 5th Symp. Poll. Versailles., 207-213.*

Feinsinger, P. and Swarm, L.A. 1978. How common are ant-repellent nectars? *Biotropica, 10* : 238-239.

Free, J.B. 1970. *Insect Pollination of Crops*. Academic Press, New York.

Gilliam, M., Moffett, J.O. and Kauffeld, N.M. 1983. Examination of floral nectars of *Citrus*, cotton, and Arizona desert plants for microbes. *Apidologie, 14* : 299-302.

Gottsberger, G. 1986. Floral Ecology : Report on the years 1981 (79) to 1985. *Prog. Bot., 47* : 384-415.

Gottsberger, G., Schrauwen, J. and Linskens, H.F. 1973. Die Sucker-Bestandeile des Nektars einiger tropischer Blüten. Portugaline. *Acta Biol. Ser., A.3* : 1-8.

Gottsberger, G., Schrauwen, J. and Linskens, H.F. 1984. Aminoacids and sugars in nectar, and their putative evolutionary significance. *Pl. Syst. Evol., 145* : 55-77.

Griebel, C. and Hess, G. 1940. The vitamin-C content of flower nectar of certain Labiatae. *Zeit. Untersuch Lebensomitt, 79* : 168-171.

Guerrant, E.O. and Fiedler, P.L. 1981. Flower defenses against nectar-piliferage by ants. *Biotropica, 13* : Supplement 25-3.

Gunning, B.E.S. and Steer, M.W. 1975. *Ultrastructure and the Biology of Plant Cells*. Edward Arnold, London.

Hainsworth, F.R. and Wold, L.L. 1976. Nectar characteristics and food selection by Hummingbirds. *Oecologia, 25* : 101-113.

Harborne, J.B. 1982. *Introduction to Ecological Biochemistry*. Academic Press, London.

Howell, D.J. 1974. Bats and pollen : Physiological aspects of the syndrome of cheiropterophily. *Comp. Biochem. Physiol., 48A* : 263-276.

Kask, M. 1938. Vitamin-C. Gehalt der estinschen Honigen. *Zeit. Untersuch Lebensmitt., 76* : 543-545.

Keeler, K.H. 1977. The extra-floral nectaries of *Ipomoea carnea* (Convolvulaceae). *Am. J. Bot., 64* : 482-488.

Keeler, K.H. 1980. The extrafloral nectaries of *Ipomoea leptophylla Am. J. Bot., 67* : 216-222.

Kevan, P.G. and Baker, H.G. 1983. Insects as flower visitors and pollinators. *Annu. Rev. Entomol., 28* : 407-453.

Kingsolver, J.G. and Daniel, T.L. 1979. On the mechanics and energetics of nectar feeding in butterflies. *J. Theor. Biol., 76* : 167-179.

Kugler. H. 1970. *Blütenokologie*. Ed. 2 Stuttgart : G. Fischer Verlag.

Lord, K.A., May, M.A and Stevenson, J. H. 1968. The secretion of the systemic insecticides dimethoate and phorate into nectar *Ann. appl. Biol., 61* : 19-27.

Linskens, H.F. and Schrauwen, J. 1969. The release of free aminoacids from germinating pollen. *Acta Bot. Neerl., 18* : 605-614.

Lüttge, U. 1961. Uber die Zusammensetzung des Nektars und den Mechanismus Seiner Sekretion II. *Planta, 59* : 108-114.

Lüttge, U. 1977. Nectar composition and membrane transport of sugars and aminoacids : A review of the present state of nectar research. *Apidologie., 8* : 305-320.

Lüttge. U. and Higinbotham, N. 1979. *Transport in plants*. Springer- Verlag, New York.

Macior. L.W. 1978. Pollination interactions in sympatric *Dicentra* species. *Am. J. Bot., 65* : 57-62.

Madel, G., 1977. Vergiftungen von Hummein dureh den Nektar der Silver-linde, *Tilia tomentosa* Moench. *Bonn Zoologische Beitr., 28* : 149-154.

Massengale, M.A., Levin, M.D., Dobrenz, A.J. and Todd, F.E. 1968. The influence of growth regulators and plant-spacing on sugar content of the nectar and seed-production in alfalfa (*Medicago sativa* L.). *J. Arizona Acad. Sci., 5* : 111-115.

Mauritzio, A. 1959. Papierchromatograpische unterschuchungen an Blutenhoningen und Nektar. *Amm. de I. Abielle, 2* : 291-341.

Mauritzio, A. 1962. From the raw material to the finished product. *Honey-bee world, 43* : 66-81.

Neff, J.L. and Simpson, B.B. 1981. Oil collecting structures in the Arthrophoridae (Hymenoptera) : Morphology, function and use in the systematics. *J. Kansas Entomol. Soc., 54* : 95-123.

Percival, M.S. 1961. Types of nectar in angiosperms. *New Phytol, 60* : 235-281.

Percival, M.S. 1965. *Floral Biology*. Pergamon Press, London.

Pivnick, K.A. and McNiel, J.N. 1985. Effects of nectar concentration on butterfly feeding : Measured feeding rates for *Thymelicus lineola* (Lepidoptera : Hespeiidae) and a general feeding model for the adult Lepidoptera. *Oecologia* (Berlin), *66* : 226-237.

Plowright, R.C. 1981. Nectar production in the boreal forest lily. *Clintonia borealis. Can. J. Bot., 59* : 156-160.

Rehr, S.S., Janzen, D.H. and Feeny, P.F. 1973. L-dopa in legume seeds : A chemical barrier to insect attack. Science, *181* : 81-82.

Revathi, V. 1982. Some biochemical evaluations of Indian honeys. MSc. dissertation, Bombay University, Bombay.

Rhoades, D.F. and Bergdahl, J.C. 1981. Adaptive significance of toxic nectar. *Amer. Nat., 117* : 798-803.

Robinson, T. 1968. *The Biochemistry of Alkaloids*. Springer-Verlag, Berlin.

Rust, R.W. 1977. Pollination in *Impatiens capensis* and *I. pallida* (Balasaminaceae). *Bull. Torrey Bot. Club., 104* : 361-367.

Shuel, R.W. 1970. Current research on nectar. *Bee Wld., 51* : 63-69.

Scogin, R. 1980. Floral pigments and nectar constituents of two bat-pollinated plants : Coloration, nutritional and energetic considerations. *Biotropica, 12* : 273-276.

Scogin, R. 1983. Visible floral pigments and pollinators. In: (eds.) C.E. Jones and R.J. Little. *Handbook of Experimental Pollination Biology*. pp. 160-173, Scientific and Academic Press, New York.

Scott-Elliot, G.F. 1890. Ornithophilous flowers in South Africa. *Ann. Bot., 4* : 265-280.

Shuel, R.W. 1955. Nectar secretion. *Am. Bee J., 95* : 229-234.

Shuel, R.W. 1957. Some aspects of the relation between nectar secretion and nitrogen, phosphorous and potassium nutrition. *Can. J. Pl. Sci., 37* : 220-236.

Simpson, B.B. and Neff, J.L. 1981. Floral rewards. Alternatives to pollen and nectar. *Ann. Mo. Bot. Gard., 688* : 301-322.

Simpson, B.B. and Neff, J.L. 1983. Evolution and diversity of floral rewards. In: (eds.) C.E. Jones and R.J. Littlee. *Handbook of Experimental Pollination Biology*. pp. 142-159. Scientific and Academic Editions, New York.

Stanley, R.G. and Linskens, H.F. 197. *Pollen : Biology, Biochemistry and Management*. Springer-Verlag, New York.

Subba Reddi, C. and Aluri, R.J.S. 1993. Chemical ecology of insect pollination — An Overview. In: (eds.) T.N. Ananthakrishnan and A. Raman. *Chemical Ecology of Phytophagous Insects*. pp. 211-225. Oxford and I.B.H. Publishing Co. Pvt. Ltd. New Delhi.

Vogel, S. 1969. Flowers offering fatty oils instead of nectar. Abstracts *XI Int. Bot. Congr*, Seattle, p. 229.

Vogel, S. 1971. Öelproduzierende Blumen, die durch Ölsammelnde Bienen bestaubt warden. *Naturwissenschaften, 58* : 58.

Vogel, S. 1974. Ölbumen and ölsammelnde Pienen. *Trop. Subtrop Pflanzenw, 7* : 1-547.

Vogel, S. 1976. *Lysimachia* : Öelblumen der Holarktis. *Naturwissen- schaften, 63* : 44-45.

Vogel, S. 1978. Evolutionary shifts from reward to deception in pollen flowers. In: (ed.) A.J. Richards. *The Pollination of Flowers by Insects*. pp. 89-96. Academic Press, New York.

Voss, R. Turner, M., Onouye, R., Fisher M. and Cort, R. 1980. Floral biology of *Markea neurantha* Hemsley (Solanaceae), a bat pollinated epiphyte. *Am. Midland Natur., 103* : 262-268.

Waller, G.D., Carpenter, W. and Ziehl, O.A. 1972. Potassium in onion nectar and its possible effect on attractiveness onion flowers to honey bees. *J. Amer. Soc. Hort. soc., 97* : 535-539.

Walker, G.D. 1973. Chemical differences between nectar of onion and competing plant species and probable effects upon attractiveness to pollinators. Ph.D. thesis, Utah State University U.S.A.

Watt, W.B., Hoch, P.C. and Mills, S.G. 1974. Nectar resource use by *Colias* butterflies. *Oecologia* (Berlin), *14* : 353-374.

Weber, F. 1942. Vitamin C in Nektar Von *Fritillaria imperials Protoplasma, 36* : 316.

Weber, F. 1951. *Impatiens*-nectar. *Phyton* (Horn), *3* : 110-111.

Willmer, P.G. 1980. The effects of insect visitors on nectar constituents in temperate plants. *Oecologia* (Berlin), *47* : 270-277.

Wood, G.W. 1961. The association between age of inflorescence and nectar production in the low-bush blueberry *Vaccinium angustifolium. Can. J. Bot., 39* : 1037-1040.

Wykes, G.R. 1952. An investigation of the sugars present in th nectar of flowers of various species. *New Phytol., 51* : 210-215.

Ziegler, H. 1956. Untersuchungen uber die Leitung und sekreti der Assimilate. *Planta* (Berl.), *47* : 447-500.

Ziegler, H., Lüttge, U. and Lüttge U. 1964. Die Wasserlosichen Vitamins des Nektars. *Flora* (Jena), *154* : 215-229.

STRUCTURE, DISTRIBUTION AND PHYLOGENETIC SIGNIFICANCE OF NECTARIES IN MALVALES

S. RAJA SHANMUKHA RAO and N. RAMAYYA

Plant Anatomy & Taxonomy Laboratory
Department of Botany, Sardar Patel College
Padma Rao Nagar, Secunderabad 500 025, India.

ABSTRACT

This study deals with the structure, distribution and phylogenetic importance of the floral nectaries in the Malvales embracing 32 genera and 64 species belonging to the Tiliaceae (including Elaeocarpaceae), Sterculiaceae, Bombacaceae and Malvaceae. In most of the species the nectaries are located at the base of the sepal adaxial or sometimes at the base of the involucre, petal adaxial or torus. They usually form a continuous lining of the sepals but rarely as in *Urena lobata* and *Decaschistia triloba*, they form a circular to oval patch towards each of the sepal bases. The nectaries in the Malvales studied are basically made up of two hair types :1) Uniseriate filiform clavate hair, 2) Uniseriate filiform pyriform hair. The position of nectaries in the Malvales seems intimately related with safety of the nectar produced. In the Elaeocarpaceae and Tiliaceae, where the sepals are usually free, the nectary is located on the torus (mostly between the petals and stamens) whereas, in the Sterculiaceae, Bombacaceae and Malvaceae, where the calyx is usually gamosepalous, it is located at the calyx base, so that the nectar does not leak out and is thus available to the pollinating insects. If positioning of nectary in a safe place is considered to be an advanced character, then the Tiliaceae and Elaeocarpaceae are primitive, which is in accord with the phylogenetic relationships within the order, on other grounds.

According to Fahn (1953), however, the floral nectaries have shifted from the perianth to the inner organs like the ovary and upto the style. The present study, however, clearly indicates that this generalisation is not acceptable with reference to the Malvales. Phylogenetically the foliar nectaries are considered to be advanced than those of floral nectaries. The present investigation also lends support to the earlier observation that the foliar nectaries provide a diversion to the crawling predators from reaching the vital floral parts.

Key words : Nectaries; structure, distribution, phylogenetic significance, Malvales

INTRODUCTION

Among the micromorphological features of plants, nectaries are not only histologically significant but also phylogenetically valuable. Nectaries have been designated as structural when they differ from the neighbouring tissues or non-structural when they do not differ (Zimmermann, 1932; Frey-Wyssling & Hausermann, 1960; Fahn, 1982). They may occur on flowers (floral nectaries) as well as on the vegetative parts (extrafloral nectaries) and secrete largely sugars to attract insects (Esau, 1965; Cutter, 1978; Fahn, 1982).

Among the extrafloral nectaries, two basic types are recognised : 1) hair nectaries and 2) epidermal nectaries (Wilkinson, 1979). On the basis of the organs on which they occur, they are referred to as foliar, petiolar etc., among the extrafloral nectaries. Similarly, the floral nectaries have also been classified according to their location viz., perigonal (perianth), toral, staminal, ovarial and stylar nectaries (Fahn, 1952; 1953; 1982).

Extrafloral nectaries in the Malvales occur mostly on the veins of the leaf adaxial or on the petiole (Masters, 1874; Zimmermann, 1932; Reed, 1917; Koernicke, 1918; Youngman & Pande, 1929; Janda, 1937; Heywood, 1938; Webber, 1938; Metcalfe & Chalk, 1950; Cristobal & Arbo, 1971; Arbo, 1972; 1973; Fryxell, 1971; 1975; Wergin *et al.*, 1975). A comprehensive survey of the literature on foliar nectaries in the Malvales with special reference to the Malvaceae and *Byttneria* (Sterculiaceae) has been made by Arbo (1972). Elias (1983) surveyed extrafloral nectaries in angiosperms and reported their occurrence in 68 families comprising 35 orders of mono and dicotyledons including the various families of Malvales. Hespenheide (1985) studied the relative importance of insects and extrafloral nectaries.

Floral nectaries of the Malvales may be located principally at the sepal adaxial base (Feldhofen, 1933; Brown, 1938; Agthe, 1951; Frei, 1955; Findlay & Mercer, 1971a; Beaslay, 1975; Shanmukha Rao & Ramayya, 1977; 1982; 1987a, 1987b), on the involucre (at the summit of bracts, especially in the Gossypieae-Janda, 1937; Fryxell, 1968, 1969), at the petal adaxial base (in *Grewia*-Tiwari, 1978; Shanmukha Rao, 1979) or on the torus (Shanmukha Rao, 1979).

In the recent past, studies have appeared on the sub-microscopic structure as well as nectar secretion in the Malvales. The sub-microscopic structure of the foliar nectaries of *Gossypium* (Wergin *et. al.*, 1975) and floral nectaries of *Abutilon* (Mercer & Rathberger, 1962; Findlay and Mercer, 1971a, 1971b, 1971c; Reed *et al.*, 1971; Gunning & Huges, 1976) have been studied with reference to particularly the dynamics of nectar secretion.

Attention has also been paid to the floral biology in several Malvales. The cinnamon humningbird (*Amazilia rutila*), fork-tailed emerald (*Chlorostilbon canivetii*), and many species of butterflies (*Eurema daira* and *Phoebis* spp.) have been found to act as pollinators (Percival, 1967; Anderson, 1976; Moffett *et al.*, 1976; Seogin, 1979a and b; Corbet *et al.*, 1979, .Webb & Bawa; 1983; Webb, 1984).

The main sugars encountered in nectar are saccharose, glucose, fructose and various oligosaccharides (Schnepf, 1974; Fahn, 1982). Recently Bahadur *et al.* (1986) studied the nectar composition in many Indian plants. They observed that the nectar of Malvaceous plants consists of three common sugars viz., sucrose, glucose and fructose along with aminoacids.

Regarding structure, it has been shown that the floral as well as extrafloral nectaries are trichomic in nature in the Malvales (Reed, 1917; Koenicke, 1918; Janda, 1937; Brown, 1938; Heywood, 1938; Webber, 1938; Ragonese, 1960; Schnell, Cusset & Quenum, 1963; Findlay & Mercer, 1971a; Cristobal & Arbo, 1971; Arbo, 1972; 1973;

Shanmukha Rao & Ramayya, 1977; 1982; 1987a, 1987b). According to these workers the nectaries consist of multicellular glandular hairs though some described them as papillae (Beaslay, 1975; Wergin *et al.*, 1975). Their structure has also been studied in the Malvales by Shanmukha Rao & Ramayya (1977; 1982; 1987a, 1987b) who reported them to consists of uniseriate filiform clavate or pyriform hairs.

The literature reviewed above, however, shows absence of detailed information on the structure and distribution of floral nectaries in the Malvales at large, hence the present study was taken up. Besides the morphology, phylogenetic value of the floral nectaries in 32 genera and 64 species in the order has also been presently analysed.

MATERIAL AND METHODS

Details of the species studied are shown in Table 1. Techniques employed in this study have been presented earlier (Shanmukha Rao & Ramayya, 1982). Trichome terminology is after Shanmukha Rao & Ramayya (1977; 1982).

OBSERVATIONS

Floral Nectaries

In the 64 species investigated, floral nectaries occur in all except in *Adansonia digitata* (Bombacaceae) and *Muntingia calabura* (Tiliaceae). In most of the species the nectaries are located at the base of the sepal adaxial whereas in some, on the involucre or bracteolar adaxial (*Gossypium*), petal adaxial base (*Grewia subinaequalis*) or *torus* (*Triumfetta* and *Corchorus*) (Table 1). The torus itself, however, occurs only in the Tiliaceae of the families studied and it is nectariferous in *Triumfetta* and *Corchorus* with the uniseriate filiform clavate hair type. In *Triumfetta*, the nectary is located on the side of the elongated torus (Fig. 10). However in *Corchorus*, the nectary is confined to the base of the shortened torus. No other trichome type (either glandular or eglandular type) is witnessed on the torus. However, in *Grewia subinaequalis* though the torus is present, it bears only multiseriate tufted hairs which are nonsecretory and hence is devoid of a nectary. As mentioned earlier the nectary is, however, located at the petal base.

TABLE 1 : Location of Nectaries in the Malvales

S.No.	Species	Locality	Leaf abaxial main	Bracteole abaxial veins	Sepal abaxial base	Sepal abaxial base	*** Petal Torus
1	2	3	4	5	6	7	8
A. TILIACEAE							
1.	*Grewia subinaequalis* DC	HYD	—	—	—	P	—
2.	*Triumfetta pentandra* A.Rich.	HYD	—	—	—	—	C
3.	*Triumfetta rotundifolia* Lamk.	HYD	—	—	—	—	C
4.	*Corchorus aestuens* L.	HYD	—	—	—	—	C
5.	*Corchorus capsularis* L.	HYD	—	—	—	—	C
6.	*Corchorus depressus* (L.) Stocks	BSI, DN	—	—	—	—	C
7.	*Corchorus fascicularis* Lamk.	HYD	—	—	—	—	C
8.	*Corchorus olitorius* L.	HYD	—	—	—	—	C
9.	*Corchorus tridens* L.	HYD	—	—	—	—	C
10.	*Corchorus trilocularis* L.	HYD	—	—	—	—	C
11.	*Corchorus urticifolius* W. & A.	HYD	—	—	—	—	C
12.	*Muntingia calabura* L.	HYD	—	—	—	—	—
B. STERCULIACEAE							
13.	*Sterculia foetida* L.	HYD	—	—	C	—	—
14.	*Helicteres isora* L.	BSI, DN	—	—	C	—	—
15.	*Kleinhovia hospita* L.	HYD	—	—	—	P	—
16.	*Pterospermum acerifolium* (L.) Willd.	HYD	—	—	C	—	—
17.	*Reevesia wallichii* B.Br.	BSI, SL	—	—	C	—	—
18.	*Eriolaena hookeriana* W. & A.	Sorola, MH	—	—	(P)	—	—
19.	*Dombeya cayeuxii* Hort.	HYD	—	—	P	—	—
20.	*Melochia corchorifolia* L.	HYD	—	—	(C)	—	—
21.	*Waltheria indica* L.	HYD	—	—	P	—	—
22.	*Abroma augusta* L.	BSI, SL	—	—	(C)	—	—
23.	*Guazuma tomentosa* Lamk.	HYD	—	—	(C)	—	—

C. BOMBACACEAE						
24. *Adansonia digitata* L.	HYD	—	—	—	—	—
25. *Bombax ceiba* L.	HYD	—	—	—	P	—
26. *Ceiba pentandra* Gaertn.	HYD	—	—	P	—	—
D. MALVACEAE						
27. *Abutilon crispum* (L.) *Medic.*	HYD	—	—	P	—	—
28. *Abutilon indicum* (L) Sweet	HYD	—	—	P	—	—
29. *Althaea rosea* Car.	HYD	—	—	P	—	—
30. *Kydia calycina* roxb.	BSI, SL	(*C)	—	P	—	—
31. *Malvastrum americanum* (L.) Torr.	CNH, HR	—	—	P	—	—
32. *Malvastrum coromandelanum* (L.) Garcke	HYD	—	—	P	—	—
33. *Modiola coroliniana* G. Don	Ooty	—	—	P	—	—
34. *Sida acuta* Burm. f.	HYD	—	—	P	—	—
35. *Sida cordata* (Burm. f.) Borss.	HYD	—	—	P	—	—
36. *Sida cordifolia* L.	HYD	—	—	P	—	—
37. *Sida mysorensis* W. & A.	HYD	—	—	P	—	—
38. *Sida rhombifolia* L.	NSR	—	—	P	—	—
39. *Sida schimperiana* Hochst.	TLK, CH	—	—	P	—	—
40. *Sida spinosa* L.	HYD	—	—	P	—	—
41. *Malvaviscus arboreus* Cav.	HYD	—	—	P	—	—
42. *Pavonia odorata* Willd.	HYD	—	—	P	—	—
43. *Pavonia patens* (Andr.) Chior.	Madgoan (Goa)	—	—	P	—	—
44. *Pavonia zeylanica* (L.) Car.	HYD	—	—	P	—	—
45. *Urena lobata* L.	SBI, SL	**P	—	—	P	—
46. *Abelmoschus crinitus* Wall.	HYD	—	—	P	—	—
47. *Abelmoschus esculentus* (L.)	HYD	—	—	P	—	—
48. *Abelmoschus ficulneus* (L.) W. & A. exWt.	HYD	—	—	P	—	—
49. *Decaschistia triloba* Wt.	Caramzol, Goa	(*C)	—	P	—	—
50. *Gossypium arboreum* L.	HYD	(*C)	(*C)	P	—	—
51. *Gossypium herbaceum* L.	HYD	(*C)	(*C)	P	—	—
52. *Hibiscus acetocella* Welwitsch ex Heirn.	HYD	—	—	P	—	—

53. *Hibiscus cannabinus* L.	HYD	—	—	P	—	—
54. *Hibiscus hirtus* L.	HYD	—	—	P	—	—
55. *Hibiscus lobatus*	HYD	—	—	(P)	—	—
56. *Hibiscus micranthus* L. (Murr.) O. Ktze	HYD	—	—	P	—	—
57. *Hibiscus rosa-sinensis* L.	HYD	(*C)	—	P	—	—
58. *Hibiscus sabdariffa* L.	HYD	—	—	P	—	—
59. *Hibiscus schizopetalus* (Mast.) Hook.f.	HYD	(*DC)	P	—	—	—
60. *Hibiscus syriacus* L.	HYD	—	—	P	—	—
61. *Hibiscus trionum* L.	HYD	—	—	P	—	—
62. *Hibiscus vitiflius* L.	HYD	—	—	P	—	—
63. *Thespesia lampas* (Cav.) Dalz. ex Dalz. & Gibs.	Nanded, MH	C	—	P	—	—
64. *Thespesia populnea* (L.) Soland. ex Corr.	HYD	C	—	P	—	—

*On the mid rib only; **D = On the main veins only;
***D = Torus is present only in the Tiliaceae.
C = Uniseriate filiform clavate hair;
P = Uniseriate filiform pyriform hair;
(C) = Indicates that uniseriate filiform clavate hair is also seen on the remaining surface of the organ concerned;
(P) = Indicates that uniseriate filiform pyriform hair is also seen on the remaining surface of the organ concerned;
— = Nectary absent; HYD = Hyderabad;
BSI, DN = Botanical survey of India, Dehra Dun;
BSI. SL = Botanical Survey of India, Shillong; MH = Maharashtra;
CNH, HR = Central National Herbarium, Howrah;
NSR = Narsapur; Medak Dist, A.P.;
TLK, CH = Talakona, Chittor Dist, A.P.

The nectaries usually form a basal lining of the sepals though rarely, as in *Urena lobata* and *Decaschistia triloba*, they are organised in the form of circular to oval patches towards the sepal base. The height of a nectary is mostly below 1 mm., but in *Bombax ceiba* and *Ceiba pentandra*, the nectary lining is upto 3 mm. in height.

The nectaries in the Malvales studied are made up of basically two hair types, uniseriate filiform pyriform hair and uniseriate filiform clavate hair, the details of which in the case of each species are given in Table 1 (Figs. 1-16). In a given species, the nectary is constituted by either of the hair types, few hundreds or thousands in number depending upon the size of the nectary. Further, the hair type constituting the nectary, occasionally also occurs as a normal hair over the rest of the sepal as in *Sterculia foetida, Eriolaena hookeriana, Melochia corchorifolia* and *Hibiscus lobatus*. In most of the species the nectary is formed by a single trichome type but in *H. cannabinus* and *Kleinhovia hospita*, unicellular conical hair occurs interspread amongst the usual nectariferous hairs.

Foliar Nectaries

In the present study, foliar nectaries have been found only in seven genera of the Malvaceae. They occur mainly on the proximal midrib excepting in *Urena lobata* where they are seen on the three main veins. These foliar nectaries are mostly located in shallow depressions or in level with the surface. Often they may also occur in pits, crypts and cavities.

The foliar nectaries are trichomic in nature (referred to as hair nectaries-Wilkinson, 1979) and they are mostly composed of uniseriate filiform clavate hair type.

Within the shallow depressions, the clavate hairs exclusively constitute the nectary and no other hair type is associated with them though several non-glandular hair types occur in general on the leaf in this taxon. These nectariferous hairs are closely packed in the nectaries and it would appear as if every protodermal cell in it develops into a hair. Further in all the species of the Malvaceae where the foliar nectaries occur (Table 1), the uniseriate filiform clavate hair is also present on the general surface of the leaf. However, unlike in the nectary, they occur in singles and structurally the head of the clavate hair here has less number of cells.

The foliar nectaries are seen prominently in *Gossypium, Kydia, Urena* but in some viz., *Decaschistia Hibiscus* and *Thespesia*, they are obscure.

Investigations on the development of trichome types constituting the nectaries in the Malvales have been scanty (Ragonese, 1960; Arbo, 1972, 1973; Tiwari, 1978; Shanmukha Rao, 1979). However, the information gathered so far indicates that each hair develops from an epidermal initial and hence trichomic in origin.

DISCUSSION

Structure

Structurally, the floral nectaries in the Malvales have been described to be trichomic (Brown, 1938; Findlay & Mercer, 1971a; Shanmukha Rao & Ramayya, 1977; Cutter, 1978; Fahn, 1979) which is presently confirmed in the context of a larger number of species. The nectaries consist mostly of uniseriate filiform pyriform or clavate hairs, glandular in character, though some have described them as papillae (Beasley, 1975; Wergin *et al.*, 1975). Shanmukha Rao & Ramayya (1977) studied the structure of floral nectaries in the Indian *Malvastrum* and reported them to consist of uniseriate filiform pyriform hairs. In the present study it is observed that the floral nectaries in most of the Malvales studied possess uniseriate filiform pyriform hairs (Table 1). However in certain members like *Sterculia foetida*, *Triumfetta pentandra*, *Triumfetta rotundiforlia* and *Corchorus*, uniseriate filiform clavate hair type also makes up the floral nectary.

The trichome types of the necatries mentioned above also occur on other parts in the respective species investigated. But those making up the nectaries are smaller in size than those of the other parts in size (cf. Figs. 3 & 4 and 5 & 6).

Organographic distribution and taxonomic importance

Distribution of the nectaries in the floral parts in the Malvales at the family level is somewhat variable (Shanmukha Rao, 1979) and hence taxonimically important (Table 1). They occur principally at the sepal adaxial base in the Malvaceae, Bombacaceae and Sterculiaceae (Brown, 1938; Shanmukha Rao, 1979, 1987, 1991; Shanmukha Rao & Ramayya, 1987a; Shanmukha Rao & Saibaba, 1988), but in the Tiliaceae they are situated on the torus (lying between the petal and stamens) — (Masters, 1874; Shanmukha Rao, 1979). The present study shows that in the Tiliaceae, the surface of the torus (between petals and stamens) is glandular in *Triumfetta* and *Corchorus* while in *Grewia*, the adaxial bases of petals usually possess nectaries (Table 1). The Elaeocarpaceae is also known for nectaries located between the petals and stamens (Masters, 1874).

Hutchinson (1967 p.485) described the ovary of *Muntingia* to be densely surrounded by glandular hairs but in *Muntingia calabura* presently studied such hairs have not been observed. On the other hand, the ovary is enveloped by tufted hairs, characteristic of Malvales in general and the flower is without a nectary as such. Likewise, *Adansonia* (Bombacaceae) is also devoid of any floral nectary.

Phylogenetic importance

According to Brown (1938), the position of nectaries in the Malvales is probably connected with lack of gamopetalous flowers in the order. But the present information is, however, suggestive that location of floral nectaries in the Malvales seems to be correlated more with availability of a safer place. For instance in the Elaeocarpaceae and Tiliaceae, where the sepals are usually free, the nectary is mostly between the petals and stamens (e.g. on the lateral surface of the torus in *Corchorus*, or petal base in *Grewia*, whereas in the Sterculiaceae, Bombacaceae and Malvaceae, where the calyx base is usually gamosepalous, it is located at the calyx base, so that the nectar does not leak out and is thus available to the pollinating insects. If positioning of nectary in a safe state is considered to be an advanced character, then the Tiliaceae as well as Elaeocarpaceae are indicated to be primitive by virtue of the nectary position in these taxa between the polyphyllous and obviously less protective petals and the stamens, whereas the Sterculiaceae, Bombacaceae and Malvaceae are advanced since the nectaries in these taxa are located at the bases of sepal adaxial, which being gamophyllous, maintain the nectar safe. Thus the nectaries in course of evolution seem to have moved from the torus to calyx or in other words from centre to the periphery. According to Fahn (1953, 1982), however, the floral nectaries have in general shifted from the perianth to the inner organs, i.e., from the sepals towards the ovary and upto the style, which the present authors consider as untenable as discussed above. The generalisation by Fahn (1953), is also not supported by the putative evolutionary relationships within the Malvales on other grounds like morphological, anatomical and embryological studies discussed by number of workers (Webber, 1934; Edlin, 1935; Venkata Rao, 1952, 1954; Hutchinson, 1967, 1969; Bates & Blanchard, 1970; Shanmukha Rao, 1979). The authors are, therefore, of the firm opinion that nectary location would have followed different trends in different grades of natural taxa or phylogenetic circles, as echoed by Brown (1938), who concluded that "nectaries appear to have arisen independently in different lines of development and then to have undergone modifications characteristic of various groups''.

Foliar nectaries as has been described in the text have only restricted occurrence being noted only in the Malvaceae in the entire order Malvales, presently examined. Previously, however, foliar nectaries have been also reported in a few Sterculiaceae. The restricted occurrence of the foliar nectaries as reviewed above assumes some significance both from phylogenetic and biological viewpoint in the light of the conclusion drawn above regarding the occurrence of the floral nectaries and phyletic relationships within the Malvales. Since foliar nectaries are absent in the putatively primitive taxa of Tiliaceae it is considered that origin of the foliar nectaries was a later development in the evolutionary history of Malvales and hence is an evolved character associated with relatively advanced taxa.

Physiologically the occurrence of foliar nectaries has been generally considered to provide a diversion to crawling predators from reaching the vital floral parts. The present information equally appears to confirm this viewpoint besides also indicating as stated above, it represents an adaptation advanced in character.

Explanation to the Figure Plate

Figs. 1—16. 1. *Sida acuta* (sepal adaxial). 2. *Sida mysorensis* (sepal adaxial). 3&4. *Pavonia odorata* (sepal adaxial and leaf adaxial respectively). 5&6. *Pavonia zeylanica* (leaf abaxial and sepal adaxial respectively). 7. *Eriolaena hookeriana* (sepal adaxial). 8. *Dombeya cayeuxii* (sepal adaxial). 9&10. *Triumfetta pentandra* (stem and torus respectively). 11&12. *Grewia subinaequalis* (petal adaxial). 13. *Gossypium arboreum* (sepal adaxial). 14. *Sterculia foetida*. (sepal adaxial). 15. *Helicteres isora* (sepal adaxial). 16. *Hibiscus cannabinus* (sepal adaxial).

(f = Foot; s = Stalk; h = Head)

Literature Cited

*Agthe, C. 1951. Uber die physiologische Herkunft des pflazennektars; *Ber. Schweiz. Bot., Ges. 61* : 240-274.

Anderson, O.J. 1976. The pollination biology of *Tilia*; *Amer. J. Bot., 63* : 1203-1212.

Arbo, M.M. 1972. Estructure y ontogenia des los nectarios foliares del ge'nero *Byttneria* (Sterculiaceae); *Darwiniana, 17* : 104-198.

Arbo, M.M. 1973. Los nectarios foliares de *Magatritheca* (Sterculiaceae); *Darwiniana, 18* : 272-276.

s
f
1
2
9
3
10
s
f
4
5
h
s
f
6
7
8
13
h
f
14
15
16
h
s
f
11
12
1
50μm
2
0.2mm
3–7
50μm
8–16
50μm

Bates, B.M. & Blanchand, J.R. O.J. 1970. Chromosome numbers in the Malvales II. New or otherwise noteworthy counts revelant to classification in the Malvaceae, tribe Malveae; *Amer. J. Bot., 57* : 927-934.

Beasley, C.A. 1975. Developmental morphology of cotton flowers and seed as seen with the scanning electron microscope; *Amer. J. Bot., 62* : 584-592.

Bahadur, B. Arthi Chaturvedi & Ramaswamy, N. 1986. Nectar types in Indian plants; *Proc. Indian Acad. Sci.* (*Plant Sci.*), *96* : 41-48.

Brown, W.H. 1938. The bearing of nectaries on the phylogeny of flowering plants; *Amer. Phil. Soc. Proc., 79* : 549-595.

Corbet, S.A., Unwin, D.M. Jones, P. & Oliver, E. 1979. Humidity, nectar and insect visits to flowers with special reference to *Crataegus, Tilia* and *Echium*; *Ecol. Entomol., 4* : 9-12.

Cristobal, C.L. & Arbo, M.M. 1971. Sobra las especies de *Ayenia* (Sterculiaceae) con nectarios foliaris; *Darwiniana, 16* : 603-612.

Cutter, E.G. 1978. *Plant Anatomy* Part I *Cells and Tissues*; (London, U.K. : Edward Arnold)

Edlin, 1935. Critical review of certain taxonomical groups of Malvales; *New Phytol., 34* :1-20 & 122-143.

Elias, T.S. 1983. Extrafloral nectaries : their structure and distribution. In: eds : Bentley, B and Elias, T. *The Biology of Nectaries*. Columbia University Press, New york. 174-203.

Fahn, A. 1952. On the structure of floral nectaries; *Bot. Gaz. 113* : 464-70.

Fahn, A. 1953. The topography of the nectary in the flower and its phylogenetic trend; *Phytomorphology, 3* : 424-426.

Fahn, A. 1979. *Secretary Tissues in Plants*: (London, U.K. : Academic)

Fahn, A., 1982. *Plant Anatomy*; (London, U.K. : Pergamon)

Esau, K., 1965. *Plant Anatomy*. 2nd ed. (New York, U.S.A. : John Wiley)

*Feldhofen, E., 1933. Beitrage Zur physiologischen Anatomie der nuptialen Nektarien ausden Reihen der Dikotylen; *Beih. bot., 50* : 657.

Findlay, N. & Mercer, F.V. 1971a. Nectar production in *Abutilon* I. Movement of nectar through the cuticle; *Aust. J. Biol. Sci., 24* : 647-656.

Findlay, N. & Mercer, F.V. 1971b. Nectar production in *Abutilon* II. Submicroscopic structure of the nectary; *Aust. J. Biol. Sci., 24* : 657-664.

Findlay, N. & Mercer, F.V. 1971c. Nectar production in *Abutilon* III. Sugar secretion; *Aust. J. Biol. Sci., 24* : 665-675.

*Frei, E., 1955. Die Innervierung der floralen Nektarian dikotylen pflanzenfamilien; *Ber. Schweiz. Bot. Ges., 65* : 60-114.

Frey-Wyssling, A. & Hausermann, E., 1960. Deutung der gestalt losen Nektarien; *Ber. Schweiz. Bot. Ges., 70* : 151-162.

Fryxell, P.A., 1968. A redefinition of the tribe Gossypieae; *Bot. Gaz., 129* : 296-308.

Fryxell, P.A. 1969. The genus *Cienfuegosia* Cav. *Ann. Mo Bot. Gard., 56* : 179-250.

Fryxell, P.A. 1971. Phenetic analysis and the phylogeny of the diploid species of *Gossypium* L. Malvaceae; *Evolution, 25* : 554-562.

Fryxell, P.A., 1975. Generic relationships of *Decaschistia* (Malvaceae) and the description of a new tribe, Decaschistieae; *Amer J. Bot., 62* : 172-175.

Gunning, B.E.S. & Hughes, J.E. 1976 Quantitative assessment of symplastic transport of pre-nectar into the trichomes of *Abutilon* nectaries; *Aust. J. Pl. Physiol., 3* : 619-637.

*Hespenheide, H.A. 1985. Insect visitors to extra floral nectaries of *Byttneria aculeata* (Sterculiaceae) relative importance and roles. *Ecol. Ent., 10* : 191-204.

Heywood, H.E. 1938. *The Structure of Economic Plants*; New York, U.S.A.; MacMillan.

Hutchinson, J. 1967. *The Genera of Flowering Plants. Dicotyledones* Vol. II; London, U.K. : Oxford.

Hutchinson, J. 1969. *Evolution and Phylogeny of the Flowering Plants*, London, U.K. : Academic.

Janda. C.H. 1937. Die extranuptialen Nektarien der Malveceen; *Desterreich. Bot. Zeitschr., 86* : 81-130.

Koernicke, M. 1918. Uber die extrafloren nectarien auf den laubblatern einiger Hibisceen; *Flora, 11-112* : 526-540.

Masters, M.T. 1874. In: *The Flora of British India* Vol. 1, J.D. Hooker, London, U.K. : Reeve.

Mercer, F.V. & Rathberger, N. 1962. Nectar secretion and cell membranes; *Proc. 5th Int. Conf. Electron Microsc.*

Metcalfe, C.R. & Chalk, L. 1950. *Anatomy of the Dictyledons* Vol. I; Oxford, U.K. : Clarendon.

Mofeett Jo Stith, L.S. Burkhardt, C.C. & Shipmen, C.W. 1976. Nectar secretion in cotton flowers and its relation to floral visits by honey bees; *Amer. Bee Jour., 116* : 32-36.

Percival. M.S. 1967. *Floral Biology*; Oxford, U.K.: Pergamon.

Ragonese. A.M. 1960. Ontogenia de los distintos tipos de trichomes de *Hibiscus rosa-sinensis* L. (Malvaceae); *Darwiniana, 12* : 58-66.

Reed, E.L. 1917. Leaf nectaries of *Gossypium. Bot. Gaz., 63* : 229-231.

Reed, M.L. Findlay, N. & Mercer, F.V., 1971. Nectar production in *Abutilon* IV. Water and solute relations; *Aust. J. biol. sci., 24* : 677.

*Schnell, R. Cusset, G. & Quenum, M. (MLLE) 1963 Contribution 'a L.'etude des glandes extra-florales chez quelques groupes de plantes tropicales; *Rev. gen. bot., 70* : 269-342.

Schnepf, E. 1974. Gland Cells; In: ed. A.W. Robards, *Dynamic Aspects of Plant Ultrastructure*. pp. 331-357. London, U.K. McGraw-Hill.

Seogin, R. 1979a. Nectar constituents In the genus *Fremontia* (Sterculiaceae) Sugars, Flavonoids and proteins; *Bot. Gaz., 140* : 29-31.

-------- 1979b. 5,7-dimethoxy-4-hydroxis of lavane from *Fremontia* (Sterculiaceae). *Aliso., 9* : 479-480.

Shanmukha Rao, S.R. 1979. *Epidermal Studies in the Order Malvales*. Ph.D. thesis Osmania University, Hyderabad, India.

Shanmukha Rao, S.R. 1987. Structure, distribution and classification of plant trichomes in relation to taxonomy : Sterculiaceae. *Feddes Repertorium* (Berlin), *98* : 127-135.

Shanmukha Rao, S.R. 1991. A Structure, distribution and classification of plant trichomes in relation to taxonomy : *Hibiscus* L. (Malvaceae); *Feddes Repertorium* (Berlin), *102* : 336-334.

Shanmukha Rao, S.R. & Ramayya, N. 1977. Structure, distribution and classification of trichomes in the Indian species of *Malvastrum*; *Phytomorphology, 27* : 40-44.

Shanmukha Rao, S.R. & Ramayya, N. 1982. Taxonomic importance of epidermal characters in the Indian *Thespesia* Corr. (Malvaceae); *Proc. Indian Acad. Sci. (Plant Sci), 91* : 509-517.

Shanmukha Rao, S.R. & Ramayya, N. 1987a. Taxonomic importance of epidermal characters in the Bombacaceae; In: *Recent Advances in Plant Sciences*, pp. 169-180 (Dehra Dun, India)

Shanmukha Rao, S.R. & Ramayya, N. 1987b. Trichome types and their taxonomic importance in Tiliaceae; *Indian J. Bot., 10* : 65-73.

Shanmukha Rao, S.R. & Saibaba, A.M. 1988. Epidermal studies as an aid to taxonomy : *Sida* l. (Malvaceae), *Feddes Repertorium* (Berlin), *99* : 19-26.

Tiwari, S.C. 1978. Some unusual features of floral trichomes and nectaries in *Grewia subinaequalis*; *Acta bot. Indica, 6* : 81-86.

Venkata Rao, C. 1952. Floral anatomy of some Malvales and its bearing on the affinities of families included in the order; *J. Indian bot. Soc., 31* : 171-203.

Venkata Rao, C. 1954. A contribution to the embryology of Bombacaceae; *Proc. Indian Acad. Sci., 39* : 51-75.

Webb, C.J. 1984. Hummingbird Pollination of *Malvaviscus arboreus* in Costa Rica; *New Zealand J. Bot., 22* : 575-581.

Webb, C.J. & Bawa, K.S. 1983. Pollen Dispersal by Hummingbirds and butterflies; A Comparative study of two lowland tropical plants; *Evolution, 37* : 1258-1270.

Webber, I.E. 1934. Systematic anatomy of the woods of Malvaceae; *Trop. Woods., 38* : 15-36.

Webber, I.E. 1938. Anatomy of leaf and stem of *Gossypium; J. Agric. Res., 57* : 269-286.

Wergin, W.P. Elmore, C.D. Hanny, B.W. & Ingber, B.F. 1975. Ultrastructure of the subglandular cells from the foliar nectaries of cotton in relation to the distribution of plasmodesmata and the symplastic transport of nectar; *Amer. J. Bot., 62* : 842-849.

Wilkinson, H.P. 1979. The plant surface; In: ed. Metcalfe, C.R. & Chalk, L. *Anatomy of th dicotyledons*; Vol. I, 2nd edition pp. 124-131. London, U.K.: Clarendon.

Youngman, W. & Pande, S.S. 1929. the epidermal outgrowth of the genera *Thespesia* and *Gossypium*; *Ann. Bot., 43* : 711- 740.

*Zimmerman, J.G., 1932. Uber die extrafloralen nektarien der Angiospermen; *Beih. Bot. Zbl., 49* : 99-196.

* Original not seen.

STAMINAL NECTARIES

BIR BAHADUR and N. RAMA SWAMY
Department of Botany, Kakatiya University
Warangal 506 009, India.

ABSTRACT

A review of staminal nectaries in various families of dicotyledons (Turneraceae, Violaceae, Mimosoideae, Fabaceae, Linaceae & related families of Geraniales, Myrtaceae, Melastomaceae, Pedaliaceae, Asclepiadaceae, Apocynaceae, Euphorbiaceae and Lauraceae) and some Monocotyledonous families is presented. Variation in the structure of various types of staminal nectaries known to date is described and their role is discussed. Nectar secretion and nectar composition for sugars and amino acids of staminal nectaries is reviewed.

A simplified classification based on the position and the structure of staminal nectaries is proposed. The sporadic occurrence of staminal nectaries in unrelated orders suggest their polyphyletic origin. Their probable role in pollination biology is briefly discussed.

Key words : Staminal nectaries, Angiosperms, Structure & classification, role in pollination.

INTRODUCTION

Staminal nectaries have been reported in different angiospermous families belonging to several unrelated orders. To-date, however, there are a few or no studies in which the structure and function of staminal nectaries has been studied, although Brown (1938) first described the structure and phylogeny of various types of nectaries based on study of 3000 live plants and also identified nectaries, derived from individual stamens in Laurales, Berberidales and Ranunculales. Later, Rendle

(1975) distinguished Caesalpinoideae and Papilionoideae on the basis of presence or absence of the staminal nectaries. Sastri (1952, 1965) studied the staminal appendages in several Lauraceae and regards them as nectaries or glandular appendages. Arthi and Bahadur (1985) have studied the gland crested anthers in some angiospermous families. Bahadur *et al.* (1987) have also studied the staminal nectaries (spur nectaries) in relation to floral biology in *Hybanthus ennaespermus* (Violaceae). Gland crested anthers have been reported in taxonomic study of Pedaliaceae (Ihlenfeldt, 1967), while Kunze (1990) studied morphology and evolution of staminal corona and staminal column in 61 taxa of Apocynaceae, Periplocaceae and Asclepiadaceae. Fahn (1979) reviewed various aspects of nectaries and classified extra floral and floral nectaries and in the latter recognised 3 types of staminal nectaries occurring in monocots and dicots respectively.

An account of staminal nectaries in various families studied to date is reviewed as under and the related aspects are also discussed.

Staminal nectaries in Turneraceae

Urban (1883) first reported floral nectaries in *Mathurina panduriflora* (Turneraceae). During this century Brown (1938) investigated 3000 species of angiosperms for their nectaries but there is no mention of the nectaries in *Turnera*. Capuron (1963) reported nectaries in *Piriqueta ansingyae*. Elias *et al.* (1975) have studied the structure of extra-floral and floral nectaries as well as nectar composition in *Turnera ulmifolia* but the floral nectaries have not been thoroughly studied. Later, Baker *et al.* (1978) have investigated the amino acid composition of the nectar from foliar and floral nectaries of *T. ulmifolia*. Barrett (1978) reported distyly and pollination biology of *T. ulmifolia* while various aspects of morphology, heterostyly and incompatibility in *T. subulata* have been studied by Rama Swamy and Bahadur (1981, 1983, 1984 a & b). They have also reported pollination biology and floral nectaries in *T. subulata* and *T. ulmifolia* (Bahadur and Ramaswamy, 1982, 1984, Bahadur *et al.*, 1985).

Flowers in both the species viz., *T. ulmifolia* and *T.subulata* are epiphyllous large showy and pentamerous. The species *T.subulata* is heterostylous bearing pin and thrum eyed flowers on different plants whereas *T.ulmifolia* is homostylous. The five stamens are inserted near the base of the floral tube and are rectangular in transverse section;

the base of each filament becoming broadened and is adnate laterally to the floral tube near the base forming a nectar pouch where the secreted nectar is stored (Figs. 1-5).

The nectar pouch is located at the base of each filament in both the *Turnera* species (Figs. 3,4). The pouch is comparatively smaller in bud condition i.e., one day prior to anthesis and is prominent and slightly longer in *T.ulmifolia* than both the pin and thrum forms of *T. subulata.* The epidermal cells of nectar pouch are cuboidal and epistomatic in both the species (Fig. 5) with the exception of pin form of *T.subulata.* The stomata occur irregularly and 3-5 stomata have been observed in the middle region of the pouch and the rest are scattered along the margin of the nectar pouch. The stomata are anomocytic and remain wide open throughout and the guard cells are devoid of chloroplasts. Higher stomatal index and stomatal frequency (6.77; 4/mm^2) on the adaxial side of pin than the thrum (1.78; 1/mm^2) of *T.subulata* and *T.ulmifolia* (4.17; 2/mm^2). Larger stomata and pore size were observed in *T.ulmifolia* (39.2 × 37.6; 16 × 14.4 μm) followed by the adaxial side of pin form (36.0 × 39.2; 16.0 × 14.4 μm), thrum form (34.4 × 32.8; 16.0 × 10.8 μm) and on the abaxial side of pin form (28.0 × 28.0; 13.6 × 5.6 μm). The cells of nectar pouch are parenchymatous, secretory, vasculated, stomatiferous, rich in starch grains and with granular contents. The granular contents and stomata are absent on the abaxial surface with the exception of pin flower form of *T.subulata* (Bahadur *et al.*, 1985). The secretory cells are cuticularised, the cuticle breaks down releasing the nectar into the pouch/nectar pocket confirming the earlier observations of Elias *et al.* (1975). It is interesting to note that just above the nectar pouch the cells are tetra to hexagonal, without starch grains and some what longer on both the surface of the filament. The nectar composition in these species for the sugars and various amino acids has been studied (see Bahadur *et al.*, 1986).

In the closely related Theales, Bixales, Caryophyllales, Polygonales, Chenopodiales and Nyctaginaceae are characterised by "nectariferous disc" as a ring below the stamens while in Guttiferales the nectar glands are modified stamens (Brown, 1938).

Staminal nectaries in Violaceae

Pollination biology of Violaceae has been documented by several authors in the recent past (for review see Bahadur *et al.*, 1987).

Hutchinson (1967) reported the presence of staminal nectaries in various taxa of Violaceae viz., *Anchietia, Corynostylis, Noisettia* and *Schweiggeria* including *Hybanthus*. Later, Beattie (1971) studied the pollination mechanisms in 3 species of *Viola*. Bahadur *et al*. (1987) have studied the structure of staminal nectary in *Hybanthus ennaespermus*.

The androecium in *H. ennaespermus* consist of five free hypogynous stamens with short filaments of which the two anterior stamens possess thick grooved greenish nectar secreting appendage; the spur (Fig. 6). The spur is a tubular concave extension that measures 810 × 290 μm with incurved margins and is devoid of vasculature with numerous small and big unicellular ornamented hairs on its surface (Fig. 6) of the lower half of the spur which projects backwards (inwards) into the saccate claw of the large petal, where the nectar is stored. The margins of the nectar secreting spur is provided with numerous open anomocytic stomata (Fig. 7). The stomatal index of the nectariferous stomata is high (5.17) and the stomatal and pore sizes measure 27.20 × 23.20 μm and 10.80 × 7.20 μm respectively. The nectar is secreted in the spur through these stomata. In *Viola* the spurs of anterior anthers similarly secrete nectar (Brown, 1938). The nectar composition and qualitative analysis of sugars and amino acids have been investigated in the species (see Bahadur *el al*., 1987).

Staminal nectaries in Mimosoideae

The presence of the gland crested anthers in Mimosoideae is reviewed in Table 1. The morphological features of the staminal nectaries of Mimosoideae varies considerably. Eight species representing six genera are characterised by stalked gland crested anthers irrespective of spicate or head inflorescence. The stamens are with glandular nectaries at the tip of the anthers (Fig. 8-20). The filament in *Xylia xylocarpa* is thicker but thinner in *Acacia nilotica*. The anther glands differ in size, shape and cellular arrangement and are devoid of vasculature (Figs. 8-20). The stalk of the gland is large in *Adenanthera pavonia* (0.300 × 0.230 mm) followed by *Prosopis spicigera*, *P. juliflora*, *Xylia xylocarpa*, *Dichrostachys cinerea*, *Neptunia triquetra* and *Acacia nilotica* while it is small in *A. campbelli*. The stalk of the glands in almost all the species are multiseriate (Figs. 9, 11, 13, 15, 17, 19) except *Acacia campbelli* which is filiform, made up of few rows of small cells. The size and shape of the stalk cells varies from species to species. Globose/rounded glands occur in *Neptunia triquetra*, *Prosopis juliflora*, *P. specigera*, *Dichrostachys cinerea* and *Acacia campbelli*, whereas conical anther glands occur in *Xylia xylocarpa*; and *Adenanthera pavonia*, *Acacia nilotica* shows oval shaped anther glands (see Arthi and Bahadur, 1985). The glands in *Adenanthera pavonia* and *Xylia xylocarpa* are cellular (Figs. 11, 19) while in *Neptunia triquetra*, *Prosopis juliflora*, *P. spicigera*, *Dichrostachys cinerae*, *Acacia nilotica* and *A. campbelli* are papillate. The papillae are double walled with cuticular striations and conspicuous nucleus (Figs. 9, 13, 15, 17). The cells in the gland of *Adenanthera pavonia* and *Xylia xylocarpa* are angular to polygonal and flattened.

TABLE 1 : Review of Staminal nectaries in Dicotyledons

S No.	Taxon	Reference
1.	Gomortegaceae	Sastri (1965)
2.	Gyrocarpaceae	Willis (1951)
3.	Hernandiaceae	Willis (1951)
4.	Monimiaceae	Sastri (1965)
5.	Lauraceae *Laurus*	McLean and Cook (1956) & Fahn (1979)
6.	Ranunculaceae (Tribe Helleboreae) *Helleborus* species	Brown (1938)
7.	Cephalotaceae *Cephalotus follicularis*	Willis (1951), Endress & Stumpf (1991)
8.	Mimosoideae	Bentham (1875), Solereder (1908), Willis (1951), Faegri & Pijl (1980) & Arthi & Bahadur (1985)
	Acacia spp. (*Gummiferae* & *Vulgares* section) *Acacia sphaerocephala* *Adenanthera*	ex. Ross (1979) Darwin (1877) Gamble (1957) Isely (1970) & Hooker (1973)
	Calliandra spp. *Dichrostachys Entada* *Neptunia* *Peptadenia* *Prosopis* spp. *Xylia*	Paul (1979) Hooker (1973) Hooker (1973) Gamble (1957) Hooker (1973) Gamble (1957) & Isely (1972) Hooker (1973)
9.	Myrtaceae	Willis (1951) & Lawrence (1964)

10.	Papaveraceae	Rendle (1975)
11.	*Xanthoceros sorbifolia* (Sapindaceae)	Endress & Stumpf (1991)
12.	Chloranthaceae	Sastri (1965)
13.	Ericaceae *Blaeria, Erica, Gaultheria*	Rendle (1975)
14.	Elacourtiaceae	,,
15.	Gentianaceae	,,
16.	Gesneriaceae	,,
17.	Platanaceae *Plantanus acerifolia*	Rendle (1975)
18.	Pedaliaceae	Willis (1951), Ihlenfeldt (1967)
	Ceratotheca triloba	Ihlenfeldt (1967)
	Harpagophytum, procumbens	,,
	Holubia saccata	,,
	Josephinia africana	,,
	Pedalium murex	,,
	Pterodiscus speciosus	,,
	Rogeria adenophylla	,,
	Sesamothamnus lugardii	,,
	Sesamum Schinzianum	,,
	Uncarina grandidieri	,,
19.	Asclepiadaceae	Fahn (1953), Kunze (1990)
20.	Melastomaceae	Rendle (1975)

The glands in all the species studied contain reducing sugar and starch with minor variations. Sugary contents and the starchy nature of the glands indicate that they are consumed by the pollinators/insect visitors as Darwin (1877) visualised and hence play important role in the pollination biology of the species. It is interesting that a correlation exists between anther gland with the pollen type in the species studied. Species with cellular gland exclusively possess pollen in polyads while the species with papillate glands show variations i.e., monads viz., *Prosopis juliflora*, *P. spicigera* and *Neptunia triquetra*; polyads viz., *Acacia nilotica* and *A. campbelli*. Pollen of *Dichrostachys cinerea* is characterized by monads and asymmetrical polyads. Symmetrical polyads are present in other taxa studied (Arthi and Bahadur, 1985).

Faegri and Pijl (1980) remarked that the function of these glands in many Mimosoideae remains unexplained despite the fact that Darwin (1877) first reported the presence of anther glands in *Acacia sphaerocephala*. Similarly, Pedley classified the Acacias and (cited by

Ross, 1979) stated that the anther gland is characteristic of the tribe *Adenantherae* but the presence of such a gland has been noted in all African species of section *Gummiferae* and *Vulgares* of the genus *Acacia* except *A. farnesiana* which probably is of American origin. Australian species except *Gummiferae* and *A. angustissima* (Filicinae) do not possess glands (ex. Ross, 1979). Isley (1970, 1972) noted the presence of anther glands in *Prosopis* and *Adenanthera* and distinguished the tribes *Mimoseae* and *Adenantherae* on the basis of the presence or absence of anther glands. Leelavathi and Ramayya (1982) have investigated 20 species of Mimosoideae for their trichomes but did not observe the anther glands.

Staminal nectaries in Fabaceae

Rao *et al.* (1958) on the basis of floral anatomical data suggested that :

1. In Mimosoideae, the disc when present is usually supplied by inward branches of staminal traces.
2. In Caesalpinoideae, the disc when present is vasculated, supplied by branches of androecial traces.
3. In Paplionaceae, a glandular staminal disc is present in all the tribes and is vasculated by inward branches of staminal traces.

Thus, the origin of nectary from stamens is supported and this is compatible with the earlier suggestion of De Candolle (cited by Rao *et al.*, 1958) that the nectary is a modified whorl of stamens.

Gulyas and Kincsek (1982) investigated the floral nectaries in 46 species comprising 26 genera of Papilionaceae and recognised 8 nectary types; of these three are staminal viz.,

1. Nectary epimorphic, the other part localised opposite to the ten free stamens forming a ring like protrusion.
   eg., *Trifolium campestre*, *Lathyrus odoratus*.
2. Nectary pipe like but on the side of free stamens.
   eg., *Phaseolus* sp.
3. Nectary ring shaped automorphic opposite to the tenth free stamen. eg., *Viciafaba*.

Endress and Stumpf (1991) have studied the dehiscence pattern in *Cephalotus follicularis* (Nepenthaceae) under SEM and showed the 'staminal nectary' over the lobes and suggested that this may be 'pseudonectary' without any secretion. They have also provided scanning micrographs of nectariferous stamen glands in *Prosopis juliflora* (Mimosoideae) and *Xanthoceros sorbifolia* (Sapindaceae) and described it as connective protrusion. Our observations on various Mimosoids support this.

Linaceae & related families of Geraniales

Narayana and Rao (1977, 1978) have studied the morphology and floral anatomy of several taxa of Humiriaceae and Linaceae which are characterised by nectariferous disc and obdiplostemenous condition. The disc is 5 lobed, adnate, extrastaminal and non-vascularised as in *Ixonanthes, Ochthcosums, Philbornea, Cathartolinum, Ctenlophon*, but in *Anisadenia* the 5 antisepalous stamens are fertile with a prominent gland at the base of filament; while the short stamens are sterile and devoid of gland. In *Humiria, Sacoglottis, Vantanea*, the massive intrastaminal disc is 10 lobed, annular to cup shaped, vascularised and adnate to the base of staminal tube.

Narayana and Rao (1977) interpreted the disc in Humiriaceae as inner sterilized part of the staminal tube. The morphology of nectariferous disc in Geraniales in relation to floral anatomical data in various orders of angiosperms is interesting and has direct bearing not only in relation to the type of pollination mechanism but nectary evolution and this will be discussed elsewhere.

According to Vandeputte, netaries of Greyiaceae and Franeoaceae show similarity as nectaries in both arise as "Pseudostaminodia" between stamens and fetals and are obdiplostemenous (cited by Rouse Decraene and Smets, 1995). These authors studied the distribution and systematic relevance of the androecial (oligomery) evolution in relation to floral evolution and angiosperm phylogeny but the nectary character has not been satisfactory discussed.

Staminal nectaries in Myrtaceae

Gland crested anthers in Myrtaceae have been reported in the past by Willis (1951) and Lawrence (1964). Despite this earlier report, to-date there is no study on the structure or function of Myrtaceous anther glands, although considerable work on the pollination biology has been done during the last 30 years on some economically important taxa viz., *Syzygium aromaticum, Psidium guajava, Pimentadioca, Eugenia* (2 species), *Eucalyptus* (7 species) and *Feijoa sellowiana* (ex. Free, 1970; McGregor, 1976). Briggs (1964) studied the pollination in ten species of *Darwinia.*

In *Callistemon linearis* and *Eucalyptus globulus* the anther glands are completely embedded on the top of the anther, while in *Psidium guajava* and *Eugenia caryophyllus* the glands are partially exposed and at the level of the anther lobes are slightly concave as seen in surface view (Fig. 24). The shape of the anther gland is circular in *Psidium guajava* oval to oblong in *Callistemon linearis*, circular to oval in *Eucalyptus globulus* and oval to elongated in *E. caryophyllus*. The anther glands in all the species studied are multicellular with variation in size and arrangement of the cells. No correlation exists between anther size and gland size and structure, although variation was observed among the species in relation to anther size and gland (Arthi and Bahadur, 1985).

The outer cells of the anther gland are rectangular and form epidermis while the inner cells are of various shapes being larger in the centre in all the four species. The cell walls are straight to wavy and the cells are polygonal with conspicuous nucleus and dense contents (Fig. 24a) while 6-10 nucleated in *Callistemon linearis*. The anther glands of all the species contain few to many oil droplets and are devoid of sugars and starch (see Arthi and Bahadur, 1985).

Although Myrtaceae are known to be insect pollinated, the West Malaysian *Eugenia malacensis* is pollinated by bats (Start and Marshall, 1976). Faegri and Pijl (1976) state that Oligolectic bees have specific pollen preferences possibly based on the odour of the pollen in Myrtaceae. On the other hand it has been shown that European hive bees often ignore the endemic plants and rely on unknown pollen sources.

Thus, in the absence of much needed information, it may be presumed that the anther gland secrete volatile oils characteristic to Myrtaceae that attract the insects and this may be related to the pollination biology of the species.

Staminal nectaries in Asclepiadaceae & related families

Staminal nectaries in these highly advanced entomophilous plants are the best studied. Kunze (1990) has reviewed the earlier literature and studied in detail the morphology and evolution of corona in 61 taxa of Apocynaceae, Periplacaceae and Asclepiadaceae. The Asclepiads in general are characterised by staminal corona and staminal column; the former is on the dorsal side of the filaments. These two structures below the nectaries form the annulus. The corona may be corolline to androecial and can be basal in the region of staminal column or higher up on the stamen below the anther slit. The staminal nectaries are functionally in close connection with the anther slit.

The corona on back of the filament evolved as a simple appendage (hence primitive) and gained complexity during evolution of new structures on the basal column (interstaminal) leading to complex annular corona.

Nectaries in Asclepiadaceae have shifted also several taxonomic lines in acro-centripetal direction. The primary position is receptacular between the filaments. The formation of interstaminal parts of an annular corona is then possible only on the receptacular basal tube, since the interstaminal segments of the corona subtend the nectaries.

Kunze (1990) has provided elegant illustrations showing the variations in position of corona and androecium in Apocynaceae, Periplacaceae and Asclepiadaceae, and recognised four variations in Asclepiadaceae viz., *Fockea* type, *Oxypetalum* type, *Tylophora* type and *Asclepias* type. The ultrastructure of nectaries in *Asclepias curassavica* and *Cynanchum vincetoxicum* show similarity since both show glandular epithelial cells with highly proliferated convoluted plasmalemma and nectar chamber filled with scented nectar comprising sugars, secretary products, tubules and coarse fibrils (Schnepf and Christ, 1980; Christ and Schnepf, 1985).

Staminal nectaries in Pedaliaceae

The Pedaliaceae is characterised by gland crested anthers (Willis, 1951). Ihlenfeldt (1967) in his taxonomic treatment reported anther glands in 11 taxa (Figs. 25-37) and also stressed on their taxonomic importance. McGregor (1976) reviewed the earlier work on pollination in *Sesamum indicum* and reported the pollen and nectar to be an excellent source for bees and other insects. Despite this early recognition and subsequent work there is so far no study on the structure and function on anther glands in any Pedaliaceae.

Gland crested anthers in two species viz., *Sesamum indicum* and *Pedalium murex* have been studied by Arthi and Bahadur (1985). The didynamous stamens in the two species of Pedaliaceae possess a sessile gland at the tip of the connective (Figs. 37, 38). Anthers are dithecous, dorsifixed and smaller in *P.murex* compared to *S.indicum*. The glands in *S.indicum* are oval, greenish and cellular whereas in *P.murex* are globose, orange and papillate (Figs. 37-41). The cellular anther gland of *S.indicum* show a row of rectangular double walled nucleated cells forming the epidermis (Fig. 39). The other cells of the gland are with wavy walls, compactly arranged and contain oil droplets. The surface of the gland possesses two open anomocytic stomata surrounded by 4-6 epidermal cells which are striated (Figs. 39, 41). The stomata secrete nectar on which the insect visitors are dependent. The gland is vasculated upto the middle region and appears to be the extension of the filament vascular tissue. The papillate anther gland of *P.murex* shows the presence of smooth papillae with double layered cell wall and conspicuous nucleus (Fig. 40). The gland of this species is devoid of stomata and vasculature but are starchy.

Staminal nectaries in Melastomataceae

Subramanyam and Narayana (1969) in their study of floral anatomy of some Melastomataceae remarked on the presence of anther nectary in *Memecylon*. Since the details of nectary are not known in *Memecylon sylvaticum*, we made the following observations.

The stamens are heterantherous being of two lengths; the antisepalous being shorter than the antipetalous ones. The connective is prolonged into a characteristic appendage bearing a saucer shaped nectary. The nectary measures 22.2 × 17.0 μm and is attached to the connective (Figs. 21, 22). The cells of the nectary in surface view are shallow with raised walls, penta to polygonal (Fig. 23) and probably secretory. Since enantiostyly is common in the family these glands probably are associated with pollination.

Staminal nectaries in Monotropoideae

Staminal nectaries in 6 genera of Monotropoideae exhibit a range in form from slender elongate projections to short stout or low ridges, usually 5 between the staminal bases with stomata on distal end and scattered trichomes (Wallace, 1977).

Staminal nectaries in Euphorbiaceae

Staminal nectaries of four *Jatropha* species viz., *J. integerrima, J. gossypifolia J. podagrica* and *J. curcas* have been studied. *Jatropha* being monoecious, the male flowers of *J. integerrima* possess five oval fleshy shining yellow nectariferous glands and at the rim are red coloured and enclose the staminal column. The glands are fleshy and flat with a depression on the upper surface encircling the staminal column in *J. gossypiifolia, J. curcas J. podagrica*. These nectariferous glands possess anomocytic stomata and are secretory.

The stomatal index is higher in *J. integerrima* (3.64) followed by *J. gossypifolia* (2.90), *J. podagrica* (1.65) and *J. curcas* (2.51). The stomatal size is higher and equal in the male flower nectaries of *J. integerrima* (36.21 × 32.63; 22.28 × 12.73 μm) and *J. curcas* (36.22 × 31.64; 16.72 × 15.52) compared to *J. gossypifolia* (22.68 × 19.10; 9.95 × 7.16 μm) and *J. podagrica* (25.47 × 21.09; 15.12 × 1.99 μm). Similar nectaries have been noted in *J. multifida, J. panduarefolia, J. tanjorensis* and *J. glandulifera*. The male flower of *Phyllanthus niruri* has 6 small pale yellow fleshy nectariferous glands surrounding the staminal column and are opposite to the petals. These glands are provided with anomocytic secretory stomata. The stomatal index is 4.59 and the stoma and pore sizes are 16.71 × 13.53 and 6.77 × 5.17 μm respectively (unpublished). The nectar composition in the species has been studied by Bahadur *et al.* (1986).

Staminal nectaries in Lauraceae

Sastri (1952) mentioned the presence of appendages in the stamens in *Cassytha* but the details are still unknown. Recently, Hickay and King (1988) have illustrated the stamens of *Laurus nobilis* showing a pair of glandular out growths on either sides of the stamen (Fig. 20). To our knowledge details of nectaries of any Lauraceae are not available. Therefore, we studied the structure of staminal nectaries in *Cassytha filiformis*. The arrangement of the stamens is in 3 tiers of 3 each while the inner whorl of three staminodes as usual in the family. A pair of staminal nectaries are present on either side of the third whorl of stamen (staminodes) (Figs. 42, 43). The nectaries in the species are hollow, round to globose and are attached at the base of the stamen (Figs. 43, 45). The surface is rough with shallow to concave cells. The cell walls are raised, straight to slightly wavy with dense contents (Fig. 46).

In addition to the nectaries, 3 conical shaped glands are also present in between the third whorl of stamens. The conical gland is larger than the staminal nectaries and shows longitudinally arranged polygonal cells. The cells are with dense contents and the surface is straited (Figs. 44 & 47). The morphology of staminal nectaries in Lauraceae has been debated but it is now considered as modified stamens in view of similarity of vascular supply with the stamens (see Sastri, 1965).

According to Ronse Decraene and Smets (1993) most of the Lauraceae eg. *Laurus* sp., possess single whorl of outer stamens opposite the outer tepals and the upper stamen whorls alternate regularly. The innermost stamen whorl are staminodial and lateral nectaries are variously attached to the base of the filament. Similar nectariferous staminodia occur in the Hamamelidae (Bogle, 1989; Endress, 1989).

Hufford and Endress (1989) have studied the diversity of anther structure, dehiscence patterns under SEM in 8 orders of Hamamelididae. In *Myrothamnus* the "distal theca" looks like nectary as per the photograph and stated the distal connective protrusion is characteristic of lower Hamemelididae. Parkin (1950) has discussed the possible primitive nature of connective and opines that this may be related to pollination.

Endress and Hufford (1989) have studied the stamen structures and dehiscence in 23 families belonging to Magnoliales, Laurales, Piperales, Nymphaeales, Aristolochiales and Ranunculales under SEM. The scanning micrograph of *Cyclanthus* (Cyclanthaceae) stamen is shown as nectariferous; likewise 'nectariferous pouches' on either sides of filaments in *Peunus* (Monimiaceae) are shown as glandular appendages but the authors make no comment.

The stamen in Proteaceae is haplostemonous and alternates with nectar secreting scales of uncertain homology (Cronquist, 1981).

According to Smets (1988) the glands are inserted inside the androecium and may represent receptacular enations or remains of inner stamen whorl.

Staminal nectaries in Monocotyledons

Fahn (1952) recognised 6 types of nectaries including the staminal type which is characterised by the nectariferous tissue found in the lower portion of the stamens as in *Colchicum ritchii.* As illustrated by Fahn the nectaries are provided with large open stomata.

Dahlgren and Clifford (1982) have observed the occurence of androecial nectaries in Liliales i.e., Colchicaceae (*Colchicum*), Iridaceae (*Iris*), Liliaceae (*Tulipa*), the nectaries occur on the filaments of fertile stamens and in Asparagales i.e., Dianellaceae (*Dianella*), Amaryllidaceae (*Hessea*), Arecaceae (*Chamaerops*). In Alismataceae (*Sagittaria*) the nectaries occur on staminodes as well as on the filaments of fertile stamens. In Hydrocharitaceae (*Stratiotes, Hydrocharis, Ottelia*) and Zingiberaceae (*Brachychilum, Globba, Hedychium, Kaempfera, Roscoea*) the nectaries occur on staminodes and rarely occur in Araceae (*Aglaonema*) and Commelinaceae (*Commelina*).

Scribailo and Posluszny (1985) have observed the presence of staminal nectaries in *Hydrocharis morsuranea* (Hydrocharitaceae). In the pistillate flower of *Hydrocharis morsuranae* three paired staminodes opposite the outer tepals are transformed and alternate with nectaries which are laterally attached to stamens.

According to Daumann (1970) androecial nectaries occur in 8% compared to perigonial (18%) and gynoecial (59%) nectaries in the investigated genera of Monocotyledonae. Further, he regards the gynoecial nectaries as advanced in comparison to perigonial and androecial nectaries.

The androceium of monocotyledons has been extensively dealt with by Rouse Decreaene and Smets (1995) but the details of nectaries are unavailable for discussion.

Prominent two lobed fossil nectaries at the base of stamens with stomata like openings on their surface have been observed in small flowers from the early Companian of Aachen. Likewise, fossil stamens with well developed apical connective are reported in Chloranthad from lower and upper Cretaceous (Friis and Endress, 1994).

CONCLUSIONS

Rao and Pankhurst (1986) have stated, ''Anther appendages, include penicillate or apiculate anthers extended sterile anther lobes, extended connectives and clearly formed appendages of whatever origin''. On page 68 & 69 of their book have provided the illustrations of anthers bearing various types of extensions either of the filament of with 'gland' like structure at the anther tip but make no comments.

McLean and Ivimey-Cook (1956) classified various types of nectaries into five main types including the staminal types. They have also sub-divided the staminal nectaries into six types and the same is reproduced on page 70 in view of special types recognised by them.

Fahn (1979) proposed a topographic classification of extrafloral and floral nectaries and the floral nectaries into 9 types of which staminal nectaries is one of them. According to his classification the staminal nectaries are of 3 sub-types : (a) on filaments, (b) transformed anthers and (c) appendages of connectives.

Staminal Type

Nectar is secreted by or in close association with the stamens.

(a) Nectar secreted by the base of the stamen flaments.
Example : From the united stamens in many Papilionaceae.

(b) Nectar secreted in grooves on the flaments.
Examples : 1. The groove is on the abaxial side in *Vaccinium* and *Tulipa*.
2. The groove is on the adaxial side in *Atragene*.

(c) Nectar is secreted by processes at the base of the stamens.
Examples : 1. The nectaries form swellings at the base of the stamens in Alsinoideae and in Geraniaceae
2. The staminal nectaries are united into a ring in Silenoideae.
3. The nectaries form swellings which may be either isolated or united in various ways, in Cruciferae.

The nectaries in Cruciferae have been used as a means of classification by Bayer. It is open to question whether these nectaries are outgrowths of the receptacle around the bases of the stamens or whether they belong to the stamens or whether they belong to the stamens themselves. As the nectaries in the closely related Fumariaceae are undoubtedly staminal, the latter alternative seems the more probable.

(d) The nectaries form appendages of the stamen filaments.
Example : Paired appendages, like stipules, in many Lauraceae.

(e) The nectaries are staminodes.
Example : 1. Nectar is secreted from the connective in *Anemone pulsatilla*
2. Nectar is secreted from staminodal appendages in *Sassafras* and *Persea*.
3. Nectar is secreted adaxially at the base of palmately branched staminodes in *Parnassia*.
4. Nectar is secreted by a ten-lobed cup with ten vascular strands, in Phaseoleae. Probably a reduced whorl of stamens.

(f) The nectaries are formed at the junction of stamen and petal in epipetalous stamens.
Examples : Nectar is secreted by a yellow-coloured nectary surrounding the base of the free part of the filament in *Colchicum* and *Trillium*. The nectar collects in a channel of the petal.

(Reproduced from McLean and Ivimey-Cook, 1956).

In the light of existing data and our own, we propose a simplified classification of the staminal nectaries as follows :

i) Nectaries enclosing the staminal column. eg. *Jatropha integerrima, Oxalis latifolia.*

ii) Nectaries on either sides of the filament. eg. *Cassytha filiformis, Laurus nobilis.*

iii) Nectaries between the bases of the filaments. eg. *Antigonon leptopus.*

iv) Filament base transformed into nectariferous pouch. eg. *Turnera subulata, T. ulmifolia.*

v) Filament spur nectaries. eg. *Hybanthus ennaespermus.*

vi) Anthers with crested nectaries/glands

a. Sessile glands embedded at the tip of anther. eg. *Psidium guajava, Eucalyptus globulus.*

b. Sessile glands at the tip of anther. eg. *Pedalium murex, Sesamum indicum, Memecylon sylvaticum.*

c. Stalked glands at the tip of anther. eg. *Dichrostachys cinerea, Adenanthera pavonia, Acacia nilotica.*

vii) Nectaries on filaments of fertile stamens or staminodes

a. On filaments of fertile stamens. eg. *Colchicum, Tulipa, Dianella.*

b. On both staminodes and fertile filaments. eg. *Sagittaria.*

c. On staminodes only. eg. *Hydrocharis, Ottelia.*

It is thus obvious that staminal nectaries occur in a wide range of unrelated taxa differing in shape, size and position suggesting that this character evolved independently along several lines and apparently related to pollination biology of the species. Guedes (1879) has discussed the morphology of stamen including the connective but without mention of nectary and regards the stamen as phyllome inserted on floral axis with a protrusion; the connective appendages, the filament which is unifacial. Guedes reported staminal 'stipules' at the base of staminal base (*Zygophyllum*) and glandular stipules makes up the disc as in *Rhizophoraceae*. Are the 'staminal stipules', nectaries? or what is their nature is presently not known? Centripetal and centrifugal stamens occur in Myrtales and Violales with various combinations in other orders. This coupled with anther dehiscence (extrorse or introse etc.) and the staminal nectaries act as a unit in pollination biology and this needs more attention in future studies.

Needless to state that a concerted comparative LM, EM, SEM, and TEM, study coupled with histochemical investigations would throw invaluable information and hopefully solve the myth and function of staminal nectaries in taxonomic and phylogenetic considerations vis-a-vis pollination biology, since nectaries have direct bearing on evolutionary development of flowering plants.

Explanation of Figures

FIGS. 1—7 : 1 & 2. Thrum and pin eyed flowers of *Turnera subulata* after removal of calyx and corolla showing nectar pockets. 3 & 4 Adaxial side of the basal swollen filament showing nectary pouch in bud and flower respectively of the same. 5. A portion of the adaxial side of nectary pouch of the same. 6. Stamen of *Hybanthus ennaespermus* showing assymetrical appendage and a nectariferous spur. 7. Open anomocytic stomata from the nectariferous spur of the same.

FIGS. 8—24a : 8, 10, 12, 14, 16 & 18. Anthers of *Acacia nilotica, Adenanthera pavonia, Dichrostachys cinerea, Neptunia triquetra, Prosopis juliflora, Xylia xylocarpa* showing staminal nectaries at their tips. 9, 11, 13, 15, 17, 19. Staminal nectaries of *Acacia nilotica, Adenanthera pavonia, Dichrostachys cinerea, Neptunia triquetra, Prosopis juliflora* and *Xylia xylocarpa* enlarged. 20. Stamen of *Laurus nobilis* showing 2 lateral glandular nectaries. 21. Anther of *Memecylon* showing staminal nectary. 22. The same staminal cupular nectary enlarged. 23. A portion of the same enlarged. 24. & 24a Anther of Psidium guajava showing partially exposed gland and a portion of the same enlarged.

FIGS. 25—41 : Staminal nectaries in various Pedaliaceae : 25. *Sesamum schinizianum*. 26. *Ceratotheca triloba*. 27. *Dicerocaryum zanguebarium*. 28. *Linariopsis Prostrata*. 29. *Josephinia africana*. 30. *Sesamothamnus lugardii*. 31. *Pedalium murex*. 32. *Holubia saccata*. 33. *Harpagophytum procumbens*. 34. *Pterodiscus speciousus* 35. *Uncarina grandidieri*. 36. *Rogeria adenophylla* 37. *Pedalium murex* 40. Papillate staminate nectary of *Pedalium murex* is enlarged. 38, 39, 41. Anther of *Sesamum indicum* showing sessile, Oval staminal nectary at tip, anther gland of the same enlarged and an anomocytic stoma with epidermal cells of the same respectively (From Ihelemfeldt, 1967).

FIGS. 42—47 : 42. Flower of *Cassytha filiformis* after removal of perianth parts showing staminal nectaries and conical gland. 43. Staminal nectaries on either side of the 3rd whorl of stamen of the same. 44. Conical nectary/gland of the same. 45 & 46. Staminal nectary and an enlarged portion of the same. 47. A portion of the conical gland enlarged.

Literature Cited

Arthi. C. and Bahadur. B. 1985. Gland crested anthers in some Angiosperms. *J. Swamy Bot. Cl. 2* : 79-86.

Bahadur. B. and Ramaswamy, N. 1982. Biochemical changes in the pistils of distylous *Turnera subulata* J.E. Smith (Turneraceae) following self and cross pollinations. *J. Palynol, 18* : 127-133.

Bahadur, B. and Ramaswamy, N. 1984. Pollination biology of heterostylous *Turnera subulata* J.E. Smith *J. Palynol, 20* : 98-109.

Bahadur, B, Ramaswamy, N. Arthi, C. and Farooqui, S.M. 1985. Floral nectaries in two species of *Turnera* L. (Turneraceae). *New Botanist, 12* : 117-127.

Bahadur, B., Arthi, C. and Ramaswamy, N. 1986. Nectar types in Indian plants. *Proc. Indian Acad. Sci.* (Plant Sci.) 96 : 41-48.

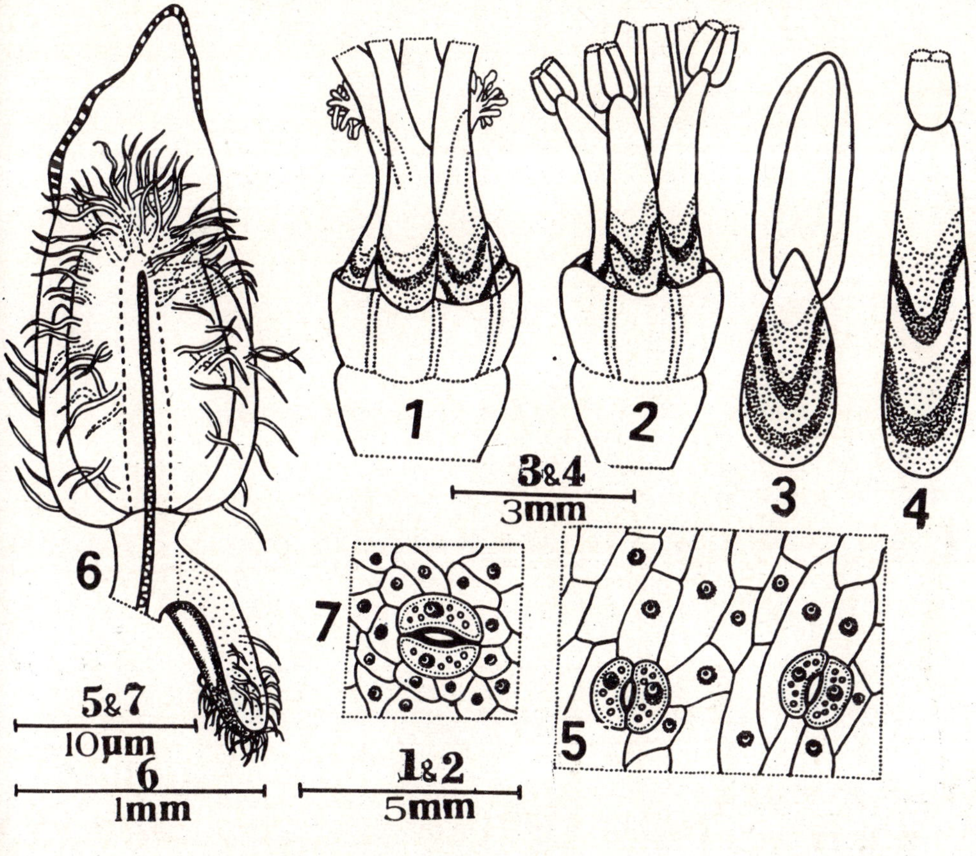

1
2
3&4
3mm
3
4
6
7
5
5&7
10µm
6
1mm
1&2
5mm

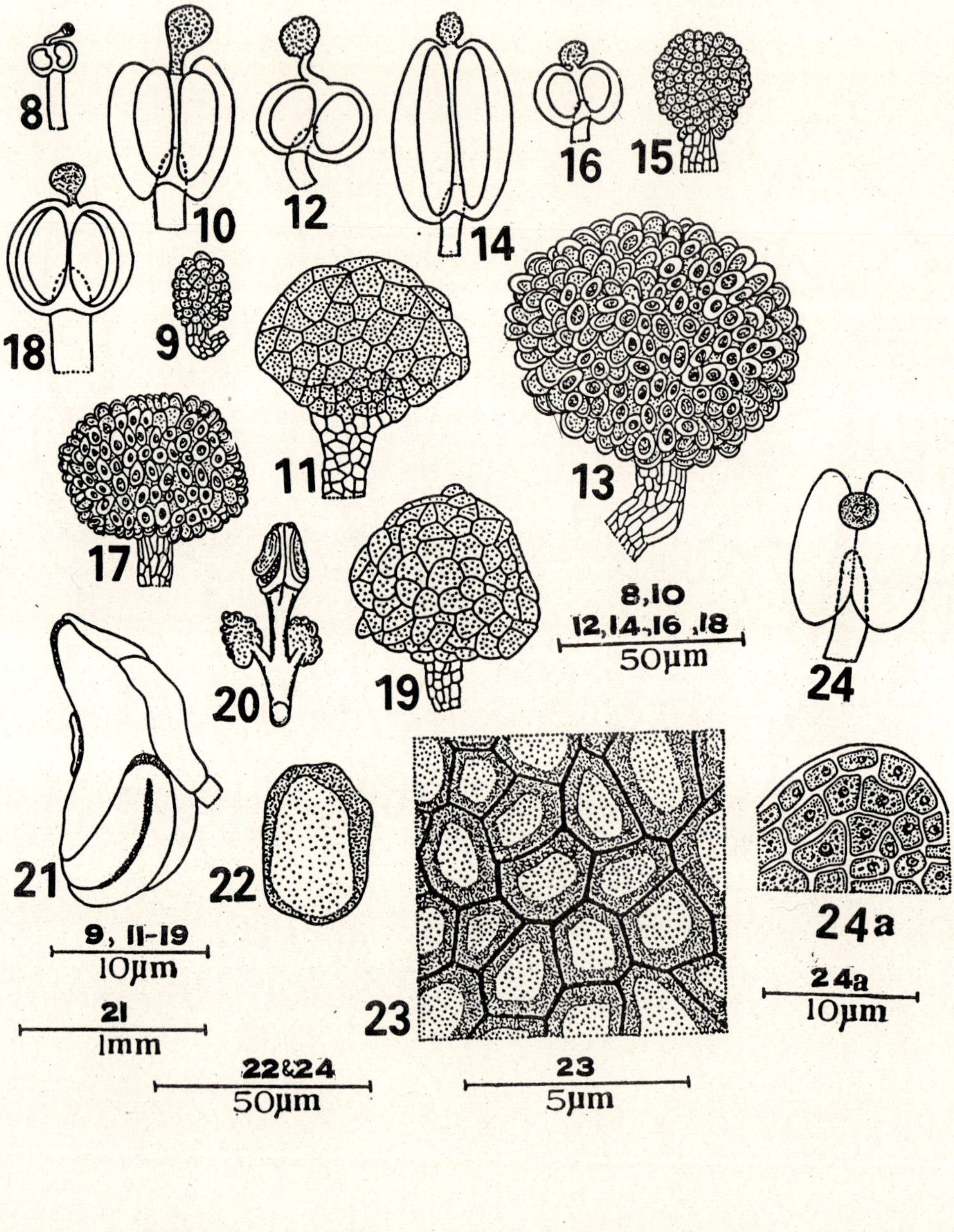

8
10
12
14
16
15
18
9
11
13
17
19
20
24
8,10
12,14,16,18
50µm
21
22
23
24a
9, 11-19
10µm
21
1mm
24a
10µm
22&24
50µm
23
5µm

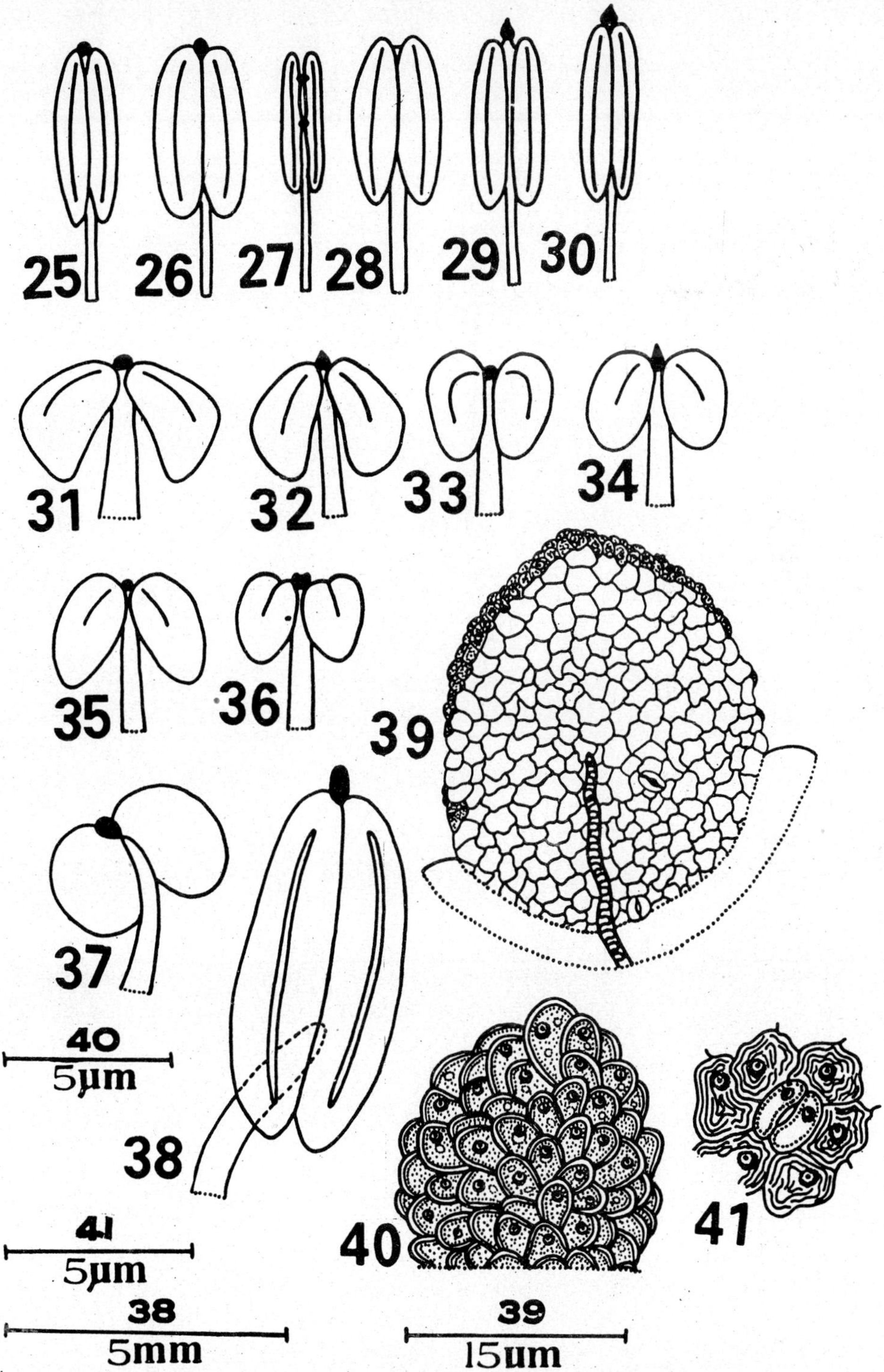
25
26
27
28
29
30
31
32
33
34
35
36
37
38
39
40
41
40
5µm
41
5µm
38
5mm
39
15µm

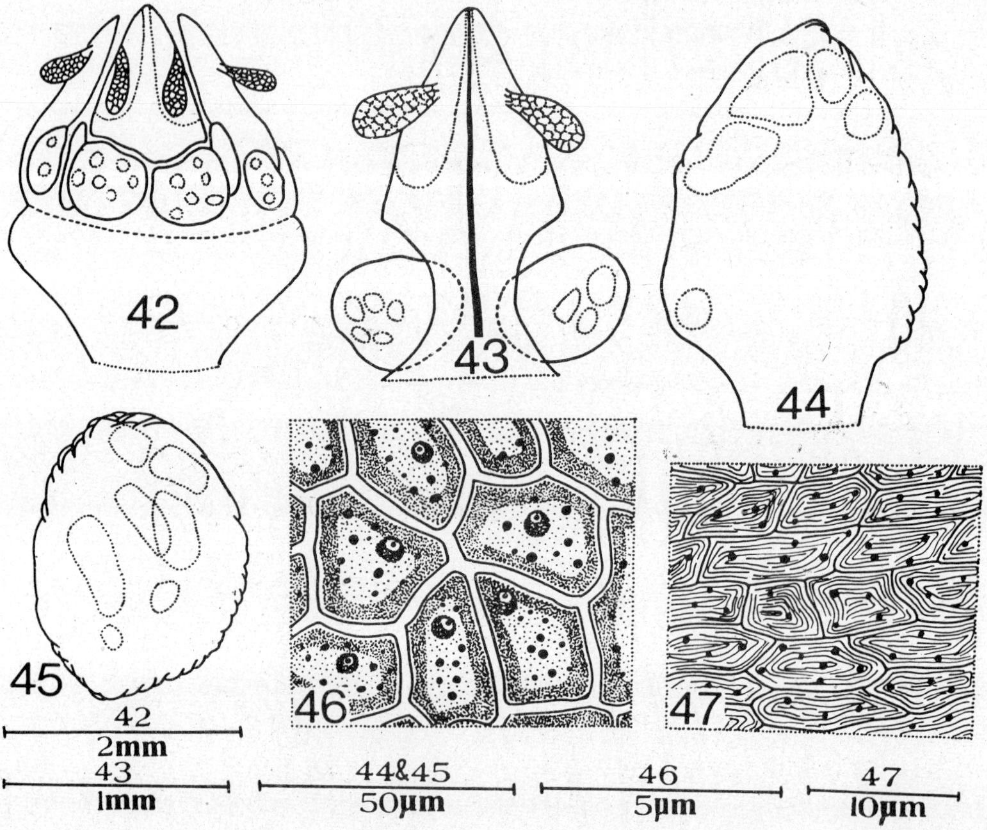
42
43
44
45
46
47
42
2mm
43
1mm
44&45
50μm
46
5μm
47
10μm

Bahadur, B., Arthi, C. and Ramaswamy, N. 1987. Floral biology of *Hybanthus ennaespermus* (L) Muell. (Violaceae). *New Botanist, 14* : 29-45.

Baker, H.G., Opler, P.A. and Baker, I. 1978. A comparison of the amino acid complements of floral and extrafloral nectars. *Bot. Gaz., 139* : 322-332.

Barrett, S.C.H. 1978. Heterostyly in a tropical weed : The reproductive biology of the *Turnera ulmifolia* complex (Turneraceae). *Can. J. Bot., 56* : 1713-1725.

Beattie. A.J. 1971. Pollination mechanisms in *Viola. New Phytol, 70* : 343-360.

Bentham, G. 1875. Revision of the sub-order Mimoseae. *Trans. Linn. Soc.* (London), *30* : 335-668.

Bogle, A.L. 1989. The floral morphology, vascular anatomy, and ontogeny of the Rhodoleioideae (Hemamelidaceae) and their significance in relation to the "lower" Hamamelids. In: eds. *Crane, P.R. and Blackmore, S. Evolution Systematics and fossil history of the Hamamelidea, Vol. I : Introduction and "lower" Hamamelidea*. Oxford : Clarendon Press, 201-220.

Briggs, B.G. 1964. The control of interspecific hybridization in *Darwinia. Evolution, 18* : 292-303.

Brown, W.H. 1938. The bearing of nectaries on the phylogeny of flowering plants. *Proc. Amer. Phil. Soc., 79* : 549-595.

Capuron, R. 1963. Note sur les Turneraceas de Madagascar. *Adansonia, 2* : 130-137.

Christ, P. and E. Schnepf 1985. The nectaries of *Cynanchum vincetoxicum. Isreal J. Bot., 34* : 79-90.

Cronquist, A. 1981. *An integrated system of classification of flowering plants*. Columbia University press, New York.

Dahlgren, R.M.T. and Clifford, H.T. 1982. *The Monocotyledons : A Comparative study*. Academic press, London.

Darwin, C.H. 1877. On the glandular bodies in *Acacia sphaerocephala* and *Cercropia peltata* serving as food for ants with an appendix on the nectar glands of the common braken fern, *Pteris aquiline. J. Linn. Soc. Bot., 15* : 398-408.

Daumann, E. (1970) Das Blutennektarium der Monocotyledonen unter besonderer Berucksichtigung seiner systematischen and phylogenetischen Bedeutung. *Feddes Repertorium, 80* : 463-590.

Endress, P.K. and Hufford, L.D. 1989. the diversity of stamen structures and dehiscence patterns among Magnoliidae. *Bot. J. Linn. Soc., 100* : 45-85.

Endress, P.K. 1989. Phylogenetic relationships in the Hamamelidoideae. *In*: eds. Crane, P.R. and Blackmore, S. *Evolution, Systematics and fossil history of the Hamamelidae, Vol. I : Introduction and "lower" Hamamelidae.* Oxford : Calrendon Press, 227-248.

Endress, P.K. and Stumpf, D. 1991. The diversity of stamen structures in "lower" Rosidae. *Bot. J. Linn. Soc., 107* : 217-293.

Elias, T.S., Rozich, W.R. and Newcomba, L. 1975. The foliar and floral nectaries of *Turnera ulmifolia* L. *Am. J. Bot., 62* : 570-576.

Faegri, K. and Pijl, L.V. 1976. *The Principles of Pollination Ecology*, Pergamon Press, London.

Faegri, K. and Pijl, L.V. 1980. *The Principles of Pollination Ecology*. Pergamon Press, III revised ed. London.

Fahn, A. 1952. On the structure of floral nectaries. *Bot. Gaz., 113* : 464-470.

Fahn. A. 1953. the topography of nectary in the flower and its phylogenatic trend. *Phytomorphology, 3* : 424-426.

Fahn, A. 1979. *Secretary Tissues in Plants*. Academic Press, London, pp.51-111.

Free, J.B. 1970. *Insect Pollination of Crops*. Academic Press, London. (also revised edition, 1995)

Fries, E.M and Endress, P,K, 1994 Origin and evolution of angiosperm flower. *In*: ed. Callow, J.A *Adv. Bot. Res., 17*: 100-162. Academic Press, London.

Gamble, J.S. 1957. *The Flora of Presidency of Madras*. Vols. I-III B.S.I. Calcutta, India.

Guedes, M. 1979. *Morphology of Seed Plants*. J. Cramer, Germany.

Gulyas, S. and Kincsek. I. 1982. Floral nectaries of species of Papilionaceae. *Acta Biol.* (Szeged) *28* : 53-63.

Hickey, M. and King, C. 1988. 100 Families of Flowering plants. Cambridge University Press, London.

Hooker, J.D. 1973. *Flora of British India*, Vol. II (Sabiaceae to Cornaceae) Bishen Singh Mahendrapal Singh, Dehra Dun, India, (Reprint).

Hufford, L.D. and Endress, P.K. 1989. The diversity of anther structures and dehiscence patterns among Hamamelidae. *Bot. J. Linn. Soc., 99*: 301-346.

Hutchinson, J. 1967. *The Genera of Flowering Plants* Vol. II. Clarendon Press, London.

Ihlenfeldt, H.D. 1967. *Uber die Abgrenzung* die naturliche Gliederung der Pedaliaceae. *R. Br. Allg. Bot. Hamburg, 12* : 43-128.

Isley. D. 1970. Legumes of the United States V. *Albizia, Lysiloma, Leucaena, Adenanthera*, and rejected genera of Mimosoideae. *Castanea, 35* : 244-260.

Isley. D. 1972. Legumes of the United States VI. *Calliandra, Pithecellobium, Prosopis. Madrono, 21* : 273-298.

Kunze, H. 1990. Morphology and evolution of the corona in Asclepiadaceae and related families. *Akad. der Wissen Chaften Mainz, 76* : 7-51.

Lawrence, G.H.M. 1964. *Taxonomy of Vascular Plants*. Oxford & IBH Publishing Co., New Delhi.

Leelavathi, P. and Ramayya, N. 1982. Trichomes in relation to Taxonomy : Mimosoideae. *Geophytology, 12* : 6-21.

McGregor, S.E. 1976. *Insect Pollination of Cultivated Crop* Plants. *Agriculture Hand Book No. 496*. Agricultural Research Service, USDA, Washington.

McLean, R.C. and Ivimey Cook, W.R.I. 1956. *Text Book of Theoretical Botany* Vol. II Longmans Green & Co., London pp.1244-1251.

Narayana, L.L. and Rao. D. 1977. Contributions to the floral anatomy of Humiriaceae. *J. Jap. Bot. 52* : 142-153.

Narayana, L.L. and Rao, D. 1978. Systamatic position of Humiriaceae, Linaceae and Erythroxylaceae in the light of the companatise floral morphology and embryology. A Discussion *J. Indian bot soc. 57* : 258-266.

Parkin, J. 1951. The protrusion of the connective beyond the anther and its bearing on the evolution of the stamen. *Phytomorphology. 1* : 1-8.

Paul, S.R. 1979. The genus *Calliandra* (Mimosaceae) in the Indian sub-continent. Feddes Repertorium (Berlin), *90* : 155-164.

Ramaswamy, N. And Bahadur, B. 1981. Heterostyly and incompatibility in *Turnera subulata* J.E. Smith (Turneraceae). *Incomp. News Lett.* (Netherlands), *13* : 20-27.

Ramaswamy, N. and Bahadur, B. 1983. pollen tube growth studies in self and cross pollinated pistils of distylous *Turnera subulata* J.E. Smith (Turneracee). *J. Bot. Res.*, 57-63.

Ramaswamy, N. and Bahadur, B. 1984a. Unilateral inter-specific hybridization between *Turnera ulmifolia* ( ) X *T. subulata* (Thrum). *Indian J. Bot., 7* : 29-35.

Ramaswamy, N. and Bahadur, B. 1984 b. Pollen flow in dimorphic *Turnera subulata* (Turneraceae). *New Phytol., 98* : 205-209.

Rao, C.K. and Pankhurst, R.J. 1986. *A Polyclave to the Monocotyledonous Families of the World* British Museum Natural History, London.

Rao, V.S., Sir Deshmukh and Sardar, M.G. 1958. The floral anatomy of the Leguminosae. *J. Univ. Bombay, 26* : 65-138.

Rendle, A.B. 1975. *The Classification of Flowering Plants Vol. II Dicotyledons.* Cambridge Univ. Press. London.

Ronse Decraene, L.P. and Smets, E.F. 1993. The distribution and systematic relevance of the androecial character polymery. *Bot. J. Linn. soc., 13* : 285-350.

Ronse Decraene, L.P. and E.F. Smets. 1995. *Bot. J. Linn. Soc., 118* : 193-247.

*Ronse Decraene, L.P. and E.F. Smets, 1995. The androecium of Monocotyledons. *In: Monocotyledons : Systematics and Evolution.* (eds.) Rudall, P.J. Gibb P. Cutter D.F. & Humphries, C.J. Kew Royal Botanic Gardens, London, 243-254.

Ross, J.H. 1979. A conspectus of the African *Acacia* species. *Mem. Bot. Surv. South Africa, 44* : 43.

Sastri, R.L.N. 1952. Studies in the Lauraceae I. Floral anatomy of *Cinnamomum iners* Reinw. and *Cassytha filiformis* L. *J. Indian Bot. Soc., 31* : 240-246.

Sastri, R.L.N. 1965. Studies in the Lauraceae. V. Comparative morphology of the flower. *Ann. Bot., 29* : 39- 44.

Schnepf, E. and P. Christ 1980. Unusual transfer cells in the epithelium of the nectaries of *Asclepias curassavica. Protoplasma 105* : 135-148.

Scribailo, R.W. and Posluszny, U. 1985. Floral development of *Hydrocharis morsus-ranae* L. (Hydrocharitaceae). *Am. J. Bot., 72* : 1578-1589.

*Smets, E.F. 1988. Florale nektarien van de Magnoliophytina Karakheriring en systematische betekenis. Doctorate thesis, Katholicke Universiteit Leuven, Belgium.

Solereder, H. 1908. *Systematic Anatomy of the Dicotyledons, Vol. I Clarendon Press*, Oxford, London.

Start, A.N. and Marshall, A.G. 1976. *Tropical Trees Variation Breeding and Conservation. Linn. Soc. Symp. Ser. No.* 2, Academic Press, London, 141-150.

Subramanyam, K. and Narayana, L.L. 1969. A contribution to the floral anatomy of some members of Melastomataceae. *J. Jap. Bot., 44*: 5-16.

Urban, I. 1883. Monographic der familie der Turneraceen. *Jahrb. Koingl. Bot. Gart.*, *2* : 1-152.

Wallace, G.D. 1977. Studies on the Monotropoideae (Ericaceae). Floral nectaries : Anatomy & function in pollination ecology. *Am. J. Bot. 64* : 199-206.

Willis, J.C. 1951. *A Dictionary of the Flowering Plants and Ferns*. 6th revd. ed. Camb. Univ. Press. London.

ONTOGENY, STRUCTURE AND HISTOCHEMISTRY OF FLORAL NECTARIES IN *KIGELIA PINNATA* DC (BIGNONIACEAE)

C.K. RUDRAMUNIYAPPA and A.R. MANURE
Department of Botany, Karnatak University
Dharwad 580 003, India.

ABSTRACT

The ontogeny and histochemistry of floral nectaries in *Kigelia pinnata* was studied. In *Kigelia* nectary begins to differentiate from the epidermis. By repeated periclinal and anticlinal divisions the initial cell gives rise capitate nectary comprising a multicellular secretory head, stipe cell(s) and basal cell(s). In the entire developing gland no PAS positive storage was noticed, but high levels of RNA, proteins, lipids and ascorbic acid were observed particularly in the disc cells. The secretory cells exhibit strong activity for all enzymes localized. The cell walls are distinctly PAS and cellulose positive. Thick callose layer around the stipe was observed.

Based on the results obtained we have tried to comprehend the information on various aspects of nectaries and to provide the functional relationship of nectaries with pollinators in the surrounding environment. We have also attempted to provide the qualitative aspects of nectar because nectar is closely related with pollination ecology, community ecology, biogeography, physiology and ultimately the evolution.

Key words : Floral nectaries; ontogeny, structure & histochemistry; *Kigelia pinnata*.

INTRODUCTION

The epidermis in most of the plants produces a wide range of uni-and multicellular secretory tissues both (nectaries and trichomes). The morphology of these structures varies greatly with the tissues and species. The literature revealed that more than 300 morphological descriptions for epidermal outgrowths have been recognised (Behnke, 1984). These characteristics have often been well documented and utilized in plants classification (Fahn, 1979). Nectaries are also the secretory systems develop on all parts of the plant body. The term nectary (nectarium) was introduced by Linne (1735).

Functionally, if the secretory systems are of simple hairs serve as a "guard" against herbivores, guide the path of pollinators or affect photosynthesis, leaf temperature or water loss through increased light reflectance as in desert species (see Kelsey *et al.*, 1984). Or if the secretory systems are of more specialised kinds (glandular trichomes/nectaries of floral or extra floral) function in producing pest-or pollinators — interactive nectar which are stored or extruded out of the plant surface. This exudate (nectar) chemically varies. The secreted compounds normally do not re-enter into the metabolic processes in plants. The nectar products in many a cases function as a source of energy for pollinators, are related to community ecology and ultimately evolution (Heinrich and Raven, 1977; Fahn, 1979). These secretory tissues also play a role in reproductive biology, because of their diverse form, structure and function. The glandular secreting systems also form an attractive systems for the study of molecular biology and gene cloning (see Wagner, 1991). Caspary (1848 see Fahn 1979) distinguished the 'floral' and 'extrafloral' nectaries. Delpino (1868-75) called them as nuptial and extra nuptial respectively. The former develops on different floral organs and the latter on vegetative organs. In angiosperms the floral nectaries are found on sepals, petals, stamens, ovary, the receptacle and even on style (see Fahn, 1988). On these organs they may be situated in different places. Ovarial nectaries occur in some plants on the surface of the ovary, as in *Spathodea*, a member of Bignoniaceae (Rudramuniyappa and Mahajan, 1991) and in some other plants (see Fahn, 1979.) Stylar nectaries may occur at the base of the style as in the species of Umbelliferae and Compositae (Fahn, 1979). Septal nectaries located in the ovary septa (Fahn, 1979; Schmid, 1988; Bernardello *et al.*, 1991). The floral and extra floral nectaries are generally classified on a functional basis. The floral nectaries are directly associated with pollination whereas the extrafloral nectaries are not (Elias and Gelband, 1976; Fahn, 1979). In the present study we denote floral nectaries that are found on the various parts of the flower and extrafloral nectaries that are found on various vegetative structures (petioles, stipules, leaves etc.).

Most of the Bignoniaceae are tropical in their distribution and majority of the genera are characterised by the presence of floral as well as extrafloral nectaries. (Rao, 1926; Parija and Samal, 1936; Seibert, 1948; Inamdar, 1969, Elias and Gelband, 1976; Subramanian and Inamdar, 1985, 1986; Mehra and Kulkarni, 1989; Rudramuniyappa and Mahajan, 1991). Bureau (1864) first described the floral and extra floral nectaries in Bignoniaceae. Later, Treub (1889) was attracted by the occurrence of glandular trichomes of the inner surface of the clayx in *Spathodea campanulata* and attributed the function of hydathodes protecting the inner floral structures from desiccation. The taxonomic importance of the nectaries in this family has been illustrated by Schumann (1895), Sandwith (1938) and Siebert (1948). Siebert (1948) surveyed extra floral nectaries for taxonomic considerations and classified as inter petiolar, neuroaxillary, glandular, scattered glands and glandular scales. Rao (1926) described the extrafloral nectaries in *Spathodea stipulata*. Dop (1927) reported the occurrence of extrafloral nectaries on the outer surface of the corolla in *Spathodea* and calycine nectaries in *Dolichandrone* and *Radermachera*. Parija and Samal (1936) described glandular hairs, patelliform glands, and extrafloral nectaries in *Tecoma*. Raghavan and Venkatasubban (1940) described the ontogeny of capitate glands occurred on the floral parts of *Spathodea campanulata* and regarded them as modified hydathodes. Inamdar (1969) described the ontogeny and structure of foliar nectaries in *Bignonia*. Laroche (1974) has reported the occurrence of nectaries on the calyx in *Adenocalyamma comosum*. Elias and Gelband (1976) described the morphology and anatomy of various extrafloral nectary system found in the genus *Campsis* and have discussed the evolutionary and phylogenetic significance of nectaries found in Bignoniaceae. Subsequently, Elias and Prance (1978) and Elias and Newcombe (1979) have also described the occurrence of floral and extrafloral nectaries in different members of Bignoniaceae. (*Crescentia, Catapla*). Similar studies have also been made on the occurrence, structure, ontogeny and biology of floral and extrafloral nectaries in some members of

Bignoniaceae (*Kigelia, Bignonia*) by Subramanian and Inamdar (1985, 1986). These authors elucidated the role of these nectaries in relation to pollination ecology also studied chemical nature of nectary cells and nectar analysis.

In 1989 Mehra and Kulkarni have made organographic survey of floral trichomes along with their distribution, ontogeny, systematic and functional significance in some species of Bignoniaceae (*Millingtonia, Jacaranda, Tabebuia, Dolichandrone, Sterospermum*). Recently, Rudramuniyappa and Mahajan (1991) have studied the morphogenesis and histochemical nature of floral nectaries found on the ovary wall of *Spathodea campanulata*.

Rao (1926) first showed the nectar secretion to contain sugars using Fehling's solution. Traces of reducing sugars were also observed in the calyx fluid of *Spathodea campanulata* (Raghavan and Venkatasubban, 1940) and in the calyx nectaries of *Adenocalyamma comosum* (Laroche, 1974). A preliminary analysis of nectar from floral and extrafloral nectaries of *Kigelia pinnata* (Subramanian and Inamdar, 1985) revealed the presence of three sugars viz., sucrose, glucose and fructose and only a few amino acids like arginine in all nectaries, glutamine and asparagine in extra floral nectaries. Methionine and tryptophan were found only in floral nectaries. Bahadur *et al.* (1986) have reported the presence of sucrose, glucose and fructose in three species of Bignoniaceae (*Spathodea campanulata, Bignonia speciosa, Tecoma grnadiflora*) and in the nectaries of *Tecomaria capensis*, glucose was not present. Amino acids were reported in traces. It is conspicuous to note that the copious nectar secreted in *Spathodea campanulata* contains only two amino acids viz., alanine and isoleucine.

Kigelia pinnata DC "Sausage tree" is a common tropical tree (family Bignoniaceae) and is a native of Africa. In India it is cultivated as an ornamental and as an avenue tree. This species is also characterised by the floral and extrafloral nectaries. In the present study the floral nectaries differentiated on calyces were studied to provide a better understanding of their ontogeny, structure and cellular composition using histochemical techniques. The diversity of secretory products produced by nectaries and glandular trichomes etc., invites the application of qualitative histochemical methods which help in *in situ* localization and identification of biochemical substances in the intact cells and tissues. A few studies have revealed the occurrence of RNA, proteins, lipids, ascorbic acid and the activities of some enzymes in the nectaries of some members of angiosperms including a few Bignoniaceae (Fahn, 1979, 1988; Peterson and Vermeer, 1984; Subramanian *et al.*, 1990). The secretory systems in general are the best suited for a variety of morphogenetic studies. Therefore, the knowledge on their structure, ontogeny, cyto/histochemistry and EM is very necessary to understand the manner in which they differentiate and function, and it is also necessary to know the *modus operandi* and the nature of secretion.

In this paper we consider some general aspects of biology of nectaries with emphasis on selected papers on histochemical basis of nectary development. The paper also deals with the chemical composition and possible function of nectar which is necessary of better understanding of the relationships between plants and animal visitors.

MATERIAL AND METHODS

Kigelia pinnata, is characterised by the presence of both floral and extrafloral nectaries. For the present study floral nectaries were selected. Different developmental stages of calyces of flowers were collected from the trees growing in the University campus. The calyces were removed and fixed in 2.5% glutaraldehyde in 0.05 M phosphate buffer, pH 7.2 for 12 hr. at 4°C. The fixed material was washed thoroughly in the same buffer, and dehydrated routinely by using ethyl alcohol-butanol series. Following dehydration, the material was embedded in paraffin following standard microtechnique methods (Berlyn and Miksche, 1976), Serial sections of a 8 µm were obtained and stained for different histochemical substances. Histochemical reactions were carried out on fixed and fresh cryostat sections.

Methods for fixed material — Total polysaccharides were detected by the PAS test (Jensen, 1962), total proteins by the mercuric bromophenol blue method (Mazia *et al.*, 1953, total RNA by the azure B method (Jensen, 1962) and ascorbic acid was localized by the $AgNo_3$ test (Shah *et al.*, 1974). Cellulose was detected by using calcofluor white-fluorescence technique (O'Brien and McCully, 1981) and callose was visualized by decolorised aniline blue fluorescence (ABF) method (O'Brien and McCully, 1981). The sections were also observed under UV source for autofluorescence.

Methods for Fresh Material — Tissue preparation for taking fresh cryostat sections occupies a special place. This is because of that enzymes will become denatured in routine tissue procedures. Similarly lipids also dissolve in organic solvents viz., ethyl alcohol. Therefore, routine tissue fixation, dehydration and infiltration procedures are to be avoided. For the present work, freeze sectioning using cryostat procedure was followed. The material under study was pre-treated before taking sections. This step minimizes alterations in the structure of cells and tissues. This step also provides a suitable supporting sectioning medium because the mixture of gelatin and an antifreeze solution viz. DMSO (Dimethyl sulphoxide) was used as a pre-treating solution to create a sort of tissue equilibriation, and all are at cold condition at 4°C. The material was freezed by using cryospray, an instant freezing aerosol (Dichloro difluoro methane). The frozen blocks were used to get serial sections of 12 μm by using mini Bright cryostat. The sections so obtained were processed for the localization of lipids and for different enzymes.

Total lipids were identified by sudan black B procedure (Chiffelle and Putt, 1951). Esterase reactivity was demonstrated by Naphthol acetate method (Gomori, 1952, cited from chayen *et al.*, 1973). Peroxidases activity was demonstrated by DAB (diaminobenzidine) method (Graham and Karnovsky, 1966). Cytochrome oxidase activity was identified by DABT (3,3'-diaminobenzidine tetra chloride) method (Pearse, 1972). Acid phosphatase activity was demonstrated by simultaneous Azo-coupling method (Modified from Pearse 1972, see Malik and Singh, 1980). Alkaline phosphatase activity was demonstrated by using Azo-coupling method (Chayen *et al.*, 1973). ATPase activity was identified by using lead method (Wachstein *et al.*, 1960).

OBSERVATIONS

Ontogeny and structure of an individual nectary gland — The nectaries differentiate from the epidermis. The development of nectary from the inner surface of calyx has been studied in detail. One of the epidermal cells becomes conspicuous and differentiate into nectary gland. The nectary initiation begins as a protrusion of an epidermal cell (Fig. A). It shows conspicuous nucleus and copious amount of cytoplasm and is easily distinguishable from the rest of the epidermal cells. This initial gradually enlarges vertically and protrudes on the surface of the inner epidermal layer and acts as a potential nectary initial. The nectary initial divides first periclinally delimiting upper head cell and a lower basal cell (Fig. B). The nuclei in these cells are conspicuous. The second periclinal division which occurs in the head cell separates the basal stalk cell, middle lenticular stipe cell and a glandular nectary head call (Fig. C). The head cell undergoes a series of anticlinal divisions that results in the formation of 2, 4, 6, 8 vertical uniseriate cells (Figs. D–F). No periclinal divisions occur in the head cell. The intermediary cell i.e. the stipe cell which is lenticular rarely undergoes one more periclinal division (Fig. G), otherwise normally remains undivided. The stalk cell or the basal cell which remains on a level with the rest of the epidermal cells generally does not undergo division. But this cell also divides occasionally, longitudinally into two basal cells (Fig. G). Thus, the mature nectary gland comprises, the top 6 to 8 vertical cells which are uniseriate constituting the secretory head of the nectary gland (Fig. G). The secretory head appears to be flattened like a disc by vertical enlargement. The cells become densely cytoplasmic and highly vacuolated. The nuclei in them are very conspicuous and large. The cells simulate papillate cells. The disc is supported by one or two auxiliary cells viz., stipe cell(s) and subjecent to stipe cell(s) are the lower basal cell(s) associated with the epidermis (Fig. G). The cytoplasm of the stipe cell is thin and its nucleus is distinct. The basal stalk cell distinguishes from the rest of the epidermal cells both in its size and cytoplasmic organisation. At times the calyx nectary gland with more than 20 to 40 uniseriate secretory cells, multicellular stipe and basal stalk layers have been observed. (Fig. H). Such nectaries were noticed regularly irregular on the outer surface of the calyx. These nectaries appear cup shaped. The cup is a multicellular head made up of one to two layered pallisade like glandular epithelium. The cells in it are arranged compactly in a vertical manner. The multicellular stipe layer comprising of 12-15 cells which are more or less rectangular in shape. Below the stipe layer is the basal cells are also arranged in a row. These cells are some what smaller than that of the stipe cells. The cuticular layer which encloses the cup is also observed. The stalk of the nectary gland does not develop in the absence of a gland head. Its differentiation seems to be dependent upon some unknown factors related to the gland proper. The stalk therefore can be regarded as the mechanical component of the whole apparatus, the secretory gland.

Histochemical composition of an individual nectary gland

Polysaccharides — The inner epidermal cells of the calyx wall do not store PAS — positive storage grains. The nectary initial also does not store polysaccharide grains but the cytoplasm of the cell reacts strongly for PAS test. The PAS-positive storage grains remain absent in the gland cells from the beginning of their differentiation until they mature. Including the initial cell, the cells subsequently formed out of it possess a very distinct PAS-positive cell walls (Figs. 1-6). These cell walls brightly fluorescent after calcofluor white stain for cellulose (Figs. 7-10). As the nectary gland matures, the secretory cells at the head region show more of PAS-positive substance in the cytoplasm (Figs. 4-6). The stipe cell is generally vacuolated and the vacuole is large at the central region, consequently the cytoplasm is pushed towards the periphery of the cell. The stipe cell generally contains poor cytoplasm which reacts feebly for polysaccharides (Figs. 4-6). Similarly the basal stalk cell(s) also react feebly to PAS test, the cells of the stipe layer and stalk cells of the large glandular nectary also react similar to the other nectaries and does not store PAS grains. As the nectary gland matures the cuticle becomes distinct and it does not react distinctly with PAS test (Fig. 6). Cuticle layer becomes undulated on the surface of the head cells. The cell walls at terminal region (head region) appear papillate and their stainability is strong for polysaccharides (Figs. 6, 10). The cuticular layer reacts to ABF test indicating the presence of callose (Fig. 11). This layer insulates the secretory head. The callose layer is comparatively very thick around the stipe cell (Fig. 11). The cup-shaped glandular head, and multicellular stipe layer show no storage deposition (Fig. 30).

Ascorbic Acid (AA) — Ascorbic acid is consistantly present all through the development and differentiation of calyx nectary glands. The initial cell of the epidermis possess comparatively more of AA deposition confined towards the tip region of elongated nectary initial (Fig. 12). At early stages of 2,3, and 4-celled stages of gland development rich AA grains are distributed in all the cells except the basal and stipe cells which exhibit comparatively less AA content (Figs. 13, 14). The cell walls also react for ascorbic acid. As the nectary glands mature no change in ascorbic acid content is observed. However at times the basal stalk cells and also stipe cell shows much accumulation of AA (Figs. 15, 16). The secretory cells of the nectary gland some times undergo further segmentation results in increase of vertical cells comprising secretory disc. The disc cells deposit plentiful of ascorbic acid which is more towards its base (Fig. 31). Distinctly the basal layer of cells possess high AA content (Fig. 31). The cuticular layer reacts feebly to $AgNO_3$ test.

RNA and Proteins — The nectary gland initial becomes conspicuous in showing higher amounts of nuclear and cytoplasmic RNA and proteins (Figs. 17, 24). This nectary initial normally maintains high RNA and protein contents greatly at its terminal region (Figs. 17, 25). Thus the cell exhibits polarity with respect to the distribution of cytoplasmic contents particularly RNA and proteins. At 2-celled stage unequal distribution of RNA and protein contents is observed, the head cell contains more of nuclear and cytoplasmic RNA and proteins (Figs. 18, 25). Subsequently, as the gland divides and differentiate into a multicellular gland, gradual reduction of both RNA and protein contents is noticed in the basal cells including the basal stalk cells of the epidermis and the auxiliary stipe cell (Figs. 21–23, 27). The reduction of RNA and proteins in these cells occur in the cytoplasm but not in the nuclei. The secretory cells in the head region maintain higher amounts of RNA and proteins in the cytoplasm as well as in the nuclei consistantly (Figs. 23, 28). At maturity of the nectary the cuticle remains almost negative to azure B and mercuric bromophenol blue tests (Figs. 23, 27, 28). The secretory cells become highly vacuolated and the vacuolation increases as they mature. The nuclei in them are large and react strongly for RNA and proteins. In the mature cup shaped nectaries both RNA and proteins are plentiful in the nuclei and the cytoplasm (Fig. 32). The two basal layers (stipe and stalk) do not show much RNA and protein deposition and they react very feebly for RNA test.

Lipids — The initial cell of the nectary gland distinguishes from the rest of the epidermal cells by showing very high lipid content (Fig.

33). This trend of synthesizing more lipids continued until the glandular initial divides and differentiates into basal cell, stipe cell and secretory cells. Both stipe and secretory cells generally maintains maximum concentration of lipids until the nectary gland matures (Fig. 34, 35). The cuticle reacts positive to lipids. However the basal cell and epidermal cells have moderate activity for lipids (Figs. 34, 35).

Enzymes — A preliminary study was made on the localization of some different classes of enzymes namely, oxidases, esterase and phosphatases in the developing nectaries by using fresh cryostat sections. The nectary gland initial generally distinguishes by showing strong activity for different enzymes viz. esterase, peroxidase, cytochrome oxidase, acid and alkaline phosphatases and ATPase (Figs. 36, 43). As the glandular initial enlarges the activity is maintained comparatively more towards the terminal region. When the initial divides and differentiates into basal and head cell, more activity of enzymes particularly phosphatases is observed in the head cell than its subtending basal cell (Figs. 44, 47, 49). The stipe cell when it differentiates show high activity. The moderate activity of the acid and alkaline phosphatase enzymes however is maintained in the basal cell as the nectary matures (Figs. 45, 48). The enzyme activity in the basal cell for esterase, peroxidase, cytochrome oxidase and ATPase remains comparatively high in the basal cell (Figs. 37, 38, 40-42, 49, 50). In the developing gland the stipe cell shows moderate activity for the enzymes esterase, cytochrome oxidase and ATPase (Figs. 37, 38, 41, 42, 50). The secretory cells (head cells) generally exhibits very strong activity for all classes of enzymes localized (Figs. 37-42, 45, 48, 50). The cuticle of the nectary normally does not exhibit distinct positiveness for the enzymes studied (Figs. 37, 38, 40-42, 45, 48, 50). The parental epidermal cells and parenchymatous cells below the epidermis generally show higher activity for all the classes of enzymes studied and this activity persists until the nectaries mature. In the cup shaped nectary higher activity of enzyme acid phosphatase confined more to the inner concave region of the cup where secretion is extruded out of the nectary. The parental epidermal cells and the parenchymatous cells subjecent to the epidermis show very strong activity. The basal area of the papillate cells and the cells of the stipe layer show minimal activity for the enzyme acid phosphatase, but the cells of the basal layer has a considerable activity for acid phosphatase (Fig. 46).

DISCUSSION

Although considerable information is available on various aspects of structure and development of nectaries, but much has not been dealt with histochemical changes. Therefore, in the present discussion we have tried to comprehend the scattered information on various histochemical substances identified by using light, FM and EM microscopic techniques.

Stipe and Stalk cells — The secretory disc is supported by one of two auxiliary cells viz., stipe cells/s and subjecent to it is the lower basal (stalk) cell/s associated with the epidermis. The stipe cell is generally lenticular in shape and this cell may undergo one or more periclinal divisions resulting in the formation of a layer of multiple cells, otherwise the cell normally remains undivided. The stipe cell is generally vacuolated and the vacuole is large at the centre of the cell. The cytoplasm is thin and shows a meagre contents of RNA, proteins and carbohydrates but the nucleus is conspicuous and reacts strongly for these substances. However the stipe cell in *Kigelia* and *Spathodea* (Rudramuniyappa and Mahajan 1991) contains conspicuous amounts of lipids, and there is no consistancy of AA content in this cell, often it shows high AA. Moderate activity of a few enzymes namely, cytochrome oxidase, esterase and ATPase is observed in *Kigelia.*

The stalk cell (basal cell) remains with the rest of the epidermal cells. The stalk forms a mechanical component of the whole secretory gland. This cell generally remains undivided and distinguishes from the rest in its size and cytoplasmic organisation. The cells of the stalk react feebly to PAS test storing no carbohydrates, but rich in AA. Cytoplasmic RNA and proteins are also low in stalk cell/s. Moderate activity for acid and alkaline phosphatases is observed. Similar reaction for RNA, proteins, PAS and AA was observed in *Spathodea* (Rudramuniyappa and Mahajan 1991).

Secretory cells — These are also called disc or head cells. Generally they possess large nuclei and dense cytoplasm both react strongly for RNA, proteins and AA. The activity of various enzymes and lipid content is also observed in these cells. The secretory cells normally devoid of PAS positive storage grains. The absence of storage carbohydrates in these cells indicates that the metabolic processes in them are probably directed towards the synthesis of other substances such as lipids and ascorbic acid and they are present abundantly in the secretory cells from the beginning to the maturity of the glands, as observed in *Kigelia* (present study) and *Spathodea* (Rudramuniyappa and Mahajan, 1991). The presence of large amount of RNA in secretory cells normally reflects the occurrence of abundant ribosomes which are generally associated with the secretory activity within the secretory cells (Schnepf, 1974). Ascorbic acid is also known to be a metabolic derivative of carbohydrates and sugars which form a basic raw materials for its synthesis (Mapson *et al.*, 1954). In the secretory cells no storage starch but PAS positive material is observed. This is true to all secretory glands of Bignoniaceae including *Kigelia* (Rudramuniyappa and Mahajan, 1991; Mehra and Kulkarni, 1989; Subramanian and Inamdar, 1985, 1986; Subramanian *et al.*, 1990). Storage starch is also not noticed in the secretory cells of other taxa studied (Ascensao and Pais, 1981; Mahlberg *et al.*, 1984; Figier, 1968). The secretory cap cells of *Pharbitis nil* (Unzelman and Healey, 1974) were shown to contain high amounts of proteins and carbohydrates. The vesicles coated with proteins have been implicated in the secretion of proteinaceous material. Similarly, the mucilage producing gynoecium papillae of *Aptemia cardifolia* (Kristen, 1976) also stains for proteins and carbohydrates. However the oleoresin producing glands of *Artemisia campestris* (Ascensao and Pais, 1987) do not react to PAS and protein tests but stains strongly for lipids. Large amount of proteins have been reported in the glandular secretory cells of *Mercurialis* (Figier 1968) and *Musa* (Fahn and Benouaiche, 1979). The presence of polysaccharides in the mucilage glands is a common feature, but the presence of ascorbic acid has also been observed in *Spathodea* (Rudramuniyappa and Mahajan, 1991). In *Pelargonium* (Peterson and Vermeer, 1984) PAS-positive material was high in young glandular cells but at maturity the polysaccharides confine to the stalk cells only. According to Schnepf (1974) the glands secreting a carbohydrate based product can be grouped with the hydrophilic type.

Variety of lipophilic substances have been reported in glandular trichomes including fats, essential oils, terpenes, resins, waxes, flavonoids aglycons (Schnepf, 1974) and oleoresins (Ascensao and Pais, 1987). The nectary glands of *Kigelia* and *Spathodea* (Rudramuniyappa and Mahajan, 1991) are also shown to react for lipids and it is therefore obvious to expect the presence of lipophilic substances in the gland cells. Histochemically using sudan dyes (Sudan black B in the present study) is very difficult to determine and/or classify the precise lipophilic compounds, but often broad classification can be made. Using sudan dyes, fats have been demonstrated in the secretory trichomes of *Nicotiana* and *Medicago* (Akers *et al.*, 1978; Kreitner and Sorensen, 1979). The great affinity for sudan dyes as observed in *Kigelia* indicates that the secretion may be of lipophilic nature. In the absence of information from thin layer or gas chromatography it is not possible to say the exact chemical nature of sudan black B positive substances.

In general the cytoplasm of gland cells is highly electron dense under TEM. The electron dense nature of cytoplasm might reflect an increase in ribosome population. The gland cells during secretory phase are further characterised by the presence of numerous mitochondria and elaborated ER (Akers *et al.*, 1978).

The activities of different enzyme systems have been observed in varied types of nectaries. In the secretory glands of *Kigelia* too several enzymes viz, esterase, peroxidase, cytochrome oxidase, ATPase, acid and alkaline phosphatases were localized histochemically. Similar activity for different enzymes has also been localized in the septal nectaries of *Aloe* (Heinrich, 1975), glandular trichomes of *Achillea* (Stahl, 1957) and secretory glands of *Hiptage* (Subramanian *et al.*, 1990), floral nectaries of *Tropaeolum* (Rachmilevitz and Fahn, 1975). Based on *in situ* localization and distribution of histochemical substances, it is infered that the secretory cells of the gland are distinguishable from the rest of the gland cells and obviously perform the vital function of secretion.

Cell wall and cuticle — Generally, the presence of rigid cell walls represents an important difference between the secretory glands present in plants and animal systems. The nature of cell walls of secretory systems has been discussed in detail (Uphof, 1962). Basically the cell walls often get modified variously either by the elaboration of additional wall layers or by the deposition of various encrusting substances. No lignification of cell walls has been observed in nectary glands to date (Fahn, 1979). In *Kigelia* also the cell walls are highly textured, PAS-positive and no lignification is observed. Thus the major composition of cell walls seems to be cellulose as has also revealed through calcofluor white-fluorescence test. In *Achillea* (Stahl, 1953) the cell walls are weakly stained for cellulose and they react distinctly for pectins. The carbohydrate nature of cell walls in nectaries appears to be a general feature. However, lipids are also observed in them. Pecto-cellulosic cell walls of secretory cells seem to possess a favourable property for absorption and transportation of secretory fluids after they are eliminated from the cytoplasm. The thick PAS-positive cell walls may influence greatly absorption and they resemble papillate cell walls observed particularly around the stipe cell in *Kigelia* and *Spathodea* (Rudramuniyappa and Mahajan, 1991). This thickened cellulosic deposition around the stipe cell is an added deposition might function in permeability because the thickening also reacts for callose which is known considerably in the function of permeability process of cell wall.

Most glandular trichomes have cuticular covering which may vary considerably in thickness and structure depending on the position of the cell in the secretory system (Uphof, 1962). The presence of cuticle can be demonstrated by a number of histochemical procedures. The most common method is through sudan dyes. Plant cuticles in general are auto-fluorescent (Van Gijzel, 1975). The cell walls with certain lipid complexes are generally exhibit autofluorescent. In some species of Bignoniaceae (Subramanian and Inamdar, 1985) it was observed that a complete insultation of cuticular layer in extra floral nectaries save at the place where the lower stalk cell wall and upper tangential walls of the foot cell layer meet. Thomson *et al.* (1969) termed this region as ''transfusion area''. The size of this area seems to vary. In *Bignonia illicium* (Subramanian and Inamdar, 1986) this area is quite large and this opening, forms as pathway for the transport of metabolites. Cuticle in *Kigelia* is feebly PAS-positive and lipid positive but not with azure B and proteins. Similar reaction was observed in *Spathodea* (Rudramuniyappa and Mahajan, 1991) and *Euphorbia* (Annigeri and Rudramuniyappa, 1984). Lipid nature of cuticle seems to be a general features noticed in many nectaries. The secretion has to pass not only through pecto-cellulosic walls (which are pathways rather than barrier) but also through the cuticular layer (Fahn, 1979). It is presumed that the kind of insulation through cutinisation and callose deposition around the stipe cell isolates the head (secretory) cells from the epidermis (Dell and McComb, 1975). Further as pointed out by Schnepf (1974) that the modified cell walls (cuticle and pecto-cellulosic) might prevent the back flow of discharged secretory materials, and alternatively the modified cell walls reduce transpirational water loss through nectaries. Regarding the mechanism by which the cutin is synthesized and deposited on the cell walls of the glandular nectaries, is little known and yet to be studied. Towards the stage of discharge of secretion the cuticle at the top of secretory cells get detached from the cellulose wall and the space is created and this is filled with secretory materials of 'lipid kind' as observed in the present as well as in other taxa studied. The intact cuticle is sufficiently permeable to allow the secretion to penetrate out (Fahn, 1979). Cuticle in *Kigelia* and *Spathodea* becomes undulated and infact cuticular flakes have been observed in these plants.

The study on nectary glands in general and particularly in *Kigelia* revealed that the nectaries are complex and form a dynamic system. Their location apparently seems to be very important in *Kigelia* because of their role in pollination. Nectar production apparently seems to be controlled by a number of factors both external and internal ones. Compositional changes of nectar, if any which occur during aging can have a little significance for the pollinators (if the birds are pollinators), because flowers will normally be exploited as soon as nectar fluid becomes available. The location of nectaries, the quality of nectar, the ecological significance of nectaries will be discussed briefly in the preceding paragraphs.

Qualitative aspects of secretion — There are number of substances eliminated from the living cells and the nectar is one such complex compound secreted by the specialised glands viz., the nectaries. Nectar is unlike fluids. Its chemical composition varies in different species. The most common constituents are sugars viz., sucrose, glucose and fructose. However, small amounts of maltose, raffinose, galactose, hexose, saccharose, melibiose have been reported. Based on quantitative relationships nectar has been distinguished into three main types (1) sucrose — dominent (2) glucose — fructose dominent (3) equal ratio of sucrose-glucose — fructose (Bahadur *et al.* 1986, Fahn, 1988). In addition polysaccharidic mucilages, proteins and proteins that are necessarily enzymatic in nature, various organic acids, amino acids, flavonoids, terpnoids, volatiles, enzymes, hormones, oxidases, phosphatases, ascorbic acid, lipids, and a number of secondary metabolites have been reported (Fahn, 1979, 1988; Baker, 1978; Stephenson, 1981; Kelsey *et al.*, 1984). Specific attractants and repellants have also been found in the nectar fluid of different plant species, and even toxins were found (Baker and Baker, 1975; Stephenson, 1981). In some special cases resin, oleoresin, oils and rubber, mineral ions and vitamins have been found to be secreted (Fahn, 1979, 1988; Ascensao and Pais, 1987). The chemical composition of nectar is therefore varies enormously among the plant species and in some cases it varies with the age of the flower, sex, season and even location (Percival, 1961; Shuel, 1975; Baker, 1978).

Knowledge of chemical constituents of Bignoniaceous nectar seems to be very meagre and only a few species have been investigated as a part of general nectar constituents (Elias and Gilband, 1975, 1976; Subramanian and Inamdar, 1985, 1986; Bahadur *et al.*, 1986). Both floral and extrafloral nectaries in some species of Bignoniaceae contain three sugars namely, sucrose, glucose, and fructose and few amino acids viz. arginine in all nectaries. Glutamine and asparagine in extrafloral nectaries, and methionine and tryptophane only in floral nectaries (Subramanian and Inamdar, 1985). In angiosperm nectars not only the number of sugars vary but also their concentrations as well, which forms a essential constituent of the feed for specific pollinators. Nectar is primarily utilized by the pollinators as a source of sugars which generally provides ready energy to them. However the presence of other components in the nectar in attracting the pollinators is not well understood.

In many species, nectar is known to contain different amino acids and their content varies form species to species. Regarding this, extensive survey has been made by Baker and Baker (1973a, b). These authors have reported the amino acids which form a regular constituents in 260 out of 266 plant nectars. Similarly, Bahadur *et al.* (1986) have also reported the occurrence of amino acids in 85 out of 100 species examined. Their quantity in the nectar although less but sufficient to provide the required nitrogen supply to the flower visitors (see Harborne, 1982).

On the basis of structural complexity of nectaries, Lüttge (1961) explained the differences in overall amino acid concentrations of nectars of floral and extrafloral kinds. According to him complex and well organized nectaries secrete nectar with a few amino acids in less concentration. Single unspecialized nectaries contain high concentrations and more number of amino acids. In *Kigelia* (Subramanian and Inamdar, 1985) contain only a few amino acids. *Spathodea campanulata* an ornithophilous taxa contains only two amino acids viz., alanine and isoleucine of which the latter being essential. The nectar of *Dianthus barbatus*, a butterfly flower contains at least, twelve different amino acids, the largest number yet to found in a single species (Baker and Baker, 1973). The presence of amino acids provides a supplementary nutritional value for the flower visitors and if they are few in number appears little significance, nutritionally. In a single visit, the pollinator derives the dual benefit of sugars and amino acids from the calyx water of *Spathodea campanulata*. In this species, for a normal development of floral organs within the flower buds the secretion of calyx fluid seems to be very essential, because, removal of this fluid from the developing buds led to the formation of a abscission layer at the basal region where the buds are attached to the inflorescence axis. Consequently flower buds begin to fall (Mahajan, 1989). It has been suggested that the secretion must be acting as a lubricant facilitating smooth gliding growth of floral parts in bud condition (Mehra and Kulkarni, 1989). Obviously it appears that the full growth and development of floral parts in *Spathodea campanulata* was achieved within the secretory fluid with running no risk of desiccation. This apparently seems to be essential because the *Spathodea campanulata* is a known tropical and an African genus. Nectar is therefore offers a great potential for further work. Corbet (1978) rightly pointed out that "the dynamic complexity of nectar can be seen as just another technical obstacle to the assessment of the calorie rewards available for flower visitors, or it can be seen as a phenomenon worth studying in its own right, as a rich source of unanswered questions for Zoologists and Micrometeorologists as well as for Botanists and beekeepers".

Secretory (Nectar) fluid and Ecology — The secretory substances (nectar) generally attract pollinators but in some cases they also play a role in repelling animal foes and are thus of considerable ecological significance. Nectar also provides a potential source of energy to the pollinators. This energetic relationship between secretory fluid of flowers and the pollinators indirectly related to community ecology, biogeography, physiology and ultimately the evolution. In many a cases the secreted chemical substances play an important role in inter-relationship between plants and animals. This interrelationship commonly leads to co-evolution of plants and animals and this aspect of co-evolution has been recently gained lot of interest by many floral and reproductive biologists.

Since long it is known that nectar is secreted by the specialised structures namely, the nectary glands within the flowers. Nectar is never secreted in quantities comparable to the flow of sap seen for example toddy palm. In nature anthophilous (flower-visiting) animals utilise nectar which provides sugars and amino acids etc and provide ready energy to the pollinators, and some feed on protein making materials. Some butterflies are known to take phloem sap. The floral nectaries are directly associated with pollination ecology whereas the extra-floral nectaries are not. Extra floral nectaries are also function in the disposal of "surplus" sugar from the phloem, thereby resulting in organs distal to the nectaries receiving a translocate significantly more enriched in nitrogen relative to sugar (Lüttge, 1977; Pate *et al.*, 1985). Nevertheless Baker and Baker (1978, 1979) have found less correlation between sugar ratios and broad spectrum nectar feeders such as honey bees than with other types of pollinators. Their data show the following general correlations : Small bees-broad spectrum; big bees-sucrose rich; flies — sucrose poor; lepidopterans — sucrose rich; humming birds — sucrose rich; passerine birds — sucrose poor; bats — sucrose poor. Similarly there seems to be some kind of relationship between the type of pollinator and concentration of amino acids in the nectar (Baker and Baker, 1973). On average basis amino acids concentration is significantly low in the nectars of flowers visited by bees than that of "butterfly flowers". Amino acids in the nectar are also important for bees than they are for butterflies. Bees have a alternative source of proteinaceous materials in pollen. Unlike bees, moths prefer a wide range of amino acids concentration in the nectars of flowers. The same is true of 'bird flowers'. Birds utilize an alternative protein source in insects.

The localization of nectaries in plants is of phylogenetic/ evolutionary interest. Extrafloral nectaries occur not only in angiosperms but also in several genera of ferns (Fahn 1988). In course of evolution the extrafloral nectaries preceded the floral nectaries (Frey-Wyssling 1933). Floral nectaries in angiosperms are found on a variety of flower parts, sepals, petals, stamens, the receptacle, ovary and style. In *Spathodea* (Rudramuniyappa and Mahajan, 1991) and

Kigelia the present authors have observed the nectaries on the outer and inner sides of both sepals and petals, on the surface of the ovary and at the base of the ovary (the receptacle). The presence of small, multiple nectaries in different plant parts is considered to be an advanced character representing on another line of evolutionary development and also specialisation, in comparison to a single large nectary, if present (Elias and Gelband, 1976). In a majority of cases the individual floral nectaries are small and the casual observer may be easily overlooked. But small dispersed nectaries function more efficiently as a collective system than the larger ones. Multiple nectaries have certain other advantages over a single, large nectary in that a malfunction or damage, from internal or external factors, than it is highly susceptible to damage, is one or two of the nectaries will not eliminate easily that site of plant body. The study on *Campsis* (Elias and Gelband, 1976) revealed that the clustering of many small extrafloral nectaries at different sites is an advanced strategy for ant attraction. This may also apply to other species of Bignoniaceae since the size and structure of nectaries seems to be almost same. It was observed that ant colonies were found feeding in some species of Bignoniaceae. This clearly demonstrate a mutual advantage, on a co-evolution principle (Commensalism), the ants receiving a source of sugar while possibly ridding the plant to phytophagous insects or discouraging grazing by vertebrate herbivores. Thus, the ants serve as "guards" against herbivores and other harmful animal visitors. According to Durkee (1982) if the extrafloral nectary is co-evolving with insect species, especially ants, as an attractant for these "pugnacious body guards" (Bentley, 1977), then selection pressure is apparently countering the nitrogen conserving systems of the plant, affording in exchange, protection against herbivory. Much work has not been done on extrafloral nectaries and the pollinators associated with them. However, some work has been initiated by Elias and Gelband (1975, 1976) and Pate *et al.* (1985). In summary the trend in the evolution of the secretory tissues first developed inside the organs and later they were scattered among other tissues of the plant system (Fahn, 1988). It is therefore inferred that plant secretory tissues are adopted to functions which confer on plants possessing them the properties of greater survival value in the surrounding environment. The adoptations may be related to the external environmental conditions and/or to the surrounding animal population.

Polarity during the differentiation of nectary initial — Polarity is specific orientation of cellular/sub-cellular activity in space and is not a character to be present originally and invariably. Polarity is expressed characteristically in some systems during differentiation, the expression may be morphological or physiological or both. Until date one of the central problems of differentiation remained to be solved is the process of unequal or asymmetric division of a parent cell leading to two daughter cells which subsequently follow divergent patterns of differentiation. There are number of examples in higher plants which are associated with polarity gradients within a single cell or across a small group of cells. The best known examples of cellular differentiation of vegetative and generative cells in pollen grain, of root hairs, stomatal initials and the subsidiary cells. To the list the differentiation of glandular/nectary initials from the epidermal cell could also be added as one of the good examples. The needed attention however has not been paid on this aspect of polarity during the differentiation of secretory glandular/nectary initial from the epidermal cell. In the present study too it is not possible to give an account on all gradients concerning to polarity. Nevertheless, a few histochemical gradients at light microscopic level observed are described during the differentiation of epidermal cell into glandular/nectary initial. Each of these examples concerned with cellular differentiation and polarity are characterised by certain sequences (see Stebbins, 1966). The most important ones are :

1) Establishment of cytoplasmic gradient within a single cell. This is very well observed during the differentiation and re-differentiation (transformation) of one of the epidermal cells into glandular nectary initial cell. The polar molecules (constituents) in this cell lines up now in a specific orientation. Since cytoplasm is a seat of polar differentiation, polarity is therefore, may be expressed in the cell contents, as evidenced in the epidermal cell of the present study.

2) The movement of nucleus to an asymmetrical position (on one side) of the cell and occurrence of a mitotic division later. The cytoplasmic organisation also becomes asymmetrical (polar), and is principally distributed around the nucleus which has moved towards the terminal tip of the glandular/nectary initial. The nectary initial becomes elongated and at the base conspicuous vacuole develops. The

first noticeable difference is cell size which becomes apparent after an asymmetrical mitosis that forms a smaller head cell and a large basal stalk cell. Differential histochemical activity apparently begins from this stage.

3) The two daughter cells differentiate from each other. Subsequently one of them divides more actively than the other. The two daughter cells formed following first mitotic division, are unequal not only in size but also in histochemical gradients (cellular). The terminal small cell inherits most of the cytoplasm, appears dense and compact, high RNA, proteins, lipids and enzymes, and subsequently divides rapidly and contributes to the major part of the glandular nectary. Bünning (1953) named this actively dividing cell as meristemoid. In the present study the meristemoid cell is small, dense in cytoplasm because of high lipids, RNA, proteins and enzymes. The meristemoid cell is produced on that side of the parental cell which has the nucleus, denser cytoplasm, and towards which the nucleus has previously (already) moved. This is true to the differentiation of glandular nectary initial in which the nucleus was found to be situated at the terminal region surrounded by dense cytoplasm. This raises many questions : what is the nature of these intracellular gradients, how are they produced, how they stimulate and what substances are or physiological status, when distributed unequally to the daughter cells, produce the observed differentiation?

The present study although does not provide a clear cut answer to these but nevertheless provide some clue to a few cellular gradients assessed in the nectary initial during its asymetrical division. More or less a similar kind of observation on the differentiation of root hairs in the grasses has been presented (Avers, 1961). In certain epidermal cells mitosis occurs and a transverse wall is formed in a position which gives rise to a smaller daughter cell with dense cytoplasm and larger cell with less dense cytoplasm. The small cell develops root hair, whereas the larger one develops into a normal epidermal cell. Vacuolation and enlargement are some of the important features of differentiation of any cell. In addition to the visible changes involved in differentiation, there are also differences of biochemical nature both at cellular and sub-cellular levels are operating. Marked difference in organelle composition occurs and varies enormously according to the tissue. In the present study although it is not possible to assess the intra-cellular (sub-microscopic) gradients and their changements but a few visible cellular gradients of polarity have been localised by using some basic dyes during the differentiation of nectary initial from the epidermal cell. The two cells formed after mitosis seem to incorporate different metabolic characteristics and therefore they exhibit different developmental capacities. This has been very well illustrated in the present study. These two cells as we have observed in the present study are different in their size. This may have an important morphological consequence. This is certainly involved in the differentiation of glandular nectary. In various meristemoid cells the cytoplasm is polarised in such a way that the nucleus of the parental cell comes to lie on the side having the denser cytoplasm, and the meristemoid cells are formed in this direction (*see* Sinnott, 1960). The unequal division is preceded by polarised differences in the cytoplasm. In some instances, the derivative cells formed from an unequal division undergo several divisions as in case of secretory cells of the glandular nectary of the present study.

The observation made on the development of floral nectary glands of *Kigelia* support the contention further that the epidermal cells of the two different maturation potentials are present. The potential nectary forming cell may not be distinguished from non-nectary forming cell on the basis of the size and shape to begin with. Subsequently differences begin to appear from the neighbouring epidermal cells. These cells stain deeply for proteins, RNA, lipids and for various enzymes localised. Their activities sharply separate the less active stalk and stipe cells and active head cells. Thus, physiological differences are deep seated in these cells.

Concluding remarks — Secretory glands (nectaries) are the specialised tissues differentiated in plants. Various aspects of their ontogeny, structures, function and secretory process needs much comparative attention using TEM, autoradiography and cyto/histochemical on different glandular types. Particularly histochemical nature of different kinds of secretory glands is very much needed at this juncture. A few studies on nectary glands revealed that they are complex and form a dynamic system. Their study is very important because they are adopted to various functions, in reproductive (floral) biology, taxonomy, they serve as a 'guard' against herbivores, affect photosynthesis, leaf temperature or water loss, the secretory products

PLATE-I

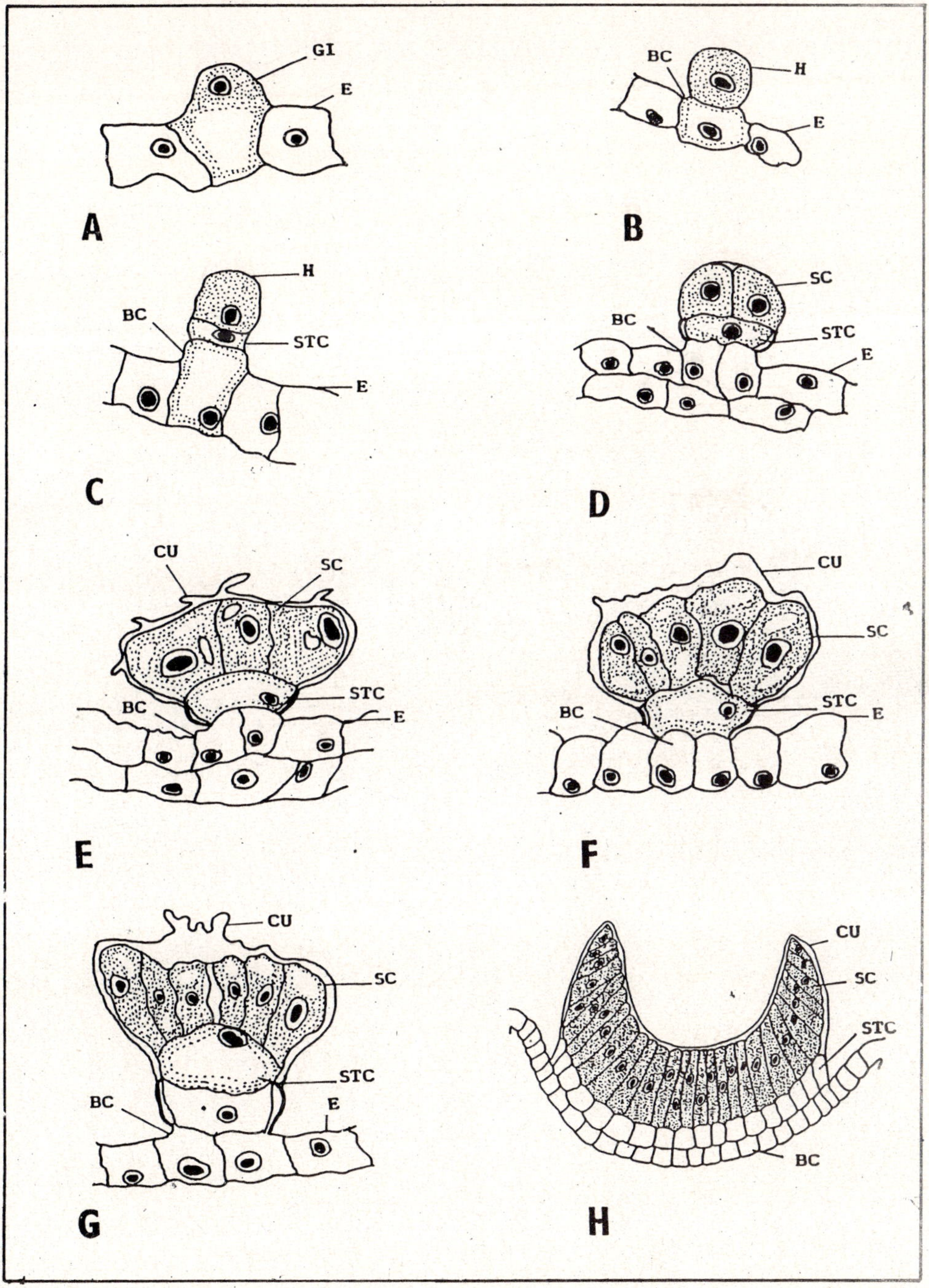
GI
E
A
BC
H
E
B
H
BC
STC
E
C
SC
BC
STC
E
D
CU
SC
STC
BC
E
E
CU
SC
STC
BC
E
F
CU
SC
STC
BC
E
G
CU
SC
STC
BC
H

PLATE-II

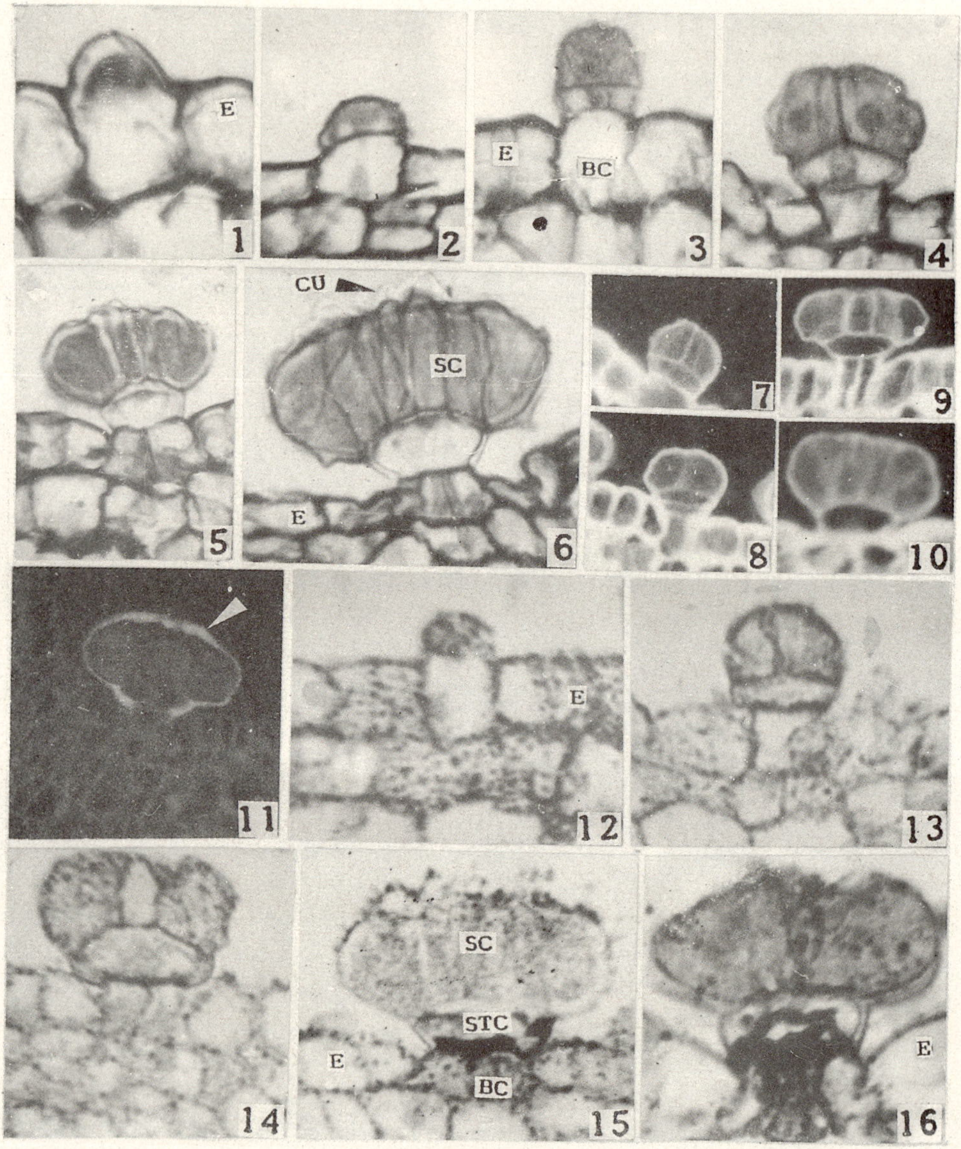

PLATE-III

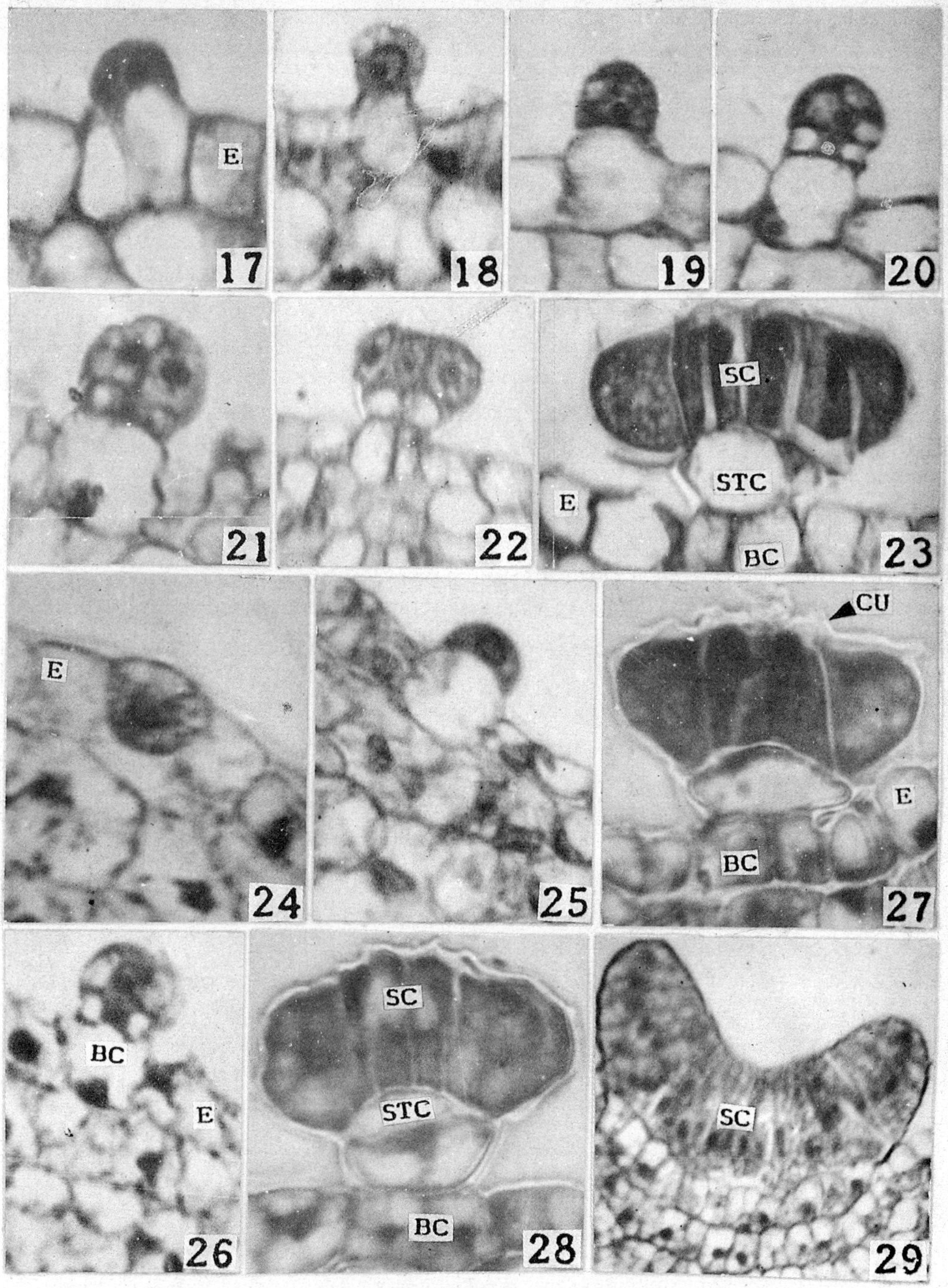

E
17
18
19
20
21
22
SC
STC
E
BC
23
E
24
25
CU
E
BC
27
BC
E
26
SC
STC
BC
28
SC
29

PLATE-IV

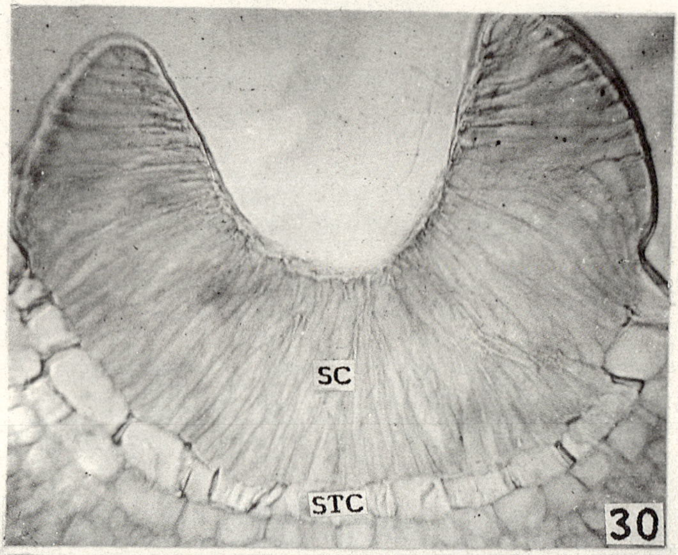

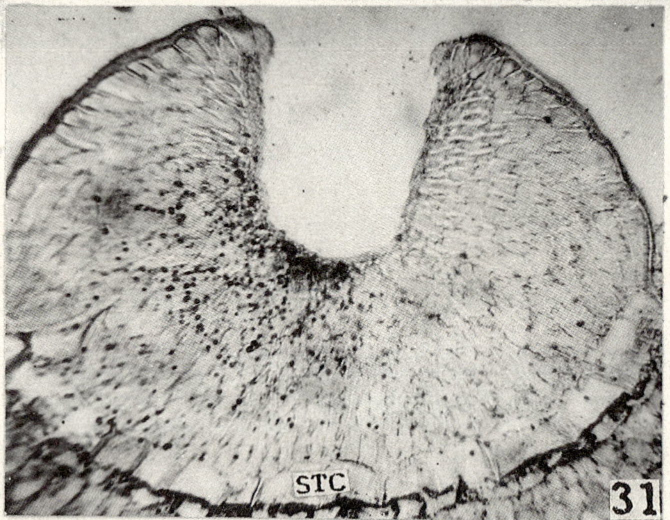

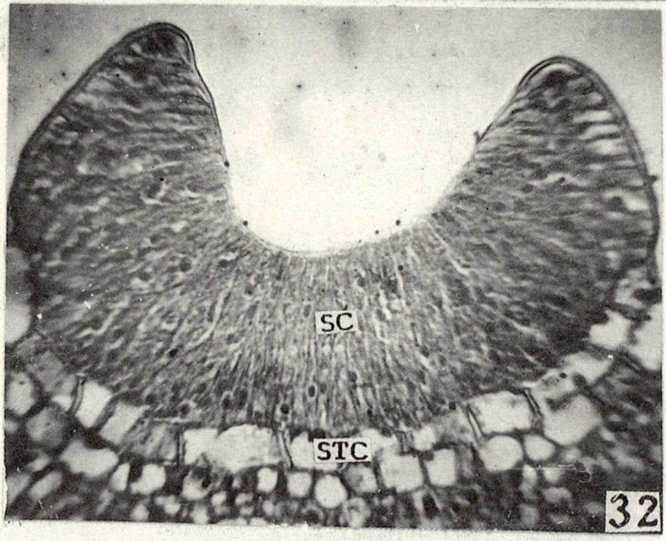

PLATE-V

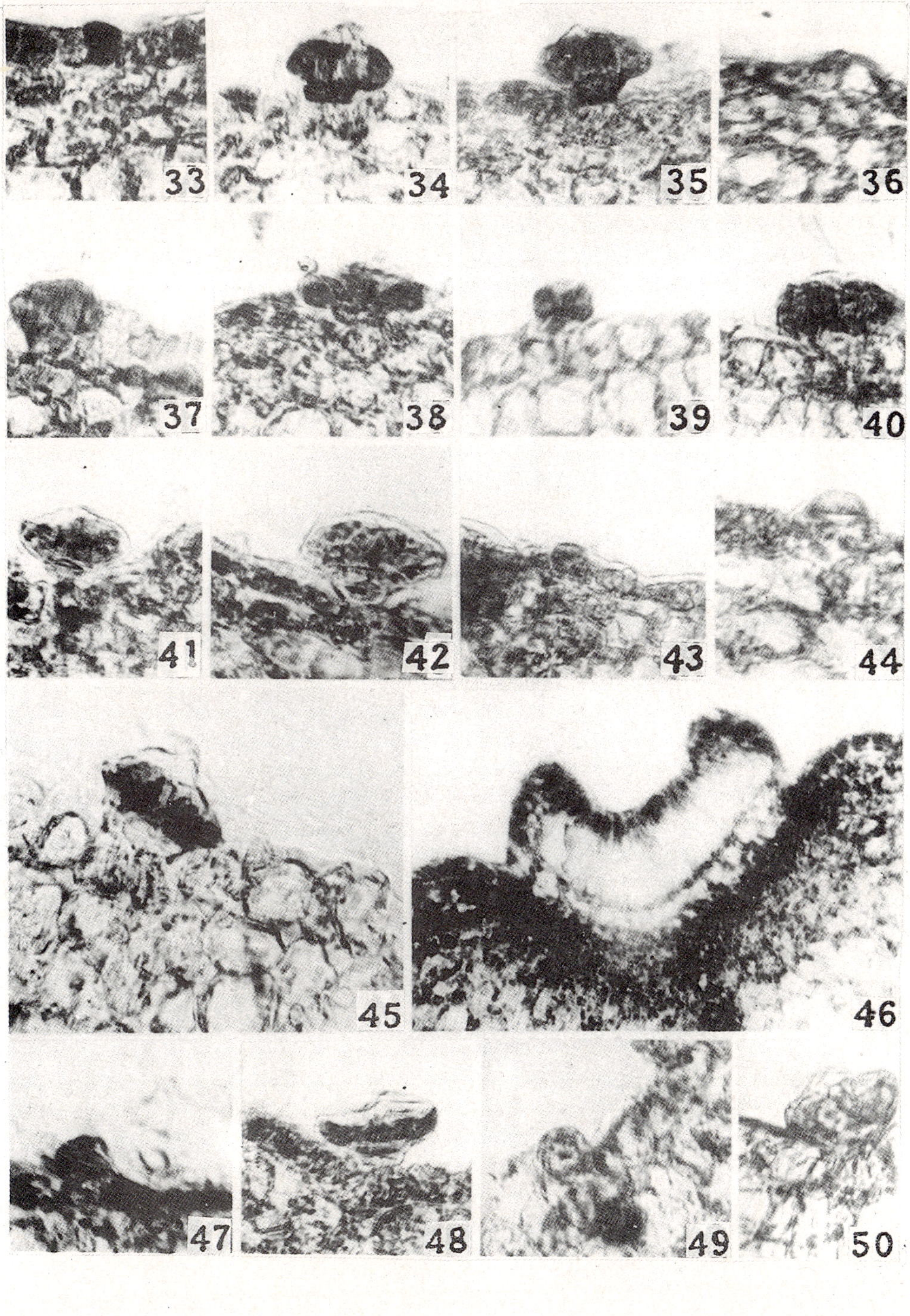

serve as energy source for pollinators, also related to community ecology and ultimately evolution. Glandular systems also form an attractive systems for the study of molecular biology and gene cloning. Their structural and functional relationships within the floral parts is particularly very important and needs to be understood further. The biochemical aspects of secretory cells, the process of secretion, the role of enzyme systems in different glands, is very much needed. It would be more appropriate if one combines TEM and histochemistry with immuno-fluorescence techniques. Critical studies on the movement of labeled substances are very much wanting. Thereby much additional information on the structure and function of plant glandular systems can be had.

Nectar unlike other fluids is a complex compound. Its composition varies in the glands of different plant species. Knowledge of chemical constituents of nectar is very meagre and only a few species have been investigated in this regard. Since nectar is very closely related to pollination ecology and it is necessary to understand the principles of energetic relationship and of co-evolution between the type of pollinator and nectar in the surrounding environment. All these are closely related to community ecology, biogeography, physiology and ultimately the evolution, therefore a critical study is very essential.

Explanations to Figures

Key : (*GI*-Gland initial; *E*-Epidermis; *H*-Head cell; *BC*-Basal cell; *STC*-Stipe cell; *SC*-Secretory cell; *CU*-Cuticle)

PLATE - I

FIGS. A—H. Diagrams of various stages of floral nectary development in *Kigelia pinnata*. Fig. A — Gland initial from the epidermal cell. Fig. B — 2-celled nectary, Fig. C — 3-celled nectary. Fig. D — 5-celled nectary. Fig. E — 6-celled nectary. Fig. F — 8-celled nectary. Fig. G — mature nectary showing multiple secretory cells with two stipe cells. Fig. H — Mature cup shaped nectary showing multicellular secretory, stipe, and basal cell layers.

PLATE - II

FIGS. 1—6. Sections of different stages of calycine nectaries of *Kigelia pinnata* tested for polysaccharides. Figs. 1, 2 — nectary initial and 2-celled nectary, respectively showing PAS- positive substance at the tip region. Figs. 3, 4 and 5 are 6-celled nectaries. Note head cells are rich in polysaccharides than the basal and stipe cells. Fig.6 is 8-celled stage of nectary. Note cuticle is becoming undulated reacts negative to PAS test and stipe cell reacts feebly to PAS test where as the secretory cells are rich in PAS positive substance in the cytoplasm. Figs. 7-10, different stages of nectaries tested for cellulose. Note cell walls are brilliantly fluorescent for cellulose. Fig. 11, tested for callose. Note cuticle and the deposition around stipe cell reacts strongly for callose. Figs. 12-16, sections tested for AA. Fig. 12, nectary initial showing more deposition of AA grains at its apical area. Figs. 13, 14. 4-and 5-celled nectaries. Note, rich AA deposition along the cell walls and in the cytoplasm of head cells. Also note deposition of more AA in the neighbouring cells. Figs. 15, 16 multicellular nectaries. Note AA deposition along the cuticle in Fig. 15 and intense deposition in the stipe and basal cells.

PLATE - III

FIGS. 17-29. Sections of different stages calycine nectaries of *K. pinnata*. Figs. 17-23, tested for RNA, Figs. 24-29 tested for proteins. Fig. 17, gland initial showing high content of RNA confined to its terminal region. Figs. 18, 19, 2-celled nectaries. Note the presence of high RNA in the head cells. The basal cell is poor in RNA content. Figs. 20-22, 3-, 4- and 5- celled nectaries, respectively showing more content of RNA in the head cells than the stipe and basal cells. Fig. 23, multicellular nectary showing high RNA in the secretory cells. Note, cuticle is negative to RNA test. Figs. 24, 25, enlarging gland initial showing high nuclear and cytoplasmic proteins confined more to its terminal region. Fig. 26, 3-celled nectary showing high protein in the head cell that its subtending basal cell. Figs. 27, 28, multicellular nectaries. Note secretory cells have high protein content and also note cuticle is negative to protein test. Fig. 29, multicellular cup shaped nectary. Note papillate secretory cells have high content of protein than stipe and basal layer cells.

PLATE - IV

FIGS. 30—32. Sections of cup shaped calycine nectaries of *K. pinnata*. Fig. 30, tested for PAS. Note multicellular papillate secretory cells do not show storage polysaccharides. Fig. 31, tested for AA. Note more deposition of AA grains in the secretory cells at the inner region of cup. Note basal layer has more deposition AA grains than stipe layer. Fig. 32, tested for proteins. Note, the secretory cells have high protein contents both in the cytoplasm as well as in the nuclei.

PLATE - V

FIGS. 33—50. Fresh sections of different developmental stages of calycine nectaries of *K. pinnata*. Figs. 33-35, tested for lipids. Fig. 33, note gland initial from the epidermis distinguishes from the rest by showing high lipid content. Figs. 34, 35, developing nectaries showing high lipid content in the secretory and stipe cells. Cuticle reacts positive for lipids. Figs. 36-38, tested for esterase enzyme. Fig. 36, glandular initial reacts strongly for the enzyme. Figs. 37, 38, developing nectaries of 5-and 8-celled react strongly for esterase. Figs. 39, 40, tested for peroxidase enzyme. 4-and 8-celled nectaries have high activity in secretory cells. Figs. 41, 42, tested for cytochrome oxidase. Developing nectaries show high activity in secretory and stipe cells. Figs. 43-46, tested for acid phosphatase. Fig. 43, note differentiation of glandular initial is demonstrated by high acid phosphatase enzyme activity. Fig. 44, 2-celled nectary. Note the head cell has more activity. Fig. 45, developing nectary showing high activity for the enzyme in the secretory cells but not in the stipe cell. Fig. 46, cup shaped nectary showing strong activity in the terminal region of the papillate secretory cells. The stipe layer has less activity. The basal area shows very strong activity for acid phosphatase enzyme. Figs. 47, 48, tested for alkaline phosphatase. Fig. 47, enlarging glandular initial cell shows strong activity. Fig. 48, the developing nectary shows strong activity in the secretory head cells and stipe cell. Figs. 49, 50, tested for ATPase. Fig. 49, enlarging glandular initial showing high activity in the terminal region. Fig. 50, 5-celled nectary shows high activity in the head cells.

Literature Cited

Akers, C.P., Weybrew, J.A. and Long, R.C. 1978. Ultrastructure of glandular trichomes of leaves of *Nicotiana tabacum* L. cv Xanthi. *Amer. J. Bot., 65* : 282-292.

Annigeri. B.G. and Rudramuniyappa, C.K. 1984. Distribution and cellular localization of some histochemical substances in the Cyathial nectary of *Euphorbia. Beitr. Biol Pflanzen, 58* : 393-401.

Ascensao, L. and Pais, M.S.S. 1981. Ultrastructural aspects of secretory trichomes in *Cistus monspeliensis. In:* (ed.). Margaris, N.S. and Mooney, H.A. *Components of Productivity of Mediterranean climate regions-basic and applied aspects.* Junk Pub., The Hague pp. 27-38.

Ascensao, L. and Pais, M.S.S. 1987. Glandular trichomes of *Artemisia campestris* (SSP Maritima) : Ontogeny and histochemistry of secretory product. *Bot. Gaz., 148* : 221-227.

Avers, C.J. 1961. Histochemical localization of enzyme activities in root meristem cells. *Amer. J. Bot., 48* : 282-292.

Bahadur, B., Chaturvedi, A. and Ramaswamy, N. 1986. Nectar types in Indian Plants. *Proc. Indian Acad. Sci.* (Plant Sci.), *96* : 41-48.

Baker, H.G. 1978. Chemical aspects of the Pollination biology of Woody plants in the tropics. *In* : (eds.) Tomlinson, P.G. and Zimmermann, M.H. *Tropical Trees as Living systems.* Cambridge University. Press, Cambridge. pp. 64-68.

Baker, H.G. and Baker, I. 1973a. Amino acids in nectar and their evolutionary significance. *Nature, 241* : 543-545.

Baker, H.G. and Baker, I. 1973b. Some autoecological aspects of the evolution of nector producing flowers, particularly aminoacids production in nectar. *In*: (ed.) Heywood, V.H. *Taxonomy and Ecology.* Academic Press, London. pp. 243-264.

Baker, H.G. and Baker, I. 1975. Studies of nectar constitution in pollinator plant co-evolution. *In*: (eds.) Gilbert, L.E. and Raven, P.H. *Co-evolution of animals and plants.* University of Texas Press, Austin. pp.100-140.

Baker, H.G. and Baker, I. 1979. Sugar ratios in nectars. *Phytochem. Bull., 12* : 43-45.

Behnke, H.D. 1984. Plant trichomes. Structure and ultrastructure, general terminology, taxonomic application, and aspects of trichome-bacteria interaction in leaf tips of *Dioscorea*. *In*: (eds.) Rodriguez E., Healey, P.L. and and Mehta, I. *Biology and Chemistry of Plant Trichomes*. Plenum Press, New York. pp. 1-21.

Bentley, B.L. 1977. Extrafloral nectaries and protection by pugnacious body guards. *Annu. Rev. Ecol. Syst., 8* : 407-427.

Berlyn, G.P. and Miksche, J.P. *Botanical Micro-technique and Cytochemistry*. Iowa State Univ. Press, Ames. Iowa.

Bernardello, L.M., Galetto, L. and Juliani, H.R. 1991. Floral nectar, nectary, nectary structure and pollinators in some Argentinean Bromeliaceae. *Ann. Bot., 67* : 401-411.

Bünning, E. 1953. *Entwicklungs and Bewegungs Physiologie der Pflanze*. Springer-verlag, Berlin.

Bureau, L.E. 1864. *Monographic des Bignoniaces*, Paris. pp. 164-169.

Chiffelle, T.L. and Putt, F.A. 1951. Propylene and ethylene glycol as solvent for Sudan black B. *Stain Technol., 26* : 51-56.

Corbet, S.A. 1978. Bees and the nectar of *Echium vulgare*. *In : The Pollination of Flowers by Insects* : (ed.) Richards, A.J. Academic Press, London. pp. 21-30.

Dell, B. and McComb, A.J. 1975. Glandular hairs resin production and habits of *Newcastelia viscida* E. Pritzel (Dicrastylidaceae). *Aust. J. Bot., 23* : 373-390.

Delpino, F. 1868-1875. Ulteriori 'osservazioni Sulla dicogamia nel regno vegetale-I and II. *Atti. Soc. Ital. Sci. Nat.*, 11, 12.

Dop, P. 1927. *Bull. Soc. Hist. Nat. Taulouse., 56* : 189.

Durkee, L.T. 1982. The floral and extrafloral nectaries of *Passiflora*. II. The extra-floral nectary. *Amer. J. Bot., 69* : 1420-1428.

Elias, T.S. and Gelband, H. 1975. Nectar : Its production and functions in Trumpet creeper. *Science, 189* : 289-291.

Elias, T.S. and Gelband, H. 1976. Morphology and anatomy of floral and extrafloral nectaries in *Campsis* (Bignoniaceae). *Amer. J. Bot., 63* : 1349-1353.

Elias, T.S. and Prance, G.T. 1978. Nectaries on the fruits of *Crescentia* and other Bignoniaceae. *Brittonia, 80* : 175-181.

Elias, T.S. and Newcombe, L.F. 1979. Foliar Nectaries and glandular trichomes in *Catalpa* (Bignoniaceae). *Acta. Bot. Sin., 21* : 215-224.

Fahn, A. 1988. Secretory tissues in Vascular Plants. *New Phytol., 108* : 229-257.

Fahn, A. 1979. *Secretory Tissues in Plants*. Academic Press, London.

Fahn, A. and Benouaiche P. 1979. Ultrastructure, development and secretion in the nectary of banana flowers. *Ann. Bot., 44* : 85-93.

Figier, J. 1968. Etude infrastructural et cytochimique des glands petiolaires de *Mercurialis annua* L. Essai d' interpretation an rapport avec La Secretion. *C.R. Hebd. Seances Acad. Sci. Ser. D. Sci. Nat., 267* : 491-494.

Frey-Wyssling, A. 1933. Uberdie extrafloralen Nektarien Von Hevea brasiliensis muell. Berichte des Schweizerischen botanischen. *Beri. der. Schw. Bot. Gesell., 42* : 109-122.

Gomori, G. 1952. *Microscopic Histochemistry.* University Press, Chicago.

Graham, R.C. and Karnovsky, M.J. 1966. the early stages of absorption of injected horse radish peroxidase in the proximal tubules of mouse kidney : ultrastructural cytochemistry by a new technique. J. Histochem. Cytochem., *14* : 291-302.

Harborne, J.B. 1982. Plant phenolics. *In* : (eds.) Bell, E.A. and Charlwood, B.V. Secondary plant products. vol. 8. Springer-Verlag, Berlin. pp. 329-402.

Heinrich, G. 1975. Uber die Lokalistion Verschiedener Phosphatase in Nektarium Von *Aloe.* Cytobiologie, *11* : 247-263.

Heinrich, G. and Raven, P.H. 1972. Energetics and pollination ecology. *Science, 176* : 597-602.

Inamdar, J.A. 1969. Structure and ontogeny of foliar nectaries and stomata in *Bignonia chamberlaynii* sims. Proc. India. Acad. Sci., *70* : 232-241.

Jensen, W.A. 1962. *Botanical Histochemistry.* Freeman, San Francisco. USA.

Kelsey, R.G., Reynolds, G.W. and Rodriguez, E. 1984. The Chemistry of biologically active constituents secreted and stored in plant glandular trichomes. *In*: (eds.) Rodrighez, E., Healey, P.L. and Mehta, I. Biology and Chemistry of Plant Trichomes. Plenum Press, New York. pp. 187-241.

Kreitner, G.L. and Sorensen, E.L. 1979. Glandular Secretory System of alfalfa species. *Crop. Sci., 19* : 499-502.

Kristen, U. 1976. Die Morphologie der Schleimsekretion in Fruchtknoten von *Aptenia* cordifolia. *Protoplasma, 89* : 221-233.

Laroche, R.C. 1974. *Ann. Mo. Bot. Gard., 61* : 530.

Linne, C.V. 1735. *Systema natuarae, Sieve regna tria nature Systematice Proposita perclasses, ordines, genera et species*, Leiden.

Lüttge, U. 1961. Uber die Zusammensetzung des Nektars und den Mechanismus Seiner Sekretion. I. *Planta, 56* : 189- 212.

Lüttge, U. 1977. Nectar Composition and membrane transport of Sugars and amino acids. A review on the present state of nectar research. *Apidologie, 8* : 305-320.

Mahajan, P.B. 1989. Histochemistry of reproductive structures in *Spathodea Camponulata* Beauv. M. Phil. dissertation, Karnatak Univ. Dharwad. India.

Mahlberg, P.G., Hammond, C.T., Turner, J.C. and Hemphill, J.K. 1984. Structure, development and composition of glandular trichomes of *Cannabis sativa.* L. *In* : (eds.) Rodriguez, E., Healey, P.L. and Mehta, I. *Biology and Chemistry of plant trichomes.* Plenum Press, New York. pp. 23-51.

Malik, C.P. and Singh, M.B. 1980. *Plant Enzymology and Histoenzymology* : A text manual. Kalyani Publ. New Delhi, India.

Mapson, L.W., Insherwood, F.A. and Chen, Y.T. 1954 : Biological Synthesis of L — ascorbic acid by plant mithochondria. *Biochem. Jour., 56* : 21.

Mazia, D., Brewer, P. and Alfert, M. 1953: A Cytochemical staining measurement of proteins with mercuric bromophenol blue. *Biol. Bull., 104* : 57-67.

Mehra, K.R. and Kulkarni, A.R. 1989. Floral trichomes in some members of Bignoniaceae. *Proc. Indian Acad. Sci.* (Plant Sci.), *99* : 97-105.

O'Brien, T.P. and McCully, M.E. 1981. *The Study of Plant Structure : Principles and Selected Methods.* Termarcarpipty Ltd., Melbourne, Australia.

Parija, P. and Samal, K. 1936. Extrafloral nectaries in *Tecoma capensis* Lindl. *J. Indian Bot. Soc., 51* : 241-246.

Pate, J.S., Peoples, M.B., Storer, P.J. and Atkins, C.A. 1985. the extrafloral nectaries of Cowpea (*Vigna unguiculata* (L) Walp.). II. Nectar Composition, origin of nectar solutes and nectary functioning. *Planta, 166* : 28-38.

Percival, M.S. 1961. Types of nectar in angiosperms, *New Phytol., 60* : 235-281.

Peterson, R.L. and Vermeer, J. 1984. Histochemistry of Trichomes. *In*: (eds.) Rodriguez E., Healey, P.L. and Mehta, I.*Biology and Chemistry of Plant Trichomes.* Plenum Press, New York. pp. 71-94.

Rachmilevitz, T. and Fahn, A. 1975. The floral nectary of *Tropaeolum majus* : The nature of the secretory cells and the manner of nectar secretion. *Ann. Bot., 39* : 721-728.

Raghavan, J.S. and Venkatasubban, K.R. 1940. Studies in the Bignoniacee 1. Chromosome number and epidermal hydathodes in *Spathodea campanulata. J. Indian Bot. Soc., 19* : 292-298.

Rao, L.N. 1926. A short note on the extrafloral nectaries in *Spathodea stipulata* wall. *J. Indian Bot. Soc., 5* : 113-116.

Rudramuniyappa, C.K. and Mahajan, P.B. 1991. Morphogenesis and Histochemistry of ovarial nectaries in *Spathodea campanulata* Beauv. *J. Indian Bot. Soc., 70* : 169-174.

Sandwith, N.Y. 1938. *Flora of Surinam., 4* : 11- 86.

Schmid, R. 1988. Reproductive versus extra-reproductive nectaries-historical perspective and terminological recommendations. *Bot. Rev., 54* : 179-232.

Schnepf, E. 1974. Gland cells. *In*: (ed.) Robards, A.W. *Dynamic Aspects of Plant Ultrastructure.* McGraw-Hill, London. pp. 331-357.

Schumann, K. 1895. Bignoniaceae : *Die Naturalichen Pflanzenfamilien. 4* : 189-252.

Shah, C.K., Pandey, S.N. and Bhat, P.N. 1974. Cytophotometric study of ascorbic acid in the developing anthers of *Aponogeton natans.* L. *Indian J. Pl. Physiol. 17* : 16-22.

Shuel, R.W. 1975. The production of Nectar. *In: The Hive and the Honey Bee.* Dandant and Son, Illinois. pp. 265-282.

Siebert, R.J. 1948. The use of glands in a taxonomic consideration of the family Bignoniaceae. Ann. *Mo. Bot. Gard., 35* : 123-136.

Sinnott, E.W. 1960. *Plant Morphogenesis.* McGraw-Hill, New York.

Stahl. E. 1953. Untersuchungen an den Drusenhaarer der Schabgarbe (*Achillea millefolium* L.). *Z. Bot., 41* : 123-146.

Stahl, E. 1957. Uber vorgange an den Drusenhaaren der Schafgarbe. *Z. Bot., 45* : 297-315.

Stebbins, G.L. 1966. Polarity gradients and the development of cell patterns. *In*: (ed.) E.G. Cutter, *Trends in Plant Morphogenesis* Longmans, London, pp. 115-126.

Stephenson, A.G. 1981. Toxic nectar deters thieves of *Catalpa speciosa*. *Amer. Midl. Nat., 105* : 381-383.

Subramanian, R.B. and Inamdar, J.A. 1985. Occurrence, structure, ontogeny and biology of nectaries in *Kigelia pinnata* DC. *Bot. Mag.* Tokyo, *98* : 67-73.

Subramanian, R.B. and Inamdar, J.A. 1986. Nectaries in *Bignonia illicium* L. ontogeny, structure and functions. *Proc. Indian Acad. Sci.* (Plant Sci.), *96* : 135-140.

Subramanian, R.B., Arumugasamy, K. and Inamdar, J.A. 1990. Studies in the secretory glands of *Hiptage sericea* (Malphighiaceae). *Nord. J. Bot., 10* : 57-62.

Tomson, W.W., Berry, W.L. and Liu, L.L. 1969. Localization and secretion of salt by the salt glands of *Tamarix aphylla. Proc. Nat. Acad. Sci.* (USA), *63* : 310-317.

Trub, 1889. Quoted from Haberlandt G. 1914 of Physiological plant anatomy. Montaque Drummon, London.

Unzelman, J.M. and Healey, P.L. Development, structure and occurrence of secretory trichomes of *Pharabitis. Protoplasma, 80* : 285-303.

Uphof, JC.T. 1962. Plant hairs. *In*: (eds.) Zimmerman, W. and Ozenda, P.G. *Encyclopedia of Plant Anatomy*. Borntraeger, Berlin., *4* : 1-206.

Van Gijzel, P. 1975. Polychromatic uv fluorescence microphotometry of fresh and fossil plant substances with special reference to location and identification of dispersed organic matter in rocks. *In*: (ed.) Alpem, AB. *Petrographic organique et potential petrolier*, CNRS : Paris.

Wanchastein, M., Meisel, E. and Niedzwiedz, A. 1960. Histochemical demonstration of mitochandrial adenosine triphosphate technique. *J. Histochem. Cytochem., 8* : 387-388.

Wagner, G.J. 1991. Secreting glandular trichomes : More than just hairs. *Plant Physiol., 96* : 675-679.

ULTRASTRUCTURE AND SECRETION OF CALYCINE EXTRA-FLORAL NECTARIES IN *KIGELIA PINNATA* DC

R. BAGAVATHI SUBRAMANIAN and J.A. INAMDAR
Department of Biosciences, Sardar Patel University
Vallabh Vidyanagar, Gujarat 388 120, India.

ABSTRACT

The ultrastructure of the calycine extrafloral nectaries in *Kigelia pinnata* is investigated at different developmental stages. The secretary cells at young stage exhibit a granular and dense cytoplasm with various organelles. Plastids and rough endoplasmic reticulum (rER) are the prominent organelles during young stage while smooth endoplasmic reticulum (sER), plastids and dictyosomes are found in the pre-secretory and secretory stages. The secretory material is probably carried by dictyosome derived secretory vesicles which fuse with plasmalemma. Ultrastructural evidences indicate a 'granulocrine' mode of secretion in the calycine nectary. At the post-secretory stage, cytolytic processes and death of cells occur.

Key words : *Kigelia pinnata*, extrafloral calycine nectaries, ultrastructure and secretion.

INTRODUCTION

Nectaries are classified into extrafloral and floral on the basis of their function (Elias and Gelband, 1975; Fahn, 1979). Floral nectaries are found on the inner floral parts and are directly involved in pollination, whereas extrafloral nectaries occur on outer floral as well as vegetative parts and are not involved in pollination. Subramanian and Inamdar (1985) studied the occurrence, structure, ontogey biology of extrafloral and floral nectaries in *Kigelia pinnata* DC. The present paper deals with the ultrastructural changes in the secretory and non-secretory cells at different stages of development and the probable mechanism of nectar elimination in the calycine extrafloral nectaries of *Kigelia pinnata*.

MATERIALS AND METHODS

Small portions of calyx, bearing nectaries were first fixed in 4% cold glutaraldehyde for 3 hrs and post-fixed with 2% cold osmium tetraoxide, both buffered with 0.1 M phosphate buffer (pH 7.2). The fixed materials were dehydrated through graded acetone series and embedded in Spurr's resin (Spurr, 1969). Sections of 0.5 to 1.0 μm and of silver to gray were cut with a Reicherts OMU_3 ultra-microtome. Semithin sections were stained with toluidine blue 0 (0' Brien and McCully, 1973). Ultrathin sections were stained with uranyl acetate followed by lead citrate (Reynolds, 1963). Formvar coated grids containing ultrathin sections were examined and photographed with a Philips EM 400 electron microscope were 81-10 μm an paraffin sections ofstained with Safranin 0 fast green FCF combination. Brightfield photomicrographs were taken with Carl-Zeiss photomicroscope I andphase-contrast photographs with AO Spencer's phase-contrast microscope.

OBSERVATIONS

The calycine nectaries of *Kigelia pinnata* are situated on the outer surface of the calyx. They are cupular in shape, composed of 2-3 layered secretory tissue and multicellular, single layered stalk as well as foot.(Fig. 1.A). The whole nectary structure is situated in a deep groove outlined by the epidermis. The radial walls of the stalk cells show thickening (Fig. 1.B).

Calycine nectaries at three developmental stage viz.; (i) young stage, (ii) pre-secretory stage, and (iii) secretory stage were selected for ultrastructural study.

(i) **Young Stage (3-5 mm buds) :** The secretory cells of the calycine nectary exhibit a granular and dense cytoplasm due to the presence of many number of ribosomes and other cell organelles such as endoplasmic reticulum (ER), dictyosomes, plastids and mitochondria. The cell walls are thin with closely appressed plasmalemma. Plasmodesmata traverse the radial and tangential walls of the secretory cells (Fig. 1.C).

Layers of ER with flattened cisternae and ribosomes studded on the outer surface (rER) are also present. The rER is found in close contact with plastids (Fig. 1.D). A number of plastids with dense osmiophilic material and starch grains are found distributed throughout the cytoplasm (Fig. 1.C). The stalk cells of the nectary exhibit an ultrastructure similar to secretory cells except for the presence of a large central vacuole (Fig. 1.E). The upper and lower transverse walls of the stalk cells are interspersed with a number of well-developed plasmodesmata, while the radial walls show heavy thickening (Fig. 1.B.E.). The foot cells show a prominent peripheral vacuole, spherical plastids and a number of mitochondria. Plasmodesmata also could be observed on the transverse as well as radial walls of the foot cell.

(ii) **Pre-secretory Stage (8-10 mm buds) :** The secretory as well as sub-secretory cells reach their maximum size. The cell walls are relatively thick. The plasmalemma is completely withdrawn from the cell walls and display wavy undulations giving rise to conspicuous extraplasmic space (the space between the plasmalemma and cell wall). Many number of dictyosomes actively giving off vesicles also could be observed (Fig. 2.C). The dictyosome derived vesicles are spherical in shape and are found in contact with or inside plasmalemma invaginations (Fig. 2.D). The topography of the dictyosome derived vesicles and vesicles nearer to or inside the plasmalemma invaginations show similarity. The vesicles are often seen in the extraplasmic space along the radial walls.

Towards the end of the secretory stage, the secretory cell wall microfibrils become loose and the middle lamella along the radial walls show dissolution. Consequently, a gap appears between the cell walls. A number of multi-vesicular bodies are seen inside the plasmalemma invaginations (Fig. 2.D). Some of the vesicles pass through the cell wall microfibrils into the gap (Fig. 2.E). Just prior to the cessation of secretion autophagic vacuoles appear (Fig. 2.F). Eventually cellular organalles and cytoplasm break down takes place leading to death of the nectary.

(iii) **Secretion :** The secretory material accumulates in the gap between the adjacent radial walls and also between the cuticle and upper tangential walls (in the sub-cuticular space). As the quantity of the secretory material in the sub-cuticular space increases, the cuticle is detached and lifted off the cell walls. Eventually the cuticle bursts open owing to the pressure exerted by a secretory material. The calycine extrafloral nectaries start secreting even when the bud is young and continues till anthesis.

DISCUSSION

The light and electron microscopic characters of the secretory cells of various types of floral and extrafloral nectaries are reported to be similar (Fahn and Rachemilevitz, 1970; Elias, 1972; Durkee, 1982; Inamdar *et al.*, 1985; Mohan & Inamdar, 1986).

Such secretory cells exhibit a dense cytoplasm rich in various cell organelles. The ultrastructural features exhibited by the calycine extrafloral nectary of *Kigelia pinnata* therefore, indicate the secretory nature of the cells. Plasmodesmatal connections traverse the walls between sub-glandular parenchyma cells and foot cells, foot cells and stalk cells and stalk cells are heavily lignified, thereby limiting the distribution of plasmodesmata to the trangential walls. Such a network of plasmodesmata offers symplastic continuity between the secretory and sub-secretory cells. Therefore, a predominantly symplastic route for the transport of pre-nectar from sub-secretory to secretory tissue would be compatible with the ultrastructural evidence. Spanswick (1976) and Gunning (1976).also supported the idea of a low resistant pathway for bulk flow of sugars through plasmodesmata. Lignification of the radial walls of stalk cells,. which prevents on apoplastic pathway of pre-nectar transport and the paucity of ER and dictyosome elements in the sub-glandular cells augment to the evidences of pre-nectar transport in the symplast.

Accumulation and the consequent breakdown of starch in the plastids at secretory stage indicates that a part of the secreted material is derived from stored food materials. Such a depletion in the inner contents of plastids has been observed in many plant glands (Dell & McComb, 1977; Werker & Fahn, 1981).

ER and dictyosomes are the dominant organelles apart from plastids during young, pre-secretory and secretory stages. Both the organelles have been often implicated in the intracellular production and/or transport of polysaccharides (Gunning & Steer, 1975, Benner

& Schnepf, 1975). The presence of a well-developed network of ER during young and pre-secretory stages and the appearance of dictyosomes during secretory stage indicates the possibility of membrane transfer from ER to dictyosomes. The close proximity exhibited by ER elements to plastids with reserve food material suggests that the ER together with membrane material transports pre-secretory product also to dictyosomes.

The abundance of dictyosome derived vesicles and their topography at the time of secretion suggest that dictyosome is the principal organelle involved in secretion. These ultrastructural evidences clearly favour granulocrine mode of secretion in which the secretory substance is transported in vesicles which are absorbed in plasmalemma invaginations and subsequently released to the exterior of the cell. Such a system of nectar elimination has been proposed for many nectaries (see Horner & Lersten, 1968; Rachmilevitz & Fahn, 1973; Fahn & Benouiche, 1979; Mohan & Inamdar, 1986).

Cellular autolysis is said to be initiated by breakdown of the tonoplast (Thomson *et al.*, 1979). the appearance of autophagic vacuoles just before the cessation of secretion indicates that they are responsible for the cellular breakdown which precedes the death of the cell (see Butler & Simon, 1971; Matile & Winkenback, 1971). Histochemical evidence shows that the secretion contains predominantly carbohydrates and proteins, as reported earlier by Subramanian & Inamdar (1985). It can be concluded that the calycine extrafloral nectary of *Kigelia pinnata* is well-organised to efficiently carry out the function of nectar secretion.

Explanation to Figure 1

FIGS. A—F : Fig. A — C.S. of calyx showing mature calycine nectary. X 340; Fig. B — Phase-contrast photomicrograph showing radial wall thickening of stalk cells. X 780; Fig. C — Longisection of calycine nectary showing secretory cells with well developed plastids ER and vacuoles. Note plasmodesmata on radial wall. X 9,600; Fig. D — Long strands of extensively developed rER in proximity to plastids in secretory cells. X 18,200; Fig. E — Stalk cell of the nectary showing plastids and a prominent central vacuole. Note radial wall thickening. X 8.200; Fig. F — Strands of rER in proximity to plastids showing dilation of membranes. X 19,600.

C – Cell wall, F – Foot cell layer; Pd – Plasmodesmata; r – Radial wall; rer – Rough endoplasmic reticulum; s – Stalk cell layer; Se – Secretory cells; St – Starch; v – Vacuole.

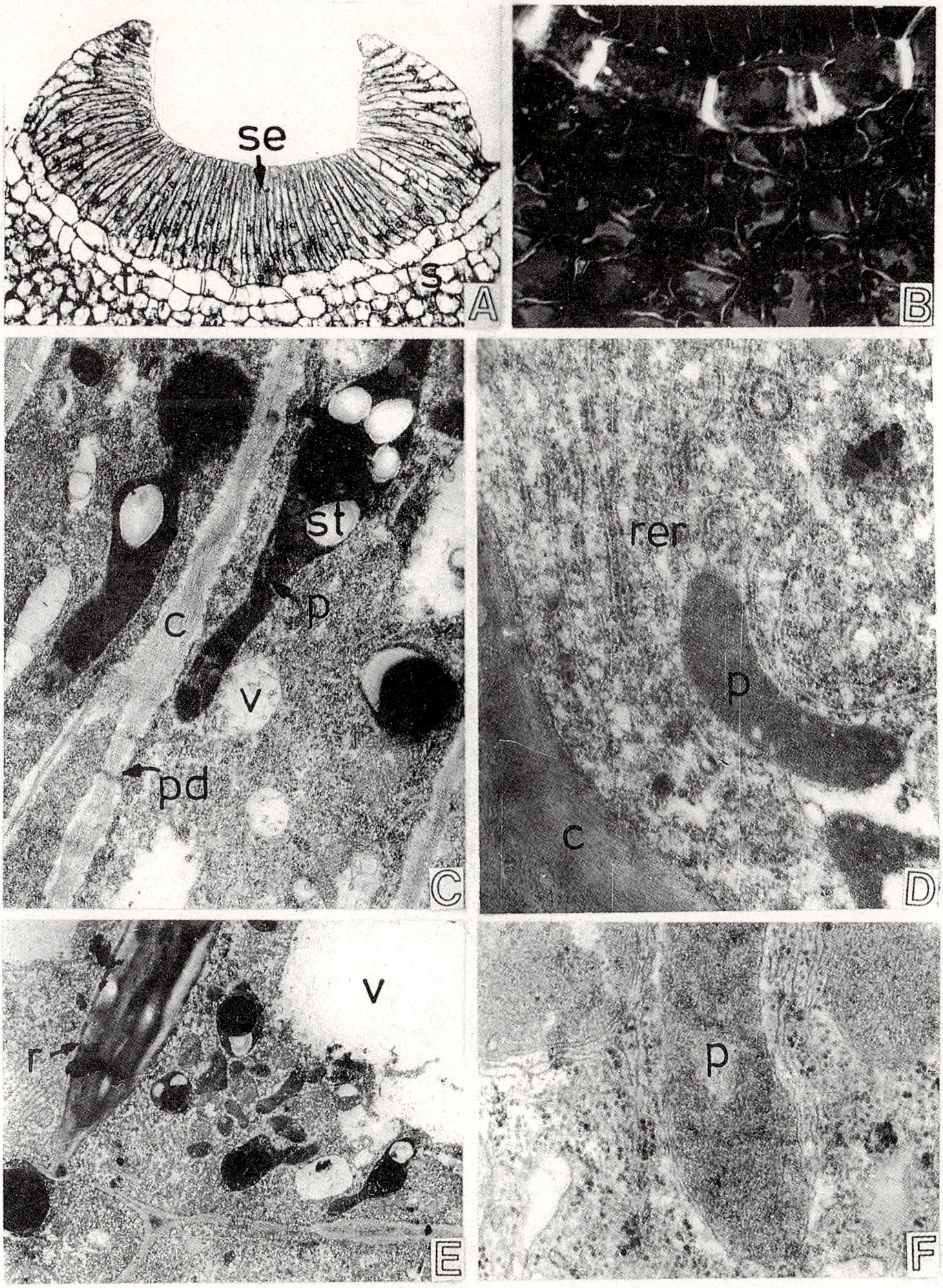

FIG. 1

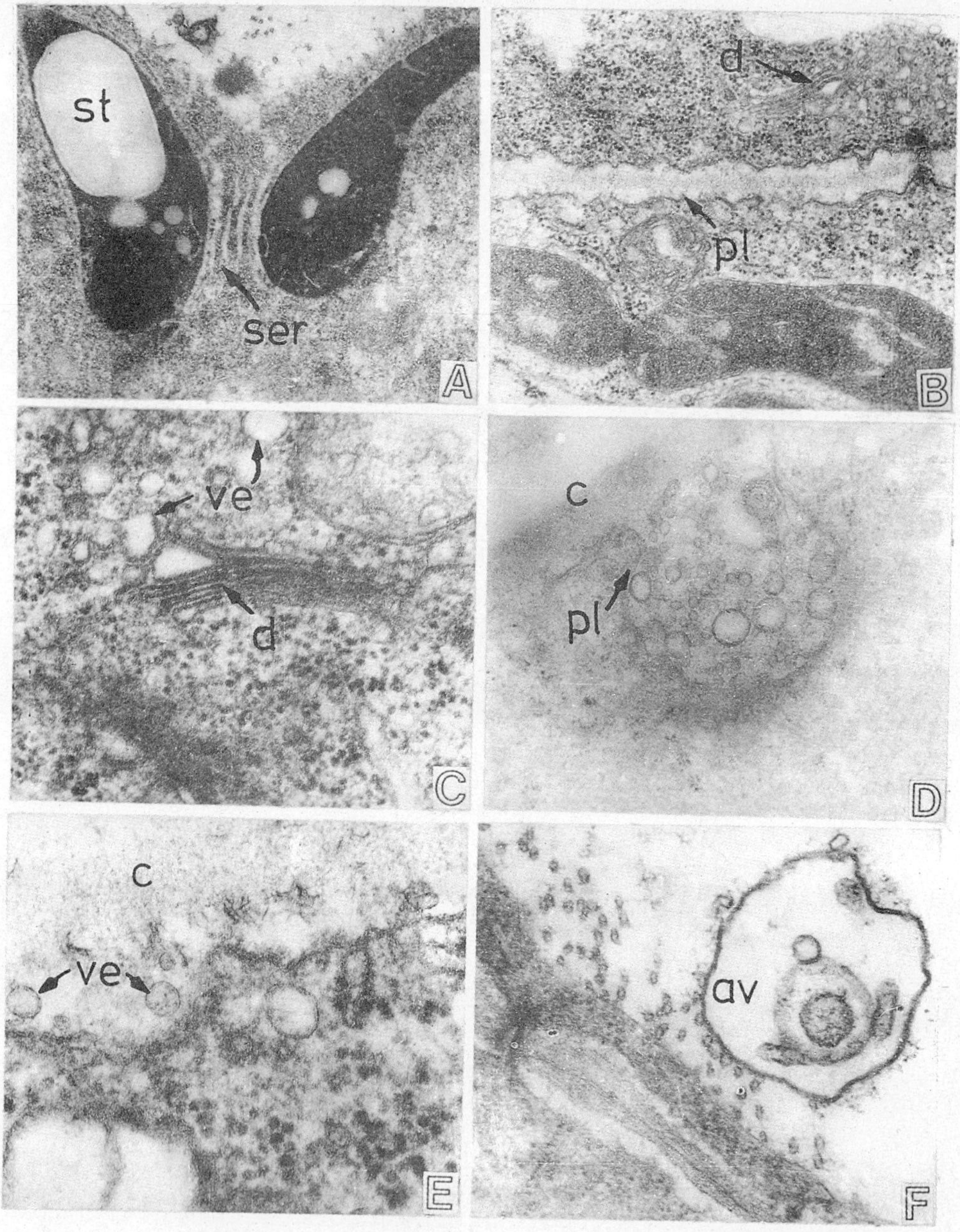

FIG·2

Explanation to Figure 2

FIGS. A—F : Fig. A — Occurrance of ser tubules with constrictions near plastids. X 9,700; Fig. B — Longisection of calycine nectary prior to secretion showing plastids without starch and vesiculation of dictyosomes. X 8,400; Fig. C — Dictyosome derived vesicles scattered in the cytoplasm of the secretory cell during secretion. X 21,400; Fig. D — Plasmalemma invagination showing multivesicular bodies inside. X 31,200; Fig. E — Secretory vesicles between plasmalemma and cell wall. Note loosening of cell wall microfibrils. X 28,600; Fig. F — Autophagic vacuoles in the secretory cell cytoplasm towards the end of secretory stage. X 11,700.

Av – Autophagic vacuoles; C – Cell wall; D – Dictyosomes; P – Plastids; pl – Plasmalemma; Ser – Smooth endoplasmic reticulum; St – Starch; Ve – Secretory vesicles.

Literature Cited

Benner, U. & Schnepf, E. 1975 Die morphologie der Naktarausschei dung bei Bromeliacean Beteligung des golgi – apparatus. *Protoplasma, 85* : 337-349.

Butler, R.R. & Simon, E.W. 1971. Ultrastructural aspects of senescence in plants. *Adv. Gerontol Res., 3* 73-129.

Dell, B. & McComb, A.J. 1977. Glandular hair formation and resin secretion in *Eremophila fraserin* F. Menll. (Myoporaceae) : *Protoplasma, 92* : 71-86.

Durkee, L.T. 1982. The floral and extrafloral nectaries of *Passiflora* II. The extrafloral nectary : *Amer. J. Bot., 69* : 1420-1428.

Elias, T.S. 1972. Morphology and anatomy of extrafloral nectaries of *Pithecellobium macradenium : Bot. Gaz., 133* : 38-42.

Elias, T.S. & Gelband, H. 1975. Nectar : Its production and functions in Trumpet creeper : *Science, 189* : 289-291.

Fahn, A. 1976. *Secretory Tissues in Plants.* (Academic Press, London).

Fahn, A. & Benouiche, P. 1979. Ultrastructure, development and secretion in the nectary of banana flowers : *Ann Bot, 44* : 85-93.

Fahn, A. & Rachmilevitz, T. 1970. Ultrastructure and nectar secretion in *Lonicera japonica : Bot. J. Linn. Soc., 63* : Suppl. (1) 51-56.

Gunning, B.E.S. 1976. The role of plasmodesmata in short distance transport to and from Phloem — *In*: (eds.) Gunning, B.E.S. and Robrds, A.W. *Intercellular Communication in plants — studies on plasmodesmata.* : (Springer-Verlag, Heidelberg).

Gunning, B.E.S. & Steer, H.W. 1975. *Ultrastructure and Biology of Plant Cells* : Edward Arnold, London.

Horner, H.T.Jr & Lersten, N.R. 1968. Development, Structure and function of secretory trichomes in *Psychotria bacteriophylla* (Rubiaceae) *Amer. J. Bot., 55* : 1089-1099.

Inamdar, J.A., Mohan, J.S.S. & Bagavathi Subramanian, R. 1985. Extrafloral nectaries of *Holarrhena antidysenterica* (L.) Wall. ex. G.Don — Development, Ultrastructure and secretion : *Trends in Plant Research* pp. 137-148.

Matile, P. & Winkenback, F. 1971. Function of lysosomes and lysosomal enzymes in the secreting corolla of the morning glory (*Ipomoea purpurea*) : *J. Exp. Bot., 22* : 759-71.

Mohan, J.S.S. & Inamdar, J.A. 1986. Ultrastructure and secretion of extrafloral nectaries in *Plumeria rubra* L. : *Ann. Bot., 57* : 389-401.

Rachmilevitz, T. & Fahn, A. 1973. Ultrastructure of nectaries of *Vinca rosea* L., *Vinca major* L. and *Citrus sinensis* Osbeck C.V. Valencia and its relation to the mechanism of nectar secretion : *Ann. Bot., 37* : 1-9.

Spanswick, R.M. 1976. Symplasmic transport in tissue — *In* : (eds.) U Lüttage and M.G. Pitman: Transport in plants II *Encyclopedia of Plant Physiology*. New Series Vol. 2 : (Springer-Verlag, New York).

Subramanian, R.B. & Inamdar, J.A. 1985. Occurrence structure, ontogeny and biology of nectaries in *Kigelia pinnata* DC *Bot. Mag. Tokyo, 98* : 67-73.

Thomson, W.W., Platt-Aloia, K. & Koller, D. 1979. Ultrastructure and development of the trichomes of *Larrea* (creosote bush) : *Bot. Gaz., 140* : 249-60.

Werker E. & Fahn, A. 1981. Secretory hairs of *Inula viscosa* (L.) Ait — Development, Ultrastructure and secretion : *Bot. Gaz., 142* : 461-476.

NECTARY BIOLOGY : Structure, Function and Utilization
(ed. BIR BAHADUR) 1997
© DATTSONS, NAGPUR, INDIA

PHYSIOLOGICAL FUNCTION OF EXTRA-FLORAL NECTARIES

D. CLAIR-MACZULAJTYS and G. BORY
Laboratory of Botany, University of Paris 7, Paris, France.

ABSTRACT

The physiological function of extrafloral nectaries in *Ailanthus glandulosa* is presented since the ecophysiological aspects of nectar secretion are poorly understood. Data from various aspects like seasonal variations occuring under controlled conditions; variations in the number of extrafloral nectaries, variations occuring under experimental condtions and effects of shoot physiology after removal of nectaries is correlated with the occurence of a requirement for photosynthetic assimilate. When the requirement is very high photosynthate are exported to the different sinks and the photosynthetic rate remains maximum. Nectar secretion is stimulated initially and extrafloral nectaries act as "sap valves" fail to prevent the accumulation of starch grains suggests that some mechanism other than secretory process prevents starch hydrolysis. It is concluded that extrafloral nectaries eliminate excess sugars play an important role in the regulation of photosynthesis.

Key words : Extra floral nectaries; Physiological function; *Ailanthus glandulosa*.

INTRODUCTION

Literature referring to secretory tissues and particularly nectaries is quite extensive. It is well known that nectaries display an enormous variability as regards their structure, morphological identity, cytological features and their mode of nectar extrusion. In many recent studies the ultrastructure of secretory cells was analysed in relation to the process of secretion. Various views were suggested for the possible ways of pre-nectar transport into a secretory cell and of nectar elimination from the cell (see literature in Fahn, 1979). The nectar composition is known also to vary among species. Of the many chemical constituents in nectars, sugars are dominant (Wykes, 1952, 1953; Percival, 1961; Bentley, 1977). Recently the methods by GLC (gas-liquid chromatography) and HPLC (high-performance liquid chromatography) have opened new possibilities in nectar-sugar analysis. The sugar concentration of the nectar (Baker, 1975; Pyke and Waser, 1981) and the composition of sugars in the nectar (Baker and Baker, 1975, 1983; Bahadur *et al.*, 1986) have been the subject of a number of works.

In other respects, our knowledge of the role of extrafloral nectaries in the life of the plant is limited except the ecological function. Extrafloral nectaries benefit plants by attracting ants that reduce the level of herbivore and seed predator damages or by attracting parasitoids that protect the plant by parasitizing herbivores (Elias and Gelband, 1975; Bentley, 1976, 1977; Keeler, 1977; Beckmann and Stanley, 1981; Koptur, 1980, 1981; Hespenheide, 1985).

Little information is available on the effects of nectar secretion on the metabolism of the organ associated. In addition the results concerning the ecophysiological properties of nectar secretion are rather fragmentary and often contradictory (Beutler and Schöntag, 1940; Helder, 1958; Southwick, 1983). It was clearly demonstrated that the nectaries represent a substantial sink for sugars (Findlay *et al.*, 1971; Reed *et al.*, 1971; Lüttge, 1977; Meyber and Kristen, 1981; Southwick, 1984). As a sink, nectaries may compete with other sinks such a developing flowers, fruits and seeds or foliar movements for nutrients (Gaillochet and Faucher, 1982; Corbet and Delfosse, 1984). The nectaries acting as a sink may have inversely a stimulation effect on the transport of the phloem sugars to the young parts of the plant (Ziegler, 1965). According to Bonnier (1878) the nectaries serve as a storage organ may be enough to help young growing organs. Another role that has been proposed is that the nectaries may serve as "sap valves" eliminating surplus sugars from a particular organ (Frey-

Wissling, 1933; Zimmermann, 1953; Mound 1962; Maheshwari and Chakrabarty, 1966). However, this proposal has not been quantitatively investigated (Lüttge and Schnepf, 1976). The quantitative results obtained by Baker *et al.*, (1978) in *Ricinus communis* do not lend any support to the "sap valves" theory.

Except these few hypothesis on the physiological function of nectaries, we have noted that the experiments in connection with this problem remained scanty. In recent years, an increasing emphasis of interest have been given to quantify the properties of floral nectar such as the volume of nectar, the rate of nectar production and the sugar concentration of the nectar. The effects of different factors (microclimatic conditions, flower age, time of the day, nectar removal ...) influencing the nectar production rate and the sugar concentration of the nectar have been also quantitatively investigated (Thyri, 1978; Baker and Baker, 1979; Corbet *et al.*, 1979a; Corbet *et al.*, 1979b; Willson and Bertin, 1979; Willson *et al.*, 1979; Brink and De Wet, 1980; Southwick *et al.*, 1981; Pleasants, 1983). Nevertheless, the cost of floral nectar has been neglected in even recent estimates of energy allocation in the reproductive effort (Soutwick, 1984).

The purpose of this review is to describe how the extrafloral nectaries functioning is closely associated with the physiological processes and conditions of organs bearing them. *Ailanthus glandulosa* has been chosen because of the importance of its secretory system. In addition, a monographic investigation of tree of heaven (which is a pioneer woody plant) has been made recently (Bory, 1983; Clair-Maczulajtys, 1984). In this work we have considered the activity of extrafloral nectaries in relation to the stage of plant growth and in response to seasonal variations and cultural treatments. Our approach of their role has included also experiments relating to the source(s) of nectar (photosynthesis carbohydrate reserve) and/or the sink itself (nectaries). Evidence that the extrafloral nectaries role in regulating the foliar functioning is presented here. Obviously a study of only extrafloral nectaries of one species cannot provide the general interpretation of this physiological problem but it can contribute to a scant literature on this subject.

DISTRIBUTION STRUCTURE AND CYTOLOGY OF EXTRA-FLORAL NECTARIES OF *AILANTHUS GLANDULOSA*

In *Ailanthus glandulosa* extrafloral nectaries have been described on cataphylls, foliage leaves and stipules (Bory, 1983). In opening bud, the number of nectaries occuring on the margins of cataphylls varies according to the type of cataphylls (150-1000 per dm^2 (Figs. 2; 5). On the first leaves appearing, nectaries are located at the base of the petiole. They are stalked and have an apical pore (Fig. 4). The stalk is also covered by hyaline non glandular hairs (Bory and Clair-Maczulajtys, 1981). These organs have been interpreted as reduced stipules consisting of one axis with its vascular system with the extremity occupied by a nectary (Clair-Maczulajtys and Bory, 1983). In spite of the diversity of these stipular appendages as regards their glandular head development and their stalk thickness, the apical pore is always present (Bory, 1983). In other respects these nectaries are early functional before the laminar nectaries are completely differentiated. The completely developed pinnated leaves bear nectaries on the abaxial surface of the lamina (Fig. 1). Each leaflet averages five nectaries situated at the tip of the secondary vein (Fig. 6). The mature nectaries are about 1. 5-2 mm in diameter and 1-2 mm in height. The nectar is extruded from the pore which is located at the top of the gland (Fig. 6). Recently it has been demonstrated that the composition of the extrafloral nectar from *Ailanthus glandulosa* varied according to the type of nectary (Bory and Clair-Maczulajtys, 1986).

The three types of extrafloral nectaries show a great homogeneity as regards their histology and cytology. They are differentiated into four concentric histological zones (Fig. 8). 1– The gland is covered with one-celled epidermis more elongated near the pere. A thick cuticle covers the epidermis which is devoid of stomata. 2– The glandular tissue (prismatic parenchyma) is composed of elongated cells converging toward the pore (Fig. 9). The prismatic cells exhibit pronounced nectariferous characters : thin walls, dense cytoplasm and the porportion of nucleus to cytoplasm relatively high. On the other hand, the occurence of active Goigi bodies in addition to the very, well developed endoplasmic reticulum led us to suppose a granulocrine way of nectar secretion (Bory and Clair-Maczulajtys, 1986). During the functional stage, schizo-lysigenous ducts appear in the prismatic parenchyma and the appearance of the pore well corresponds to the schizo-lysigenous process of the nectary (Clair-Maczulajtys and Bory, 1982). 3– Surrounding immediately the glandular tissue, two to four layers of still elongated cells constitute the transition zone (Fig. 10). 4– The tannin-containging cells form a belt around the glandular tissue and the transition zone except under the pore (Fig. 11). The periglandular parenchyma is characterised by numerous cells containing crystals of calcium oxalate. Outside of the periglandular parenchyma, an association of four to eight alkaloid-containing fells form a ring more or less complete. They are very different in shape and size (50–120 μm in diameter) from the neighbouring cells (Fig. 12). A recent ultrastructural study of these cells has revealed a large space between the wall and the hyaloplasm and numerous little particles in the large vacuoles showing a very sinuous tonoplast (Bory, 1983). Under the gland, the palisadic parenchyma is interrupted at the level where the glandular tissue is connected with the subjacent vascular system. The secretory tissue is supplied by both phloem and xylem. The vascular strand of the secondary vein branching from two or three principal traces (also ramified) approaches the gland in the mesophyll and is bifurcated abaxially and adxially, never penetrating it (Fig. 7). The extrafloral nectaries of *Ailanthus glandulosa* are initiated early and simultaneously with the development of the veins. The different histological zones constituting the nectaries come from a set of divisions in subepidermal and deeper layers without renewal of meristematic activity (Bory and Clair-Maczulajtys, 1978).

VARIATIONS IN THE SECRETORY ACTIVITY OF EXTRA-FLORAL NECTARIES OF *AILANTHUS GLANDULOSA*

Seasonal Variations

In the same year where the analysis of seasonal variations in the secretory activity took place, we have also determined the photosynthetic rate and followed the changes in lipid and carbohydrate content of leaves. Four types of threes differing by their reproductive state have been retained : 1. staminate trees; 2. hermaphroditic trees; 3. trees in which inflorescences abort precociously; 4. sterile trees in which the shoot growth continues later in the season. At the beginning of July, the inflorescences occur at the end of the branch and suppress the vegetative growth of the shoot. Staminate trees and those with aborted inflorescences are characterised by a demand of photosynthetic products reduced early in the season; staminate flowers fall at mid-July and inflorescences abortion occurs in May. On the contrary in the hermaphroditic and sterile trees, the demand of photosynthates remain high later in the season : the stage of fruit maturity is reached in September and the sterile shoot growth is continuing until the mid-October.

For each type of tree, the rate of photosynthesis remain maximum as long as the requirement for photosynthates exist (Fig. 13). In the same way, the activity of extrafloral nectaries varies according to the type of tree. In hermaphroditic and sterile trees, this activity continue later in the season than in staminate trees and those with aborted inflorescences (Fig. 13).

The decline in photosynthetic rate is also associated with the lipid and carbohydrate content of leaves. For instance, starch accumulation preceding lipid accumulation is followed by a marked decrease in photosynthesis (Figs. 13; 14).

Electron microscopic investigations of plastids from leaves of staminate trees and those of trees with aborted inflorescences have also revealed this process of starch and lipid accumulation (Bory, 1983), (Figs. 15; 16).

Variations occuring under controlled conditions

Variations in the secretory activity can be also induced experimentally (Fig. 17). In the case of *Ailanthus* seedlings growing in a greenhouse, it has been demonstrated that the conditions required for an optimal nectar secretion and those required for an optimal photosynthetic rate of leaves are completely similar (Bory and Clair-Maczulajtys, 1978; Bory, 1983; Clair-Maczulajtys, 1984; Bory and Clair-Maczulajtys, 1986). The influence of light intensity and temperature on nectar secretion is particularly evident (Beutler, 1930; Walker *et al.*, 1974; Southwick, 1983). For many plants, a link between rate of photosynthesis and nectar secretion has been also suggested (Huber, 1956; Corbet and Delfosse, 1984).

Influence of water stress

A short period of water stress applied to *Ailanthus* seedlings (5 months old) induces a stimulation of the nectar secretion (Clair-Maczulajtys, 1984). Under these conditions, starch is partially converted into soluble sugars and the level of these components is then particularly high in all parts of the seedling (Dubroca and Bory, 1981). In this case, there is a positive correlation between the temporary soluble sugars excess and the amount of nectar secreted. Recently Pleasants and Chaplin (1983) have expressed a view that the quantity of nectar produced by the individual plant depends of the importance of its available ressources. The positive relationship between root weight and nectar production rate has been also noted by these authors.

Effect of nectaries removal

Partial removal of nectaries from leaflets of *Ailanthus* seedling affects the nectar production rate. According to the results of Bory (1983), this ablation stimulates the nectar secretion in the remaining nectaries. The amount of nectar secreted increases with the number of removed nectaries.

Effect of leaf area reduction

Inversely, the reduction of leaf area by removal of the apical part of the leaflet (devoid of nectaries) induces a decrease in the amount of nectar produced about 30-40% of its original value (Bory, 1983).

Effect of nectar removal

Removal of nectar from foliar nectaries of *Ailanthus* has no effect on total production (Bory, 1983). The same result has been obtained by Pleasants (1983) from the floral nectaries of *Ipomopsis aggregata* in which the nectar was removed periodically to stimulate pollinator visits. In other species, repeated nectar removal can increases (Raw, 1953) or decreases (Corbet and Willmer, 1981) net rates of nectar secretion.

Influence of relative humidity

Experimental changes in ambient relative humidity have no effect on the amount of sugars secreted by extrafloral nectaries of *Ailanthus* but modify the volume of the nectar drop (Bory, 1983). Recent studies have shown that there is a significant negative correlation between nectar solute concentration and relative humidity; the drier the air, the more concentrated the nectar (Corbet, 1978; Southwick *et al.*, 1981; Pleasants, 1983; Corbet and Delfosse, 1984).

VARIATIONS IN THE NUMBER OF EXTRAFLORAL NECTARIES IN *AILANTHUS GLANDULOSA*

Variations occuring under natural conditions

Relations between heterophyllous development and number of nectaries

In all type of trees (described p. 6), starch and soluble sugars stored in the catalphylls are partially used in early stages of heterophyllous development of the shoot (Bory and Clair- Maczulajtys, 1986). The level of soluble sugars is particularly high in the first lowermost fleshly scales (Bory, 1983) which also exhibit a large number of nectaries (Fig. 18). In contrast, during the heterophyllous development of the seedling, the number of nectaries enlarges with the increase in the amount of soluble sugars in the leaves (FIg. 18). The cotyledons which are devoid of nectaries contain only small amount of soluble sugars (Clair-Maczulajtys, 1984).

Relations between reproductive state of tree and number of nectaries

According to the type of tree, the leaves display important differences as regards their size, morphology, cytological features and their amounts of metabolites (Bory, 1983). In the same way, the variations in the number of nectaries are particularly significant (see Table 1).

TABLE 1 : Variations in the number of Extrafloral Nectaries of *Ailanthus gandulosa*

Reproductive state of tree	*Staminate tree*	*Herma-phroditic tree*	*Tree with aborted inflorescences*	*Sterile tree*
Number of nectaries dm^{-2}	18.5	7.7	42.6	11.8
Number of nectaries g^{-1} MS	19.4	8.7	22.9	14.8

Sample size : 10

Variations occuring under experimental conditions

In a recent study, Bory (1983) has shown that the increase or the decrease in available sugars induced variations in the number of extrafloral nectaries.

Experiments allowing to a decrease in available sugars
Cataphylls removal

In spring, when the bud opens, fleshy scales and foliaceous cataphylls represent a lipid and carbohydrate reservoir for the shoot (Clair-Maczulajtys and Bory, 1985). Removal of these cataphylls induces a decrease in the number of nectaries of the new developed leaves (Bory, 1983).

Decrease in light intensity

The growth of *Ailanthus* seedlings (5 months old) can be reduced experimentally by decreasing the light intensity in the greenhouse. The shape of their leaves is then modifyed; they remain composed of three leaflets only. The number of foliar nectaries is also affected by the decrease in light intensity (Fig. 19). Under these conditions, the extrafloral nectaries are reduced in size and their secretory tissue (prismatic parenchyma) is less developed (Clair-Maczulajtys, 1984).

Partial defoliation

The growth of *Ailanthus* seedlings (1 year old) is affected by the removal of completely developed leaves under the terminal bud (Bory and Clair-Maczulajtys, 1986). The new leaves appearing after this partial defoliation show a number of nectaries very reduced (Fig. 20).

Experiments allowing to an increase in available sugars

Nectaries removal

The removal of foliar nectaries from seedlings (5 months old) in active growth induces in increase in the number of nectaries in the following leaves. So, certain leaflets appears multilobate bearing a nectary on each lobe (Fig. 3). This result has been related with the effect of nectaries removal on the increase of available sugars in the leaf (Bory and Clair-Maczulajtys, 1986).

Ringing

Ringing treatment applied to seedlings (5 months old) is followed by photosynthate accumulation allowing to the stimulation of the nectar secretion (Bory and Clair-Maczulajtys, 1986). In addition, the number of extrafloral nectaries is higher in the few leaves developed after the stem has been ringed (untreated seedlings : 15.9 nectaries per dm^2; treated seedlings : 24.5 nectaries per dm^2).

Water stress

The renewal of activity succeeding to a water stress (see p.8) is marked by an important enlargment of the number of nectaries on the new developed leaves (control : 15.9 nectaries per dm^2; water stress : 21.5), (Clair-Maczulajtys, 1984). Therefore, the important increase in soluble sugar content noted by Dubroca and Bory (1981) in response to a water stress influences positively the initiation of foliar nectaries.

The results of these experimental studies suggest that any process allowing to a reduction of carbohydrate metabolism induces also a diminution of the number of foliar nectaries. On the contrary the increase in the photosynthate production or the soluble sugars accumulation have a positive effect on the initiation of foliar nectaries.

EFFECTS ON SHOOT PHYSIOLOGY OF REMOVING NECTARIES FROM LEAVES

At the beginning of July, total removal of nectaries from new shoots of hermaphroditic trees was done. Each 15 days, leaves from treated or untreated shoots were collected. Their photosynthetic activity and their content in starch, soluble sugars and lipids were mesured. The results are given in the Table 2.

In the foliage of treated shoots, accumulation of soluble sugars occurs very rapidly and is succeeded by an increase in starch content. The accumulation of lipids appears much later in the season. The photosynthetic rate declines about 50% by the time the highest starch level is reached. In other respects, starch accumulation is also accompanied by the deformation of chloroplasts of palisade cells (Bory, 1983).

TABLE 2 : Effect of Nectaries Removal on soluble sugar, Starch and lipid content and on Photosynthesis of Leaves from Hermaphroditic Tree *(Ailanthus glandulosa)*. outset of ablations : 1-7-1981.

Dates	*Soluble sugar mg mg^{-1} MS*		*Starch g^{-1} MS*		*Lipids mg g^{-1} MS*		*Photosynthesis mg CO_2 $dm^{-2}h^{-1}$*	
	untreated	*treated*	*untreated*	*treated*	*untreated*	*treated*	*untreated*	*treated*
1/7	65	65	112	112	15.9	15.9	20.1	20.1
15/7	72	90	78	82	16.7	16.4	21.5	20.4
1/8	28	94	77	101	14.9	15.1	20.9	13.2
15/8	31	125	71	117	13.0	14.5	22.7	10.4
1/9	39	137	58	105	14.2	20.9	21.4	10.1
15/9	35	129	61	138	13.3	31.0	23.0	9.5
1/10	86	74	75	112	12.9	38.9	8.7	8.7

Sample size : 6

A possible role of starch in regulating photosynthesis is supported by studies in which a negative correlation between starch content of leaves and their photosynthetic activity has been found (Chatterton *et al.*, 1972). It has been also suggested that starch accumulation may also inhibit photosynthetic reactions physically by disrupting chloroplast lamellar organisation (Throughton, 1975). In contrast, Carmi and Shomer (1979) reported that the accumulation of starch in the chloroplasts is not inevitably a limiting factor in photosynthesis. In *Ailanthus*, we can suppose that the increase in starch content of leaves and the deformation of chloroplasts due to the nectaries removal cause the decrease in photosynthesis. Such a phenomenon contributes to slow down the reconstitution of starch reserves in the branch (Bory and Clair-Maczulajtys, 1986).

Several examples concerning the regulation of sugars status of the plant have been reported by Helder (1958). The function of extrafloral nectaries of *Gossypium* has been interpreted as being the elimination of excess hexoses (Mound, 1962). In this species, Butler *et al.* (1972), Elmore *et al.* (1977) have also suggested that nectaries may compete with the developing fruits for nutrients. In this case, nectar secretion represents a loss of sugars for the plant. On the contrary, extrafloral nectaris of *Ailanthus* preventing sugars accumulation in leaves permit the maintenance of high photosynthetic efficiency.

CONCLUSIONS

The different observations and experiments relating to the function of extrafloral nectaries of *Ailanthus glandulosa* are summarised in the diagram 21 A-C.

It seems clear that the activity of foliar nectaries is correlated with the occurence of a requirement for photosynthetic assimilates. When the requirement is very high (vegetative growth, flowering or fruits development), photosynthates are exported to the different sinks (and not stored) and the photosynthetic rate remain maximum. The nectar secretion is equally important (Fig. 21A). If the requirement for assimilates is reduced suddenly by cessation of vegetative growth or inflorescence abortion, an irreversible accumulation of starch occurs in the leaves (Fig. 21B). Although the nectar secretion is stimulated at the outset, extrafloral nectaries acting as "sap valves" do not succeed in preventing this accumulation. This phenomenon suggests the existence of another mechanism independent of the secretory process which prevent starch hydrolysis.

The total ablation of foliar nectaries on the shoot leads to a starch accumulation in the leaves. The important decline in photosynthetic rate occuring under these conditions slows down the reconstitution of starch reserves in the shoot (fig. 21 C). So, the extrafloral nectaries permitting the elimination of excess sugars play an appreciable role in the regulation of photosynthesis.

Explanation to Figures

FIGS. 1–7 : Distribution and morphology of extrafloral nectaries of *Ailanthus glandulosa* (*f*, fleshy scale; *g*, glandular hairs *l*, leaflets; *ls*, leaf- shaped cataphylls; *n*, nectary, *nh*, non glandular hairs; *p*, pore; *s*, stalk; *st*, stomata ; *v*, secondary vein). Fig. 1. Pinnate leaves of seedling. x o,2. Fig. 2. When the bud opens, marginal nectaries occur on flexhy scales. x 0,8. Fig. 3. Increase in the number of nectaries under experimental conditions. x 1,2. Fig. 4. Stalked nectary x 110. Fig. 5. Detail of the margin of fleshy scales. x 50. Fig. 6. Scanning electron micrograph of foliar nectary. x 36. Fig. 7. Connection between nectary and venation of the leaflet (cleared with chloralphenol). x 70.

1
l
l
2
ls
n
f
f
f
n
n
n
v
4
p
s
nh
5
n
n
g
g
nh
6
P
st
7
P

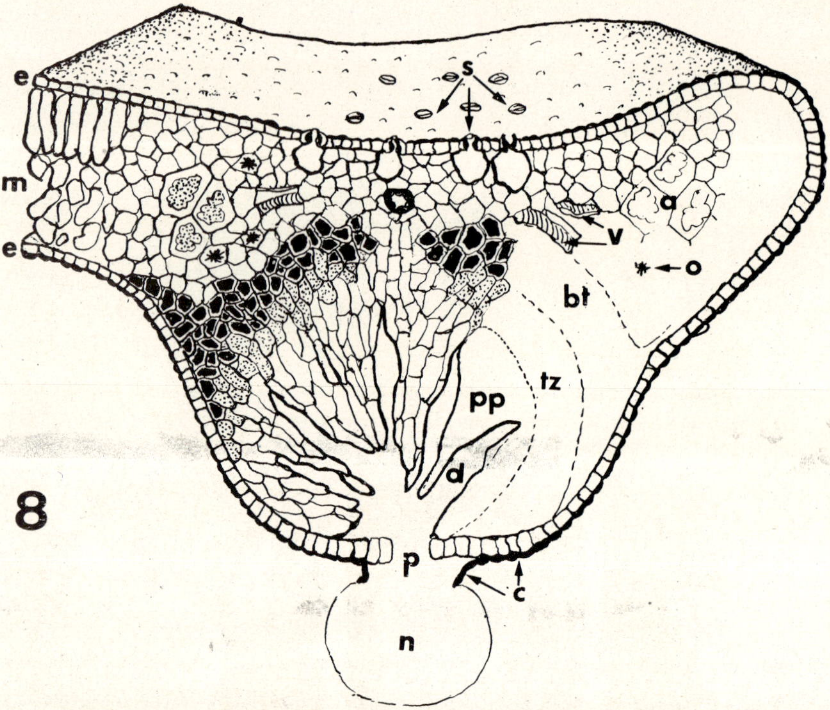

8

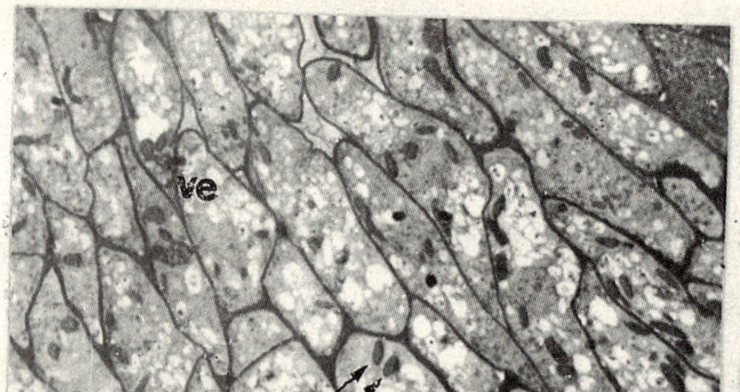

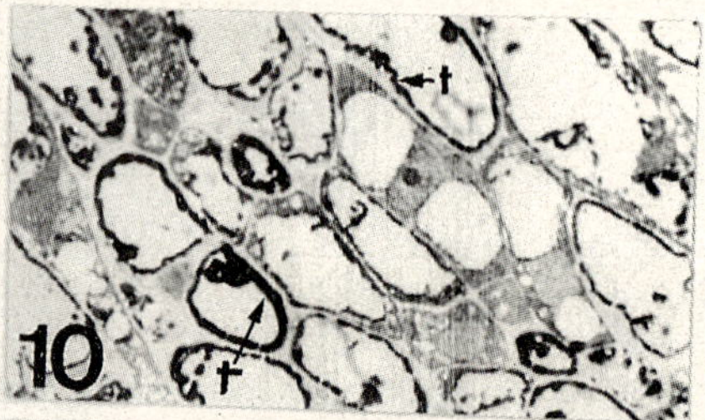

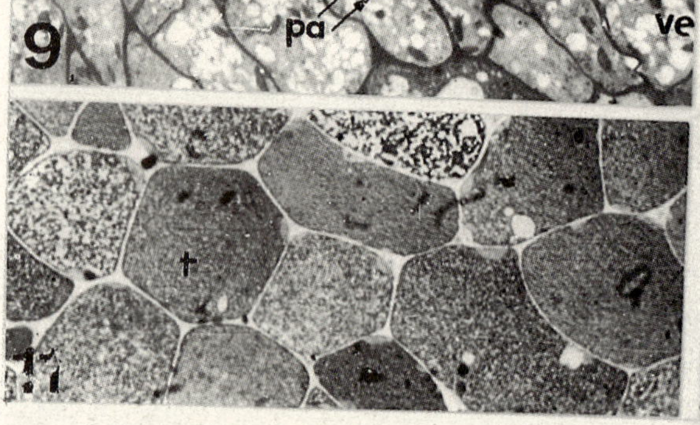

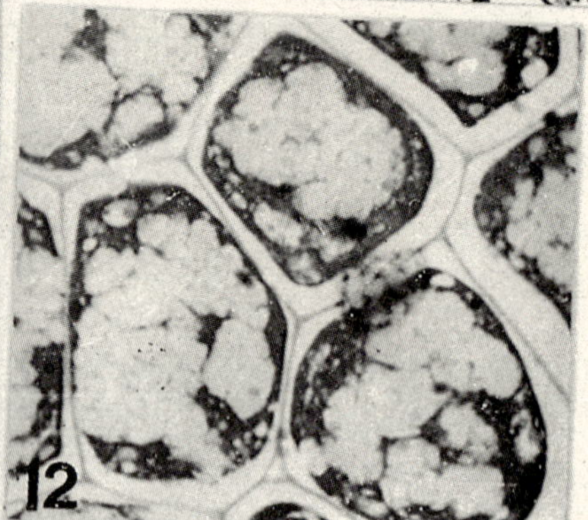

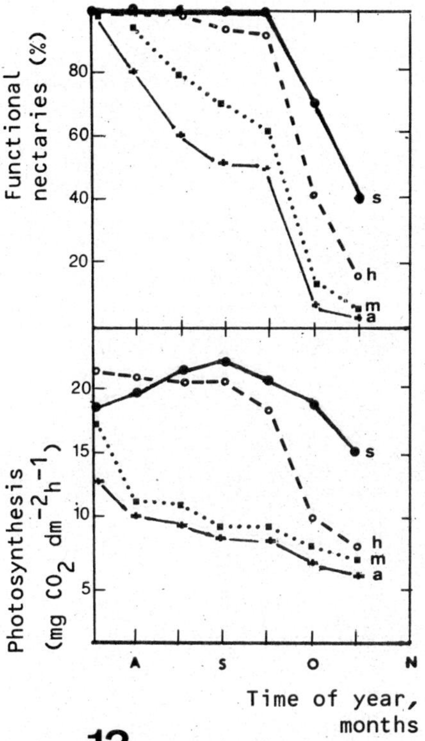

Functional nectaries (%)
80
60
40
20
s
h
m
a
Photosynthesis (mg CO_2 dm^{-2} h^{-1})
20
15
10
5
s
h
m
a
A
S
O
N
Time of year, months

13

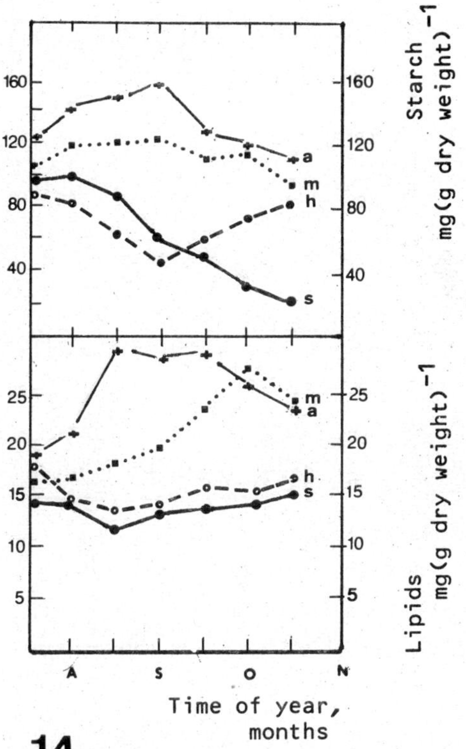

160
120
80
40
a
m
h
s
Starch mg(g dry weight)$^{-1}$
25
20
15
10
5
m
a
h
s
Lipids mg(g dry weight)$^{-1}$
A
S
O
N
Time of year, months

14

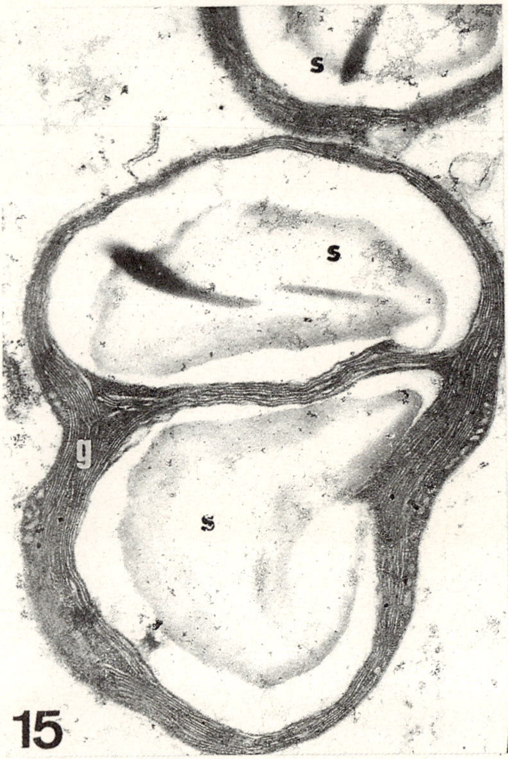
s
s
g
s
15

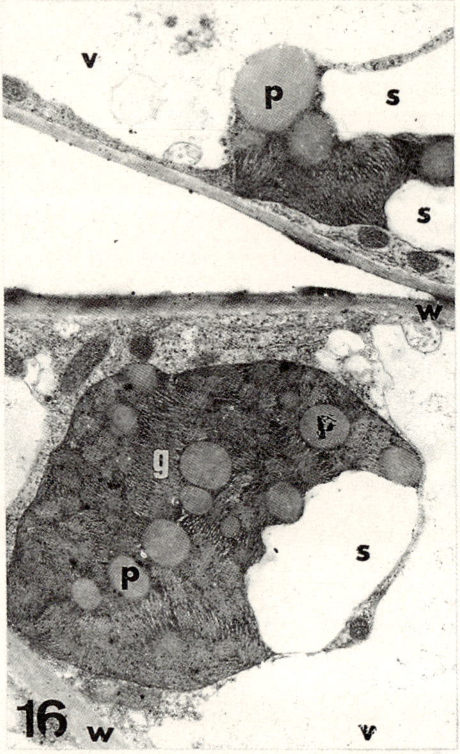
v
p
s
s
w
g
p
p
s
16
w
v

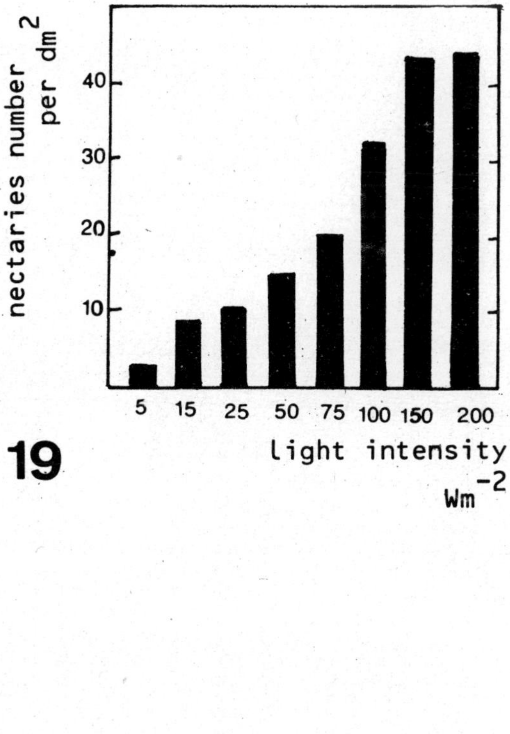
nectaries number per dm2
40
30
20
10
5
15
25
50
75
100
150
200
light intensity
Wm-2

19

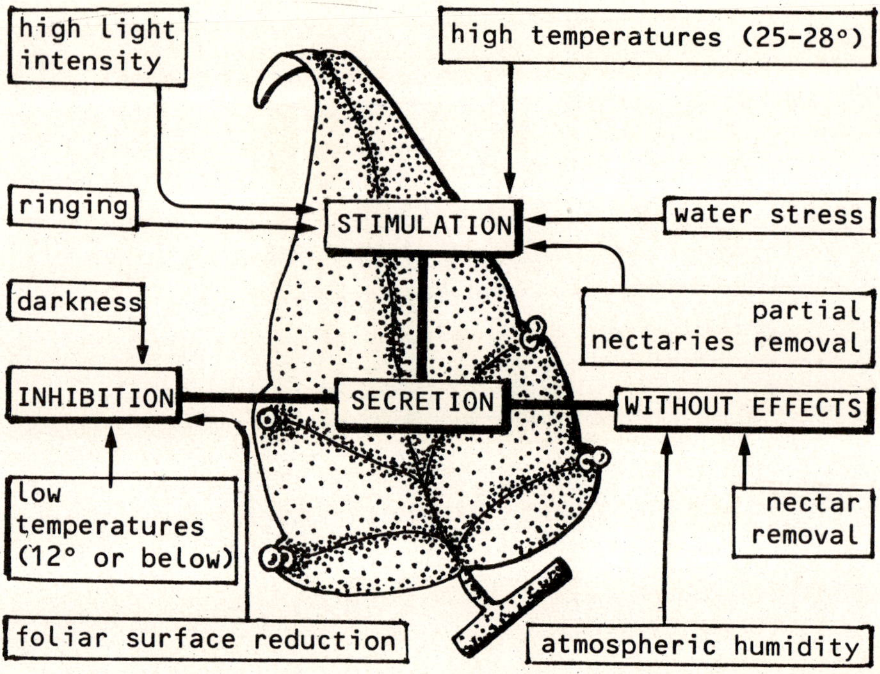
high light intensity
high temperatures (25-28°)
ringing
STIMULATION
water stress
partial nectaries removal
darkness
INHIBITION
SECRETION
WITHOUT EFFECTS
low temperatures (12° or below)
nectar removal
foliar surface reduction
atmospheric humidity

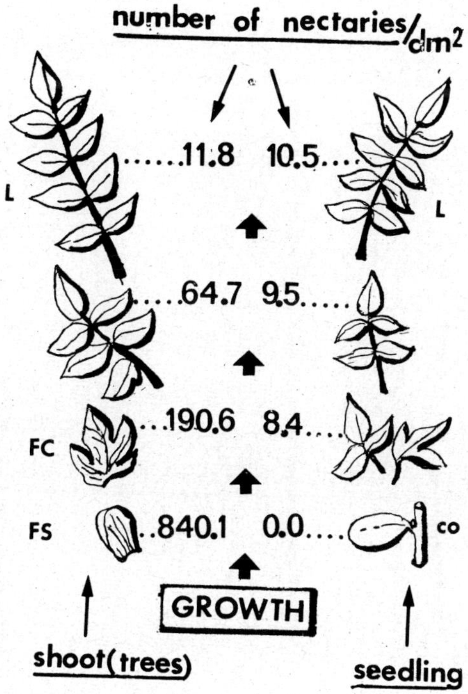

number of nectaries/dm2
L
......11.8
10.5....
L
....64.7
9.5.....
FC
...190.6
8.4....
FS
..840.1
0.0....
co
GROWTH
shoot(trees)
seedling

18

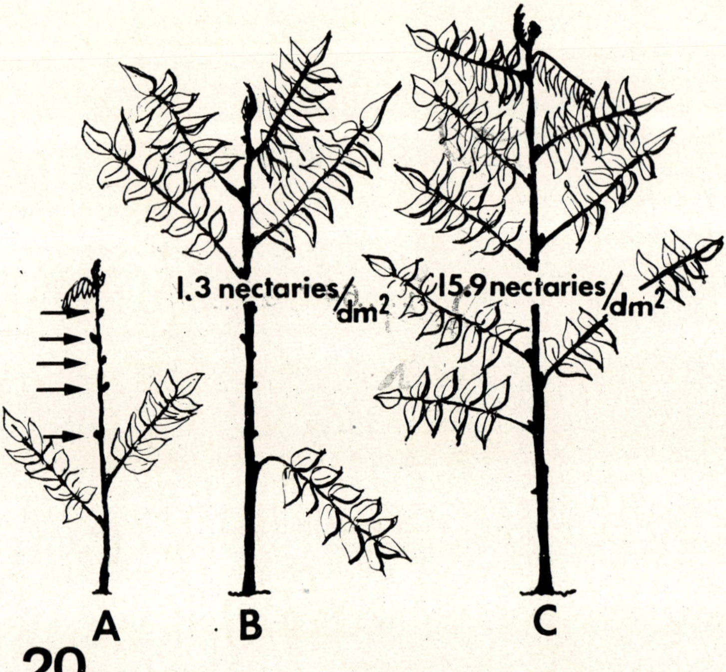

20

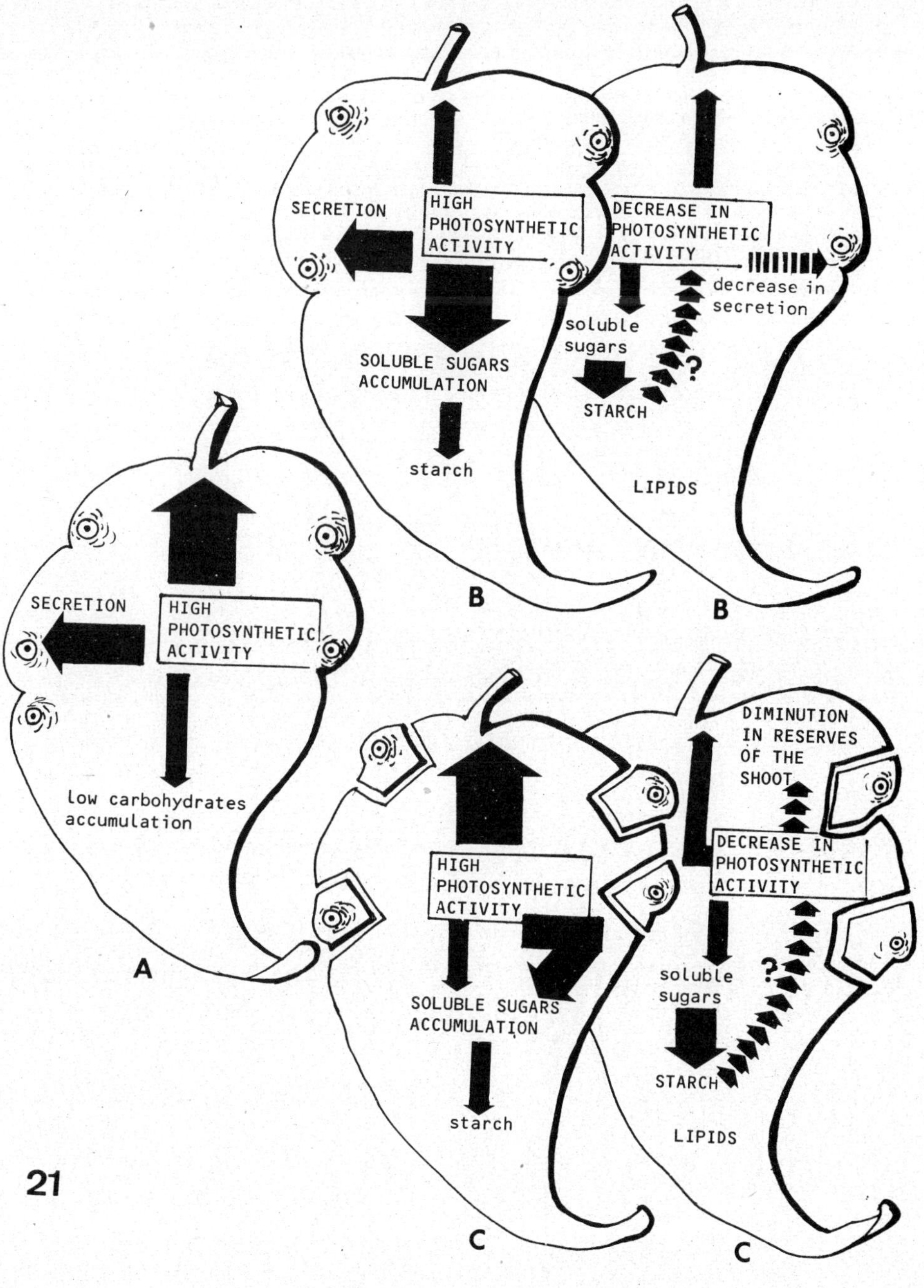
SECRETION
HIGH PHOTOSYNTHETIC ACTIVITY
SOLUBLE SUGARS ACCUMULATION
starch
B
DECREASE IN PHOTOSYNTHETIC ACTIVITY
decrease in secretion
soluble sugars
?
STARCH
LIPIDS
B
SECRETION
HIGH PHOTOSYNTHETIC ACTIVITY
low carbohydrates accumulation
A
HIGH PHOTOSYNTHETIC ACTIVITY
SOLUBLE SUGARS ACCUMULATION
starch
C
DIMINUTION IN RESERVES OF THE SHOOT
DECREASE IN PHOTOSYNTHETIC ACTIVITY
soluble sugars
?
STARCH
LIPIDS
C

21

FIGS. 8–12 : Anatomy and cytology of foliar nectaries of *Ailanthus glandulosa* (*a*, alkaloid-containing cells; *bt*, belt of tannin-containing cells; *c*, cuticle; *d*, schizo-lysigenous ducts; *e*, epidermis; *m*, mesophyll; *n* nectar; *o*, calcium oxalate cells; *p*, pore; *pa*; plastids; *pp*, prismatic parenchyma; *s*, stomata; *t*, tannins; *tz*, transition zone; *v*, vascular system; *ve* vesicles). Fig. 8 Longitudinal section of foliar nectary showing histological zones. x 60. Fig. 9. Detail of prismatic parenchyma composed of elongated glandular cells. x 550. Fig. 10. Cells of the transition zone. x 550. Fig. 11. Alkaloid-containing cells. x 400. Fig. 12. Details of tannin-containing cells. x 550.

FIG. 13 : Seasonal changes in photosynthesis and extrafloral nectaries activity of the different types of trees of *Ailanthus glandulosa* (*a*, tree with aborted inflorescences; *h*, hermaphroditic tree; *m*, staminate tree; *2* sterile tree).

FIG. 14 : Seasonal changes in lipid and starch content of leaves of the different types of trees of *Ailanthus glandulosa* (*a*, tree with aborted inflorescences; *h*, hermaphroditic tree; *m*, staminate tree; *s* sterile tree).

FIGS. 15–16 : Electron micrographs of plastids of palisade cells of leaves from tree with aborted inflorescences in *Ailanthus glandulosa* (*g*, grana; *p*, plastoglobuli; *s* starch; *v* vacuole; *w*, wall). Fig. 15. Plastid showing large starch grains. x 12000. Fig. 16. Plastid containing starch and numerous plastoglobuli. x 10000.

FIG. 17 : Diagram summarizing the variations in the secretory activity of extrafloral nectaries of *Ailanthus glandulosa* under experimental conditions (From Bory, 1983; Bory and Clair- Maczulajtys, 1986).

FIG. 18 : Variations in the number o extrafloral nectaries occuring in the course of heterophyllous development of tree shoot and seedling of *Ailanthus glandulosa* (*co*, cotyledon; *fc* foliaceous cataphyll; *fs*, fleshy scale; *l*, leaf).

FIG. 19 : Effect of light intensity on the number of extrafloral nectaries of *Ailanthus glandulosa* seedling (5 months old). *Sample size* : 10.

FIG. 20A–C : Influence of partial defoliation on the number of extrafloral nectaries in *Ailanthus glandulosa* seedling (1 year old). A. defoliation under apical bud (arrows). B : treated seedling. C : untreated seedling. (*sample size* : 5).

FIG. 20D : Clair-Maczulajtys et G. Bory — "Observations on the physiological function of ext. n. of *Ailanthus glandulosa*.

FIG. 21A–C : Diagram summarizing the results relating to the function of extrafloral nectaries of *Ailanthus glandulosa*. A : high requirement for assimilates; B : low requirement for assimilates; C : total ablation of foliar nectaries.

Literature Cited

Bahadur, B., Arthi, C. and Ramaswamy, N. 1986. Nectar types in Indian plants. *Proc. Indian Acad. Sci.* (Plant Sci.), *96* : 41-48.

Baker, D.A.; Hall, J.L. & Thorpe, J.R. 1978. A study of the extrafloral nectaries of *Ricinus communis*. *New Phytol., 81* : 129-137.

Baker, H.G. 1975. Sugar concentrations in nectars from hummingbird flowers. *Biotropica*, *7* : 37-41.

Baker, H.G. & Baker, I. 1975. Studies of nectar constitution and pollinator-plant coevolution. *In*: (eds). Gilbert, E. & Raven, P.H. *Coevolution of Animals and Plants*. pp.100-140. University of Texas Press, Austin.

Baker, H.G. & Baker, I. 1983. Floral nectar constituents in relation to pollinator type. *In*: (eds). Jones, C.E. & Little, R.J. *Handbook of Experimental Pollination Biology*. Van Nostrand Reinhdold Co. Inc. New York.

Baker, I. & Baker, H.G. 1979. Sugar ratios in nectars. *Phytochem. Bull., 12* : 43-45.

Beckmann, R.L. & Stanley, J.M. 1981. Extrafloral nectaries and plant guarding in *Ipomoea pandurata* (Convolvulaceae). *Amer. J. Bot., 68* : 72-79.

Bentley, B.L. 1976. Plant bearing extrafloral nectaries and the associated ant community : interhabitat differences in the reduction of herbivore damage. *Ecology, 57* : 815-820.

Bentley, B.L. 1977. Extrafloral nectaries and protection by pugnacious bodyguards. *Annu. Rev. Ecol. Syst., 8* : 407-427.

Beutler, R. 1930. Biologisch-chemische Untersuchungen am Nektar von Immenblumen. *Z. Vergl. Physiol., 12* : 72-172.

Beutler, R. & Schontag, A. 1940. Über die Nektarabscheidung einiger Nutzpflanzen. *Z. Vergl. Physiol., 28* : 254-285.

Bonnier, G. 1878. *Les nectaires. Ann. Sci. Nat. Bot. Biol. Veg., 8* : 1-206.

Bory, G. 1983. Quelques aspects de la biologie de l'*Ailanthus altissima* (Mill.) Swingle. Mouvements de metabolites, croissance, developpement, sécrétion et floraison chez divers types d'arbres. Thése Doctorat d'Etat Univ. Paris 7, Paris, France.

Bory, G. & Clair-Maczulajtys, D. 1978. Morphologies et développement des glands foliaires chez l'*Ailanthus glandulosa* Desf. (Simarubacées). *Revue gén. Bot., 85* : 137-157.

Bory, G. & Clair-Maczulajtys, D. 1981. Morphology, ontogeny and cytology of trichomes of *Ailanthus altissima*. *Phytomorphology, 30* : 67-78.

Bory, G & Clair-Maczulajtys, D. 1986. Composition du neetar et role des nectaires extrafloraux chez l' *Ailanthus glandulosa*. *Can J.Bot., 64* : 247-253.

Brink, D. & De Wet, J.M.J. 1980. Interpopulation variation in nectar production in *Aconitum columbianum* (Ranunculaceae). *Oecologia, 47* : 160-163.

Butler, G.D.; Loper, G.M.; Mc Gregor, S.E.; Webster, J.L. & Margolis, H. 1972. Amounts and kinds of sugars in the nectars of cotton (*Gossypium* spp) and the time of their secretion. *Agron. J., 64* : 364-368.

Carmi, A. & Shomer, I. 1979. Starch accumulation and photosynthetic activity in primary leaves of Bean (*Phaseolus vulgaris* L.). *Ann. Bot., 44* : 479-484.

Chatterton, N.J.; Carlson, G.N.; Hungerford, W.E. & Lee, D.R. 1972. Effect of tillering and cool nights on photosynthesis and chloroplast starch in *Pangola*. *Crop. Sci., 12* : 206-8.

Clair-Maczulajtys, D. 1984. Quelques aspects de la biologie de l'*Ailanthus altissima* (Mill.) Swingle. Etude de la double stratégie de reproduction par graines et par drageonnement en relation avec les métabolites de réserve. Thése Doctorat d'Etat Univ. Paris 7, Paris, France.

Clair-Maczulajtys, D. & Bory, G. 1982. Invasion and destruction of extrafloral nectaries in *Ailanthus altissima* by sooty moulds. *Phytomorphology, 32* : 206-211.

Clair-Maczulajtys, D. & Bory, G. 1985. Evolution de la composition lipidique des cataphylles chez *Ailanthus glandulosa* au cours de l'ouverture du bourgeon. *Physiol. Vég., 23* : 275-282.

Clair-Maczulajtys, D. & Bory, G. 1983. Les nectaires pédicellés chez l'*Ailanthus glandulosa. Can. J. Bot., 61* : 683-691.

Corbet, S.A. 1978. Bee visits and the nectar of *Echium vulgare* L. and *Sinapis alba* L. *Ecol. Ent., 3* : 25-37.

Corbet, S.A.; Unwin, D.M. & Prys-Jone, O.E. 1979a. Humidity, nectar and insect visits fo flowers with special reference to *Crataegus, Tilia* and *Echium*. *Ecol. Ent., 4* : 9-22.

Corbet, S.A.; Willmer, P.G.; Beament, J.W.L.; Unwin, D.M. & Prys-Jone, O.E. 1979b. Post secretory determinants of sugar concentration in nectar. *Plant Cell Environ., 2* : 293-308.

Corbet, S.A. & Willmer, P.G. 1981. The nectar of *Justicia* and *Columnea* : composition and concentration in a humid tropical climate. *Oecologia, 51* : 412-418.

Corbet, S.A. & Delfosse, E.S. 1984. Honeybees and the nectar of *Echium plantagineum* L. in southeastern Australia. Aust. *J. Ecol., 9* : 125-139.

Dubroca, E. & Bory, G. 1981. Composés glucidiques et azotés et résistance à la sécheresse chez *Ailanthus altissima. Biochem. Syst. Ecol., 9* : 283-288.

Elias, T.S. & Gelband, H. 1975. Nectar : its production and functions in trumpet creeper. *Science, 189* : 289-291.

Elmore, C.D.; Meredith, W.R.; King, E.E. & Ranney, C.D. 1977. Effect of the nectariless trait on cotton seed protein and amino acid composition. *Crop. Sci., 17* : 687-689.

Fahn, A. 1979. *Secretory Tissues in Plants*. Academic Press, New York.

Findlay, N.; Reed, M.L. & Mercer, F.V. 1971. Nectar production in *Abutilon*. III. Sugar secretion. *Aust. J. Biol. Sci., 24* : 665-675.

Frey-Wissling, A. 1933. Über die extrafloralen Nektarien von *Hevea brasiliensis Ber. Schweiz. Bot. Ges., 42* : 109-122.

Gaillochet, J. Y Faucher, M. 1982. Le nectaire du *Cassia fasciculata* Mich. et son influence sur les mouvements foliaires. *Bull. Soc. bot. Fr., Actual. bot., 129* : 41-45.

Helder, R.J. 1958. The excretion of carbohydrates (nectaries). *Handb. Pflanzenphysiol., 4* : 978-996.

Hespenheide, H.A. 1985. Insect visitors to extrafloral nectaries of *Byttneria aculeata* (Sterculiaceae) : relative importance and roles. *Ecol. Ent., 10* : 191-204.

Huber, H. 1956. Die Abhangigkeit der Nektarsekretion von Temperatur, Luft-und Bodenfeuchtigkeit. *Planta, 38* : 47-98.

Keeler, K.H. 1977. The extrafloral nectaries of *Ipomea carnaea* (Convolvulaceae). *Am. J. Bot., 64* : 1182-1188.

Koptur, S. 1980. Multiple role of extrafloral nectar production in *Inga spp*. (Fabaceae : Mimosoideae). *Bull. Ecol. Soc. Am., 61* : 100.

Koptur, S. 1981. Antiherbivore defenses in *Inga spp* (Fabaceae : Mimosoideae). Ant protection, chemical protection and defense by the third trophic level. *Bull. Ecol. Soc. Am., 62* : 99.

Lüttge, U. 1977. Nectar composition and membrane transport of sugars and aminoacids : A review on the present state of nectar research. *Apidology, 8* : 305-319.

Lüttge, U. & Schnepf, E. 1976. Organic substances. *In*: (eds.) Lüttge, U. & Pitman, M.G. *Encyclopedia of Plant Physiology*. Vol. 2B : Springer-Verlag. Berlin.

Maheshwari, J.K. & Chakrabarty, B. 196. Foliar nectaries of *Clerodendron japonicum* Sweet. *Phytomorphology, 16* : 75-90.

Meyber, M. & Kristen, U. 1981. The nectaries of *Aptenia cordifolia*. Ultrastructure, translocation of ^{14}C-labelled sugars and a possible pathway of secretion. *Z. Pflanzenphysiol., 104* : 139-147.

Mound, L.A. 1962. Extrafloral nectaries of cotton and their secretions. *Cotton Grow. Rev., 39* : 256-261.

Percival, M.S. 1961. Types of nectars in angiosperms. *New Phytol., 60* : 235-281.

Pleasants, J.M. 1983. Nectar production patterns in *Ipomopsis aggregata* (Polemoniaceae). *Amer. J. Bot., 70* : 1468-1475.

Pleasants, J.M. & Chaplin, S.J. 1983. Nectar production rates of *Asclepias quadrifolia* : causes and consequences of individual variation. *Oecologia* (Berlin), *59* : 232-238.

Pyke, G.H. & Waser, N.M. 1981. The production of dilute nectars by hummingbird and honey eater flowers. *Biotropica, 13* : 260-270.

Raw, G.R. 1953. The effect on nectar secretion of removing nectar from flowers. *Bee Word, 34* : 23-26.

Reed, M.L.; Findlay, N. & Mercer, F.V. 1971. Nectar production in *Abutilon*. IV. Water and solute relations. Aust. *J. Biol. Sci., 24* : 677-688.

Southwick, E.E. 1983. Nectar biology and nectar feeders of common milkweed, *Asclepias syriaca* L. *Bull. Torrey Bot. Club, 110* : 324-334.

Southwick, E.E. 1984. Photosynthate allocation of floral nectar : a neglected energy investment. *Ecology., 65* : 1775-1779.

Southwick, E.E.; Loper, G.M. & Sadwick, S.E. 1981. Nectar production, composition, energetics and pollinator attractiveness in spring flowers of western New-York. *Amer. J. Bot., 68* : 994-1002.

Thyri, H. 1978. Faktorer som Pavirker Nektar produksjonen hos Rosslying (*Calluna vulgaris*). (Factors affecting nectar production in *Calluna vulgaris*). *Agr. Univ. Norway, Inst. Beekeeping Beebreeding Rept., 62* : 447-458.

Troughton, J.H. 1975. *Photosynthesis and Productivity in Different Environnements.* (ed.) Cooper, J.P. Cambridge Universily Press, London.

Walker, A.K.; Barnes, D.K. & Furgula, B. 1974. Genetic and environmental effects on quantity and quality of alfalfa nectar. *Crop Sci., 14* : 235-238.

Willson, M.F. & Bertin, R.I. 1979. Flowers visitors, nectar production and inflorescences size in *Asclepias syriaca. Can. J. Bot., 57* : 1380-1388.

Willson, M.F., Bertin, R.J. & Price, P.W. 1979. Nectar production and flowers visitors of *Asclepias verticillata. Am. Midland Naturalist, 102* : 23-35.

Wykes, G.R. 1952. An investigation of the sugars present in the nectar of flowers of various species. *New Phytol., 51* : 210-215.

Ziegler, J. 1965. Die Physiologies pflanzlicher Drüsen. *Ber. dt. bot. Ges., 78* : 466-477.

Zimmermann, M. 1953. Papierchromatographische Untersuchungen über die pflanzliche Zuckersekretion. *Ber. Schweiz. Bot. Ges., 63* : 402-429.

DYNAMICS OF PRODUCTION AND EXPLOITATION OF NECTAR : LESSONS FROM *IMPATIENS GLANDULIFERA* ROYLE.

ALBERTO BÚRQUEZ[1, 2] and SARAH A. CORBET[1]

[1]Department of Applied Biology, Pembroke St
Cambridge, CB2 3DX, England.

[2]Instituto de Biología, Departamento de Ecología
Universidad Nacional Autónoma de México
México 04510, DF. México.

ABSTRACT

This review explores the dynamic patterns in the secretion, reabsorption and concentration of nectar, and their relation with microclimate, flower visitors and the innervation of the nectary. Himalayan balsam (*Impatiens glandulifera* Royle) is used an example. Nectar secretion rates and nectar concentration are affected by the environment, and probably by the genetic composition of the plants. Significant differences in nectar secretion rate and nectar concentration are found between plants, within times of the day and between days, but not among flowers in the same plant. Correlation matrices and correlograms help us to disentangle multiple interactions. The factors most likely to affect nectar secretion rate in *Impatiens* seem to be air temperature and stand age (probably acting through the relative sink strength of the flowers); nectar concentration seems to depend mainly on the relative humidity of the air. Other factors probably play a role, but their effects are obscured by complex physiological interactions. We conclude that in a given plant the nectar secretion rate will depend mainly on its physiological age, and on variations in air temperature, while the nectar solute concentration at a given moment will be mainly the product of the short-term plant-microclimate interaction. In this context, constraints on the evolution of nectar presentation systems are considered.

Key words: Nectar; dynamics of production, exploitation; *Impatiens glandulifera* Royle.

INTRODUCTION

The spectrum of flower visitors to be found on a given species of flower varies from place to place, from day to day and even from hour to hour. To some extent this variation can be related to spatial or temporal patterns in the activity of the visitor species, or to their direct responses to microclimatic change. But foraging activity is influenced also by changes in the rewards available in the flowers. Nectar is one such reward. Changes in its nature and abundance result from the effects of environmental change on the nectar itself and on patterns of secretion and reabsorption, as influenced by the physiology of the whole plant. Here we explore the nature and causation of changes in the abundance and concentration of nectar, and the consequences of those changes for flower visitors, focusing on one species of flower, the Himalayan balsam, *Impatiens glandulifera* Royle. Correlations emerging form the analysis of several all-day sequences of field observations and measurements gave clues about causation. Some of these clues have been examined further by field experimentation.

The Plant and its Flowers

Impatiens glandulifera (= *I. royleii* Walpers; Balsaminaceae) is a tall annual herb introduced in the middle of the last century from the Himalayas and now naturalized, often along riven banks and on waste ground, in the British Isles and much of Europe. Its ecology, distribution and pollination biology have been described by Coombe (1956), Lhotska and Kopecky (1966), Daumann (1967) and Valentine (1978). In Cambridge, flowering lasts from mid August until frosts kill the senescent plants in October or November. Our study took place in August and September 1985 and 1986 in a large (100 m^2) plot in the Cambridge University Botanic Garden and in a natural population beside the River Cam at Grantchester, near Cambridge.

The flowers (Fig. 1) are zygomorphic with a saccate sepal which forms a large chamber into which visiting bees crawl, and almost disappear. this sepal ends in a spur lined with nectariferous tissue similar to that described for *I. sultanii* by Bahadur, Chaturvedi and Swamy (1986). Vascular strands run dorsally forming a thick vein which supplies the nectary.

A typical flower life history begins in the early morning, between 0400 and 0900 hr GMT, when most of the flowers open. Soon the anthers dehisce, releasing sticky pollen, which is usually exhausted by the early afternoon (about 1500 hr GMT). At this stage the stamens still cover the stigma and ovary. The next day the androecium is shed, exposing the stigma. Later that day, from the afternoon onwards, the perianths begin to fall. This floral behaviour can be described as protandrous dichogamy, with a male phase lasting 24-36 hr and a brief female phase lasting 3-12 hours. We recognize four stages of flowering, from newly opened flowers to flowers with the stigma exposed.

Flower visitors

Visitor abundance was assessed by regular counts along a transect 24 m long and 1 m wide. Flower visitors comprised a varied fauna (Table 1), in which the Hymenoptera were most important, both in abundance and in number of species. Species differed widely in the timing of their foraging activity. Visitor density increased rapidly in the early morning, exploiting the accumulated standing crop of nectar. Density remained high until the evening, when it fell equally rapidly. Wasps were the first visitors to arrive early in the morning, but were absent for the rest of the day. Soon afterwards came bumblebees (especially *Bombus pascuorum*) and, later in the day, honeybees, *Apis mellifera*. At night, noctuid moths were observed. Other species were usually less abundant, and more variable in their numbers from day to day (Fig. 2). Syrphid flies licked the leaves, perhaps for extrafloral nectar (Weber, 1951) or honeydew, but they rarely visited the flowers. The beetles were seen visiting flowers only in the male stage.

TABLE 1 : Visitors to *Impatiens glandulifera* in Cambridge. The starred spcies were seen carrying pollen, and visiting flowers in both male and female stages.

Hymenoptera	*Bombus pascuorum* Scopoli*
	B. terrestris L*
	B. lucorum L*
	B. Lapidarius L*
	B.pratorum L*
	B. hortorum L*
	Psithyrus vestalis (Geoffroy in Fourcroy)*
	Vespula germanica L*
	Apis mellifera L*
Diptera	*Episyrphus balteatus* DeGeer
	at least 2 unidentified species of Syrphidae
Lepidoptera	*Autographa gamma* L
	at least 3 unidentified species of Noctuidae
Coleoptera	*Meligethes* sp.

Nectar and microclimate

Methods

Nectar was sampled with 1 and 5 mm^3 disposable microcapillaries (Camlab, Cambridge) or, for larger volumes, autoclavable nylon tubing of 0.5 mm internal diameter (Portex, Hythe, Kent). Solute concentration was measured at once in the field using pocket refractometers modified for small samples (Bellingham and Stanley, Tunbridge Wells), and expressed as percentage sucrose (g sucrose per 100 g solution). The sugar content of nectar was calculated after converting this to concentration by volume (Bolten *et al.*, 1980), using the following quadratic equation

$$S = C\,(0.009224) + C^2\,(5.96 \,.\, 10\text{-}5) + 0.007081$$

where S is sucrose concentration by volume and C is solute concentration in g sucrose equivalents per 100 g solution. This equation gives an error of less than 1% for values of nectar solute concentration between 10% and 80%. Flower visitors were excluded from some flowers by 2.5 mm mesh nylon gauze bags, which had no measurable effect on the temperature and relative humidity inside the flowers. Patterns of secretion were examined by taking samples repeatedly from bagged flowers at regular intervals through the day from 0430 to 2200 hr GMT. At the same time, continuous measurements of air temperature at flower height, total irradiance and photosynthetically active radiation were taken using a data logger equipped with thermistor probes (Grant Instruments, Barrington, Cambridge) and pairs of tube solarimeters oriented at right angles (Delta-T, Burwell, Cambridge). Relative humidity at flower height was measured at each sampling time with a Vaisala thermohygrometer. At hourly intervals, leaf temperature and leaf diffusive resistance were measured with a diffusion porometer (Delta-T mark II), and leaf thickness, as an index of plant water status, was measured with a spring-loaded micrometer (Búrquez, 1987). The analysis described here is based on 10 all-day studies of this kind, and 12 additional days with observations for part of the day.

Secretion and reabsorption

In *I. glandulifera* nectar was secreted from early morning to late evening, with a maximum rate at midday (Fig. 3). Secretion was almost undetectable (% of peak rate) at night. Analysis of variance indicated marked variation in nectar secretion rate between days, even when only midday values are taken ($F_{(8, 564)} = 23.42$; $P << 0.0001$), with time of the day, and between plants, but not between flowers on the same plant nor between different floral stages (Table 2; Fig. 3; Fig. 5).

TABLE 2 : Anlalysis of variance showing the effects of time of the day, floral stage, plant, and flower on the rate and concentration of nectar in *Impatiens glandulifera*, ns = not significant; asterisks indicate P (0.0005).

Nectar secretion rate Source	SS	DF	MS	F	P
Main effects	14.63	18	0.81	12.16	***
Time of day	4.01	6	0.67	10.00	***
Floral stage	0.44	3	0.15	2.17	ns
Plant	8.29	6	1.38	20.68	***
Flower	0.09	3	0.03	0.43	ns
Residual	21.18	116	0.18		
Nectar concentration Source	**SS**	**DF**	**MS**	**F**	**P**
Main effects	166.68	19	8.77	37.65	***+
Time of day	121.46	7	17.35	74.36	***+
Floral stage	5.10	3	1.70	7.30	***
Plant	6.72	6	1.12	4.80	***
Flower	0.65	3	0.22	0.93	ns
Residual	190.45	121	0.23		

If nectar left in the flowers were reabsorbed, frequent repeated sampling over a period would yield more nectar than a single sample taken at the end of the period. In *I. glandulifera* we could find no significant difference in the cumulative amounts of nectar sugar yielded by bagged flowers sampled every 3 hr or once only at the time of abscission ($\overline{X}$ = 27.7 mg sugar (± 2.0 SE, n = 22) and $\overline{X}$ = 25.1 mg sugar (± 2.5 SE, n = 17), respectively; $F_{(1, 37)} = 0.46$; $P > 0.05$), nor differences in the expected direction between the nectar secretion rates at midday in flowers sampled every 3 hr or every 15 min ($\overline{X}$ = 0.71 mg sugar h^{-1} (± 0.26 SE, n = 43), and $\overline{X}$ = 0.56 mg sugar h^{-1} (± 0.29 SE, n = 41) respectively; $F_{(1, 82)} = 6.41$; $P < 0.05$). Thus we found no evidence for reabsorption in this species.

The standing crop of nectar in unprotected flowers was too small to measure for most of the day (probably because of removal by visitors). Nectar volume slowly increased after sunset, reaching about 2 µl per flower by the next morning, and concentration decreased from about 40% in the evening to 20% in the early morning. Total sugar content increased only slightly during this period. In the early morning and late evening, when major pollinators were absent, secretion rates were low, and little sugar could accumulate.

Solute concentration

The solute concentration varied from day-to day, even when midday mean concentration is used ($F_{(8, 547)} = 30.39$; $P < 0.0001$). with time of the day, and from one plant to another, and between floral stages, but did not show significant differences between flowers on the same plant (Table 2, Fig. 3; Fig. 5). In general, concentrations were low in the early morning (about 20-30%), rose towards midday to a maximum of 60%, and then fell slowly towards evening. The diel solute concentration curve closely followed the curve of relative humidity (Fig. 5).

Correlations

Within-day correlations

A matrix of Pearson correlation coefficients shows that all the environmental and physiological variables are highly correlated with one another. To allow for delayed responses, the matrix includes

TABLE 3 : Pearson product-moment correlation matrix showing the association of the nectar solute concentration (NC) and nectar secretion rate (NSR) with several environmental factors in *Impatiens glandulifera* flowers. NSR and NC were shifted by half, 1, 2, 3, and 4 hours to allow for delays in response [$n_{(t_0)} = 17$].

TIME LAG (hrs)	0		1/2		1		2		3		4	
	NC	NSR	NC	NSR	NC	NSR	NC	NSR	NC	NSR	NC	NSR
NECTAR CONCENTRATION (NC)	—	0.94	—	0.83	—	0.79	—	0.46	—	0.13	—	–0.12
NECTAR SECRETION RATE (NSR)	0.94	—	0.92	—	0.93	—	0.70	—	0.20	—	–0.29	—
RELATIVE HUMIDITY	–0.96	–0.95	–0.88	–0.79	–0.85	–0.79	–0.52	–0.40	–0.10	–0.02	0.30	0.32
AIR TEMPERATURE	0.88	0.92	0.95	0.97	0.95	0.93	0.83	0.81	0.54	0.52	0.15	0.12
TOTAL IRRADIANCE	0.71	0.74	0.82	0.95	0.82	0.88	0.85	0.91	0.74	0.74	0.46	0.36
PHOTOSYNTHETICALLY ACTIVE RADIATION	0.70	0.72	0.80	0.94	0.81	0.87	0.85	0.90	0.74	0.75	0.48	0.38
LEAF THICKNESS	–0.92	–0.94	–0.96	–0.96	–0.94	–0.95	–0.80	–0.75	–0.48	–0.41	–0.04	–0.02
LEAF RESISTANCE	–0.43	–0.46	–0.52	–0.71	–0.64	–0.67	–0.81	–0.80	–0.88	–0.85	-0.80	–0.77
LEAF TEMPERATURE	0.88	0.93	0.92	0.94	0.91	0.91	0.78	0.73	0.44	0.37	0.00	–0.08

correlations based on a time-lag of 1/2, 1, 2, 3 and 4 hr. Table 3 and figure 4 illustrate such a matrix for a typical day. Intercorrelation of environmental variables is to be expected; for instance, air temperature is expected to follow total irradiance, and relative humidity to show a negative correlation with air temperature. Nectar secretion rate correlates best with current relative humidity (negatively) and solute concentration; with air temperature, leaf temperature and (negatively) with leaf thickness about 0-1 hr earlier; with total irradiance and photosynthetically active radiation (PAR) 1/2 hr and also about 2 hr earlier; and (negatively) with leaf resistance about 3 hr earlier (Fig. 4). Nectar solute concentration correlates with current relative humidity (negatively) and secretion rate; with leaf thickness (negatively), leaf temperature and air temperature about 0-1 hr earlier; with total irradiance and PAR about 2hr earlier; and with leaf resistance (negatively) about 3 hr earlier.

With the exception of leaf resistance, all the variables in Table 3 are associated with correlations above 0.90. Correlations are highest for time-lags between 0 and 1 hrs. The only correlations with coefficients equal to or greater than 0.95 are those of secretion rate with current relative humidity, with total irradiance and air temperature 1/2 hr earlier, and with leaf thickness 1/2 and 1 h earlier; and those of solute concentration with current relative humidity, with leaf thickness 1/2 hr earlier and with air temperature 1/2 and 1 hr earlier.

Between-day correlations

Some of the correlations identified form within-day sequences will result from the more or less coincident diel patterns of fluctuation of the variables. We have therefore constructed a second independent matrix by taking the means of the hourly values of solute concentration and secretion rate between 1200 and 1700 hr on 10 days in August and September, and correlating these with environmental variables, including mean relative humidity and air temperature for the same period, total accumulated wind, total hours of sunshine, mean cloud cover, date (stand age), and other measures of temperature (minimum, maximum, range, and soil temperature; leaf thickness and leaf resistance were not available for all days). This treatment largely removes the variance in nectar secretion rate and solute concentration due to diel changes such as the large changes in microclimate that

TABLE 4 : Pearson product-moment correlation matrix showing the relationship between the mean nectar secretion rate and nectar concentration in *Impatiens glandulifera* and the means for several environmental variables for the period between 1200-1700 hr GMT (n = 10 days). Soil temperature, accumulated wind, sunshine and cloudiness are values for the whole day. The asterisks indicate values of probability below 0.05; all other values are not significant (P) 0.05).

	1	2	3	4	5	6	7	8	9
Nectar Secretion rate (1)	1.00	0.43	–0.42	0.68**	0.67**	–0.07	0.38	–0.28	–0.72**
Nectar Concentration (2)		1.00	–0.83***	0.60**	0.22	–0.43	0.40	–0.44	–0.22
Relative Humidity (3)			1.00	0.65**	0.12	0.28	–0.76***	0.78**	0.08
Air Temperature (4)				1.00	0.75**	0.22	–0.62*	0.60*	–0.47
Soil Temperature (5)					1.00	–0.05	–0.55	–0.56*	0.19
Accumulated wind (6)						1.00	–0.13	–0.11	–0.27
Accumulated sunshine (7)							1.00	–0.84***	0.18
Cloudiness (8)								1.00	0.02
Stand age (9)									1.00

occur in the mornings and evenings. This between-day correlation matrix (Table 4) shows significant ($p < 0.05$) correlations between nectar secretion rate and date (stand age), soil temperature and air temperature, and between nectar solute concentration and relative humidity and air temperature. The other measures of temperature did not reveal significant correlations with nectar secretion rate or solute concentration and are omitted.

A multiple regression following a stepwise method (Harris, 1975) was used to allow unbiased selection of the most likely between- days causal factors. Nectar secretion rate (NSR) correlates significantly with stand age and air temperature. The inclusion of other variables does not increase the explained variance (NSR = 1.3731 – 0.0153 days after August 1st; multiple r = 0.7199; $F_{(1,8)} = 8.61$; $P < 0.05$, and with the inclusion of air temperature NSR = 0.0612 °C – 0.0137 days after August 1st + 0.1356; multiple r = 0.9368; $F_{(2, 7)} = 25.09$; $P < 0.005$) although nectar solute concentration is significantly correlated with mea did may relative humidity and mean did may temperature (Table 4), the multiple regression accepts only relative humidity as a genuine factor; all other factors are intercorrelated or do not account for significant explained variance (nectar solute concentration = 76.0117 – 0.3480 relative humidity; multiple r = 0.83; $F_{(1, 8)} = 17.26$; $P < 0.005$).

Defoliation and light exclusion experiments

In some species, a link has been suggested between nectar secretion rate and the physiological status of the plant, especially in relation to its rate of photosynthesis and transpiration (Bonnier, 1878; Corbet and Delfosse, 1984). The correlation in *I. glandulifera* between secretion rate or solute concentration on the one hand, and irradiance or leaf thickness about 2 hr earlier or leaf resistance about 3 hr earlier (Table 3) on the other, indicates that a similar link may be found in this species too. We explored this possibility by experimentally modifying the physiological status of the plant, in such a way as to preclude photosynthesis and reduce transpiration and water deficit (Búrquez, unpublished observations).

In one experiment, two sets of 12 plants were selected randomly. Just before dawn, one set was darkened by covering each plant with a "barrel" of opaque black cloth supported on a wire frame (and shaded to prevent heating). The flowers were allowed to protrude through a slit, allowing for sampling. The other set constituted the controls. Both sets of flowers were bagged, and sampled repeatedly through the day. In another experiment, we defoliated the sampled branch instead of enclosing the plant in a light proof ''barrel''. The flowers were sampled as before.

In both defoliated and darkened plants, the nectar secretion rate on the first day of the experiment was lower than that of control plants (Fig. 5). On subsequent days the secretion rate decreased until no nectar was secreted, and new flowers ceased to be produced. Evidently the physiological status of the plant is not without effect on secretion rate. In *I. glandulifera*, light as the agent for production of immediate transportable carbohydrates is probably among the most influential factors. The pattern of change of nectar solute concentration was unaffected by the experimental treatments on the first or subsequent days (Fig. 5).

DISCUSSION

In this study *Impatiens glandulifera* showed a consistent diel pattern of nectar secretion, with a peak at about did may and virtually no secretion at night (Figs. 3, 5). Flower-visiting insect numbers were low at night, rose just before secretion began in the morning, remained high all day, and fell just before secretion stopped in the evening (Fig. 2). These patterns of supply and removal of nectar defined a regular pattern of change in the standing crop of nectar in unprotected flowers; nectar was present briefly in the early morning, but nectar sugar did not accumulate during most of the day, when it was removed by abundant insect visitors, or during the night, when secretion rates were low.

Visitors

Nectar secretion continued for a short time after insect visits ceased in the evening. The resulting accumulation of nectar increased in volume by hydration during the night. By the following morning its volume was great enough to fill the spur so that even the short-tongued wasps could reach it. As this nectar became depleted the level retreated down the spur until it was accessible only to longer-tongued bees. The first to exploit it were the bumblebees

Bombus pascuorum. As the relative humidity fell, the nectar became more concentrated, and the sugar content per flower increased, other bumblebee species and honeybees arrived, producing a high visitor density in the afternoon. In the evening, honeybees were the first visitors to depart followed by most species of *Bombus*. The last to leave was *B. pascuorum*, which continued to forage until just after sunset. Noctuid moths were seen visiting the flowers late at night. Their role as pollinators could not be established because of their small numbers and the difficulty of approaching and observing them.

Secretion and reabsorption

We found no evidence for reabsorption of nectar in *I. glandulifera*; repeatedly-empties flowers yielded no more sugar than flowers sampled once when secretion was completed. Other species in which reabsorption has been sought but not found include *Asclepias syriaca* (Southwick, 1983), *Clintonia borealis* (Plowright, 1981) and *Ipomopsis aggregata* (Pleasants, 1983). But a large body of data, that can be traced back to Bonnier (1878), shows that reabsorption does occur in some plants. It has been demonstrated in many species as net movement of nectar constituents into the plant (Wilson, 1881; Boetius, 1948; Raw, 1953; Corbet, 1978; Corbet *et al.*, 1979; Corbet and Delfosse, 1984), or by the use of radioactive tracers (Pedersen *et al.*, Ziegler and Lüttge, 1960; Shuel, 1961; Lüttge, 1962).

Why should reabsorption occur in some species but not in others? In some species, nectar is offered to pollinators at a site remote from the secretory areas. This is particularly noticeable in plant families with highly modified flowers, such as Asclepiadaceae, Violaceae and some Orchidaceae. *Asclepias* species provide a good example of this phenomenon. Nectar is deposited in the cucullus, where physical barriers would impede reabsorption (Galil and Zeroni, 1965; Southwick, 1983). Reabsorption might be expected in species in which the nectar remains in contact with the nectary, but it does not occur in all of them. It seems from the scant literature that reabsorption occurs mainly among those flowers in which the nectaries (with the nectar) remain attached to the plant after the corolla has fallen, as seems to be the case of *Rubus, Trifolium, Vicia, Sinapis, Medicago, Abutilon, Streptosolen, Echium, Eucalyptus* (according to : Boetius, 1948; Raw, 1954; Pedersen *et al.*, 1953; Shuel, 1961; Nuñez, 1977;

Corbet, 1978; Corbet and Delfosse, 1984), and for our observations in *Brassica* (unpublished data). However, slight modifications of the morphology and wettability of the flower might isolate nectar droplets from the nectary, preventing their reabsorption. Species reported as lacking reabsorption, despite contact of the nectar with the nectary, are those in which the nectaries occur in the corolla or in floral tissues that are shed soon after fertilization, such as *Impatiens* and *Ipomopsis* (this work, Pleasants, 1983), and may be expected in *Delphinium, Aquilegia, Symphoricarpos* and *Lonicera* among other genera (and probably other members of the Ranunculaceae, Caprifoliaceae, Fumariaceae and Lentibulariaceae among others).

Reabsorption of nectar may have functional significance beyond the recovery of an energy investment. It might be of adaptive advantage to a plant to prevent insect visits after pollination, so perhaps reducing the risk of injury to the flower or focusing pollinator visits on unpollinated flowers (see Gori, 1983). Repeated insect visits can reduce seed set (Burquez *et al*, 1987; Young MS), and floral changes post-fertilization can enhance pollination efficiency (Schaal and Leverich, 1980). Nectar dilution at the end of the flower's lifetime seems to be associated with the beginning of net nectar reabsorption in several plants, in particular in *Echium, Sinapis* and *Borago* (Boetius, 1948), and *Brassica, Fritillaria, Asphodeline* and *Impatiens* (Bürquez and Corbet unpublished data). Dilution may prove to be a prerequisite for reabsorption. Plants with the nectaries in the corolla might deter visits to older flowers by dilution and/or reabsorption of residual nectar, by changes in flower appearance and orientation (Gori, 1983), or by shedding the nectaries with the corolla, so losing the chance of taking back the nectar.

The genetic components of variation in nectar secretion and concentration have been investigated by Pedersen (1953), Teuber and Barnes (1979), and Murrell, Tomes and Shuel (1982) among others. They have demonstrated the existence of genetic variation that could form the basis of breeding programmes or, ultimately, evolution.

Environmental factors also play an important role, although the factors controlling diel patterns of nectar secretion remain poorly understood in *I. glandulifera* and other species. The interaction between environmental change, plant physiological status and nectar secretion involves problems of considerable complexity.

The variables influencing nectar secretion rate are different from those that affect nectar solute concentration, but both features correlate well with most of the measured environmental and physiological variables when different time lags are allowed. Air temperature and stand age accounted for most of the day-to- day variance in the nectar secretion rate. The failure of PAR or total irradiance to account for even a small portion of the day- to-day variance suggests that photosynthetic saturation was reached at low irradiance. The light deprivation experiments indicate that some fraction of the day's nectar secretion depends on that day's photosynthesis, while another fraction must be mobilized from stored photosynthates.

It has been shown for some plants that a high proportion of photosynthate can go into nectar (Southwick, 1984). Light deprivation and defoliation experiments make it possible to evaluate the relative contribution to nectar of recently produced, as opposed to stored, assimilates. When plants are temporarily deprived of light, nectar secretion might : (i) continue unchanged, (ii) show an immediate reduction in rate, or (iii) cease. The first case is illustrated by species that flower before the leaves emerge, and by night flowering plants. In these, nectar secretion is likely to be nearly independent of immediate light conditions, and nearly all the nectar secreted must come from short or long term storage organs. These plants case, in which interference with the supply of new assimilates leads to an immediate decrease in the secretion rate, is exemplified by *Asclepias quadrifolia*, a plant with underground storage organs. Pleasants and Chaplin (1983) found that the nectar secretion rate fell to 70% of its initial value four days after removal of half the leaves, and to 16% of its initial values after total defoliation. A similar situation was reported by Nuñez (1977) for *Eucalyptus melliodora*. The third case seems to occur in *Tilia* and *Symphoricarpos* which cease to produce nectar when shaded or defoliated (Czarnowski, 1952). In the case of *Impatiens glandulifera* day-to-day variation in irradiance, although large (0.2-1.0 Kw m^{-2} daily maximum), did not correlate significantly with nectar secretion rate. The extreme experiments of light exclusion and defoliation, on the other hand, led to an immediate decrease in nectar secretion rate, with subsequent stabilization at a lower value. This new plateau must depend on sugar translocation from storage, perhaps in the enlarged stem. Secretion rate later decreased. probably because of exhaustion of the source.

Water deficit, although it has been invoked since the times of Bonnier (1878) as a factor in the regulation of nectar secretion, seems to play only a minor role. In *Impatiens glandulifera*, water deficit (measured in terms of leaf thickness and leaf resistance) is apparently without important effects on nectar secretion rate. The correlations are the least significant of all those in fig. 4. In some cases, a reduction in water availability, or an increase in water deficit, does not affect solute transport in the phloem or the solute content of exuded sap (Wardlaw, 1967; Canny, 1973). In other cases sucrose flux increases significantly with increasing water stress (Smith and Milburn, 1980; Avigad, 1982). This has also been observed for plants of *Brassica napus* subjected to strong water deficits (Burquez unpublished data). Obviously, long term water deficits can produce such physiological deterioration that most processes are stopped. Zimmermann (2983) and Marden (1984) suggest that soil moisture has a major effect on nectar secretion in *Delphinium nelsonii* and *Impatiens capensis* respectively. They observed that after a long series of hot rainless days, nectar secretion decreased. Here we do not consider long-term effects.

The correlation of nectar secretion rate with temperature has been noted by Wilson (1881), Kenoyerc, 1917), Nuñez (1977), and particularly Huber (1956). Temperature is the environmental variable that is most often cited as related to nectar secretion rate. Sugar translocation rates are known to correlate with temperature (Canny, 1973; Walker and Ho, 1977; Smith and Milburn, 1980; Marowitch, Richter and Hoddinot, 1986), so this relationship is not surprising. Moreover temperature affects the rate of photosynthesis which, as the light exclusion experiment indicates, contributes to a limited extent to the nectar secretion rate.

In *Impatiens glandulifera* the multiple regression indicates that in the field only air temperature and stand age seem to influence day-to-day variation in the secretion rate. The effect of stand age may be related to sink strength of the nectary, as well as to the availability of photosynthates (Ho, 1980). The effect of flower and fruit numbers per raceme support this view (unpublished data). Older plants are expected to have an increased fruit load. This factor affects the flowers' relative sink strength which will be greater for those flowers produced early in the season when competition with other sinks is weak. Similar results are reported by Pleasants and Chaplin (1983) for *Asclepias quadrifolia*.

Nectar solute concentration

In *Impatiens glandulifera*, within-day variation in nectar solute concentration correlated significantly with all measured variables, but most strongly and without any time-lag with the relative humidity of the air. Between-day variation in mean didmay values of nectar solute concentration correlated significantly only with relative humidity and temperature. Multiple regression showed that relative humidity of the air was the only significant factor. A similar relationship was observed by Bonnier (1878), and later documented by Kenoyer (1917) and park (1929). The most parsimonious explanation seems to be a direct effect of air humidity on the water content of nectar. This approach was used with the different degrees of precision by Vansell (1940), Scullen (1940), Huber (1956), Nuñez (1977), Corbet (1978), Corbet, Unwin and Prys-Jones (1979) and by Corbet *et al.* (1979), who gave a detailed account of the post-secretory changes of nectar solute concentration. An alternative explanation is that internal physiological factors linked to air humidity determine the nectar solute concentration as proposed by Bonnier (1878), and more recently by Bertsck (1983). Neither explanation is incompatible with our data. Leaf resistance was significantly correlated with nectar concentration, but the weakness of the correlation makes transpiration unlikely as a primary causal factor. Leaf thickness, which has been shown to be a good predictor of leaf relative water content (Búrquez, 1990), was well correlated with nectar solute concentration with a small delay. It is possible that a combination of pre-and post-secretory factors affect nectar concentration.

A description of nectar concentration dynamics cannot be complete without at least a crude knowledge of the nectar secretion pattern. It has been suggested that the concentration of nectar at the time of secretion is related to the relative amounts of xylem and phloem supplying the nectary (Agthe, 1951; Frey-Wyssling, 1955; Frei, 1955). Changes in water potential affect the xylem more readily than the phloem and its translocates (Wardlaw, 1967; Smith and Milburn, 1980). Thus a water deficit might reduce the water supply to the nectaries without affecting sugar transport, and so might increase the nectar solute concentration at secretion. This effect might be amplified later by post-secretory changes, because the condition that create a water deficit in plants are likely to promote evaporation at the nectary (eg. a combination of high irradiance and low relative humidity). However, the experiments involving light exclusion (which reduced the rate of transpiration, the water deficit, and the rate of sugar translocation; Burquez unpublished data) did not affect nectar concentration. This indicates that for nectar solute concentration internal effects due to water potential or transpiration are far less important than immediate environmental effects.

In view of the importance of time of sampling (Fig. 3), microclimate and plant physiological status as determinants of nectar concentration it is surprising that many authors have disregarded these effects when considering the significance of the nectar concentration for pollinators (eg. Baker, 1975; Bolten and Feinsinger, 1978; Marden, 1984). As Corbet *et al.* (1979) and Plowright (1981) have pointed out, reports of field studies on nectar solute concentration are of enhanced value if they include information on relevant microclimatic variables such as relative humidity and temperature (see Unwin, 1980).

The rate of post-secretory equilibration of nectar with the relative humidity of the air depends on the nectar secretion rate and the volume of nectar accumulated in the flower. Environmental post-secretory effects will be attenuated if nectar secretion rates are high and nectar volumes large. *Brassica napus* has relatively low secretion rates and exposed nectaries, and its nectar rapidly equilibrates with the relative humidity of the air (Búrquez unpublished data). *Fritillaria imperialis* has equally exposed nectaries, but high rates of secretion and a large standing crop of nectar, and its nectar concentration is largely independent of relative humidity (Corbet *et al.*, 1979). an interesting contrast is found in nocturnal or crepuscular flowers, in which increasingly less negative water potentials, decreasing transpiration rates and increasing relative-humidity do not seem to alter nectar solute concentration. No significant changes in nectar solute concentration were detected either in *Mirabilis jalapa*, a tubular flower pollinated by hawkmoths, or in *Manfreda brachystachya* an open, bat- pollinated flower (Martínez del Río and Búrquez, 1986; Eguiarte and Búrquez, 1990 respectively) despite changes in their rate of nectar secretion and in their environment. In *Mirabilis* a long narrow pseudocorolla protects the nectar and prevents it from equilibrating with the ambient air, while in *Manfreda* the effect of the environment is dampened because of the speed at which large volumes of nectar are secreted.

It has been suggested that diel changes in nectar concentration can be interpreted as a regular pattern, adaptive because of differential attraction of specific groups of pollinators at different times of day (Cruden *et al.*, 1983). For flowers that show similar concentration/humidity relationships when growing in localities differing in pollinator spectrum, and especially for those in which diel variations in nectar concentration range beyond the preference limits of supposed pollinators, we prefer to regard temporal variation in nectar concentration as a consequence of post-secretory effects of a changing environment (Corbet *et al.*, 1979). Nectar is perhaps exploited opportunistically by an array of visitors in relation to their specific preferences (Heinrich, 1976; Willmer and Corbet, 1981; Eguiarte and Búrquez, 1990). No doubt selection acts on the flower/visitor interaction, and on factors influencing nectar concentration as a major component of it, but selection must act not on the concentration itself, but on the machinery that determines it in any given environmental and physiological conditions. Constraints limiting the extent to which nectar concentration can match pollinator preference probably include a physiological limit on the concentration at which nectar can be secreted, and a practical limit on the rate and extent of post-secretory evaporative concentration related to the degree of protection and nectar volume. The concentration at which nectar is secreted can sometimes be determined by collecting newly secreted nectar which has been protected from post-secretory equilibration with the ambient air. It is usually found to lie within the range 6 — 47% (Huber, 1956; Corbet *et al.*, 1979; Corbet and Delfosse, 1984). The concentration of nectar at the time of secretion is unlikely to be much higher than that of the phloem sap from which it is derived (sugar concentration in the phloem with few exceptions ranges from 18 to 38%, Kluge, 1970 in Lüttge and Schnepf, 1976; but see Bertsch, 1983), but refractometry might indicate higher values if the nectar were to include compounds of high molecular weight which would raise the refractive index more than the osmolality (Corbet *et al.*, 1979).

From the relatively low initial concentration, high concentrations can be produced by post-secretory equilibration in dry air if the nectar droplets are small, with a high surface/volume ratio, and have free exchange with the air. Thus in relatively open flowers with small nectar volumes, such as those pollinated by short tongued insects, post-secretory equilibration can achieve high concentrations within a day. But in flowers with pollinators that have high demands for energy, such as hummingbirds, hawkmoths, bats, perching birds and small mammals, the large nectar volumes will result in a slower equilibration, especially if the rate of loss of water vapour to the air is restricted by a long corolla tube (such as would exclude other visitors from hummingbird and hawkmoth flowers), or by a high ambient relative humidity (as in nocturnal flowers pollinated by bats and small mammals). In perching-bird pollinated species which have an open flower, both water and sugar are relevant to the pollinators (Toledo and Hernàndez, 1979; Toledo and Búrquez, 1980; Vogel *et al.*, 1984; Olesen, 1985). Xylem innervation is likely to be important, keeping nectar volumes large and slowing equilibration.

Thus the nectar solute concentration found in a given flower at a given time will be the product of a short-term plant microclimate interaction which is itself influenced by features (such as corolla length, nectar volume and secretion rate) whose evolutionary significance relates also to other aspects of the plant-pollinator association. It may be optimistic to expect that this compromise will result in a nectar solute concentration exactly matching that preferred by the pollinator.

Explanation to Figures

FIG. 1. Flower of *Impatiens glandulifera (A, B) front and side view of the flower, (C) side view of the androecium enclosing the ovary (dotted line), (D) spur showing different levels of accumulated nectar.*

FIG. 2. Density of visitors to *Impatiens glandulifera* in Cambridge on two different days. ■ = *Bombus pascuorum*; □ = *B. lapidarius*; Δ = *B. terrestris*; ∇ = *Apis mellifera*; = *Vestpula germanica.*

FIG. 3. Cumulative nectar secretion and nectar solute concentration changes in a day in 2-3 flowers on each of 3 plants of *Impatiens glandulifera* randomly selected among the plants sampled on that day. Sampling of nectar began at 0500 GMT, shortly after flower opening. Nectar solute concentration is shown only for the first day.

FIG. 4. Correlograms showing the change in the Pearson product- moment correlation coefficient when nectar solute concentration and secretion rate of *Impatiens glandulifera* are delayed with respect to selected environmental factors, r = air temperature: ■ = leaf thickness; Δ = relative humidity; ∇ = Leaf resistance; O = total irradiance. Other variables in Table 3 are ommitted here for clarity.

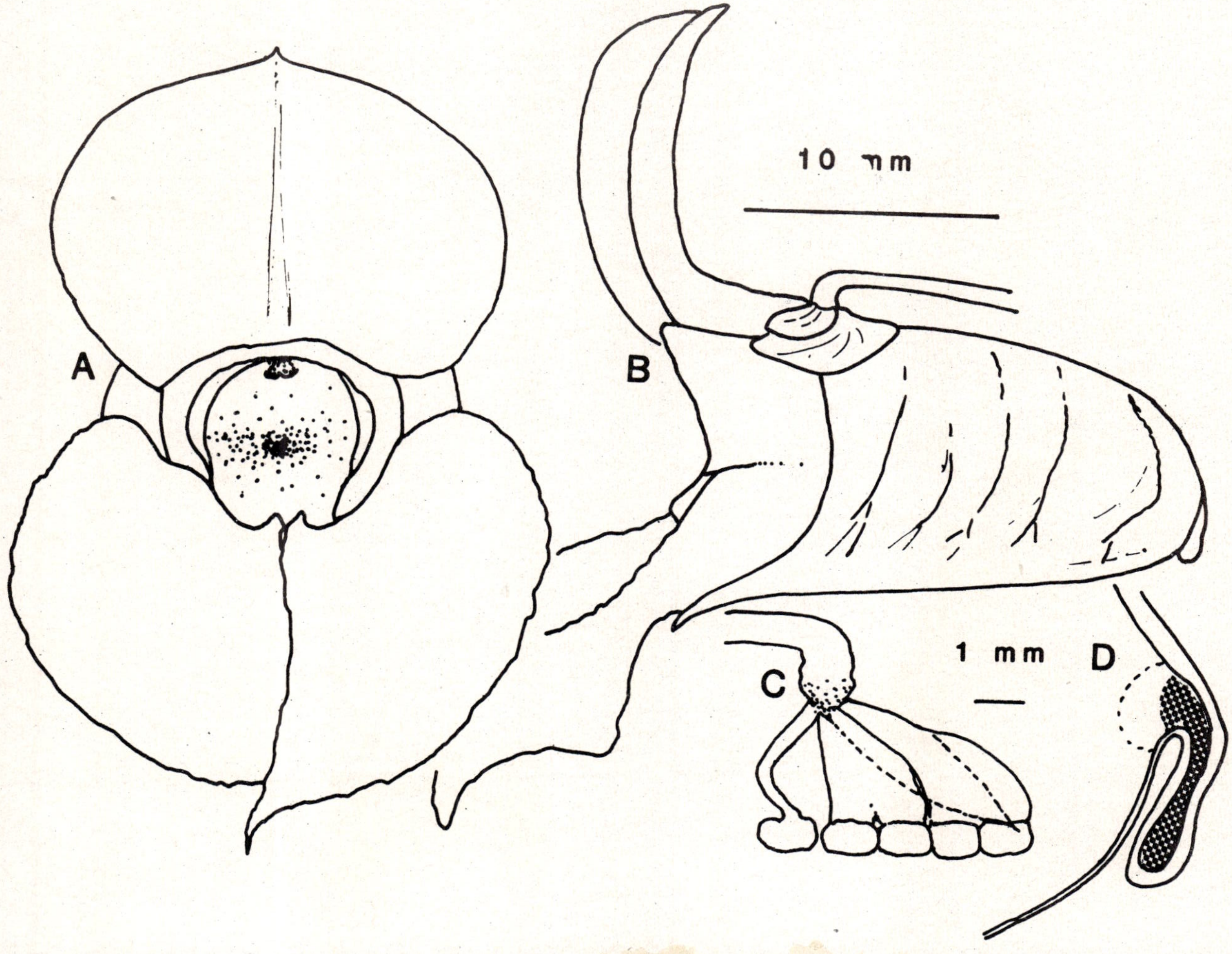

A
B
10 mm
C
1 mm
D

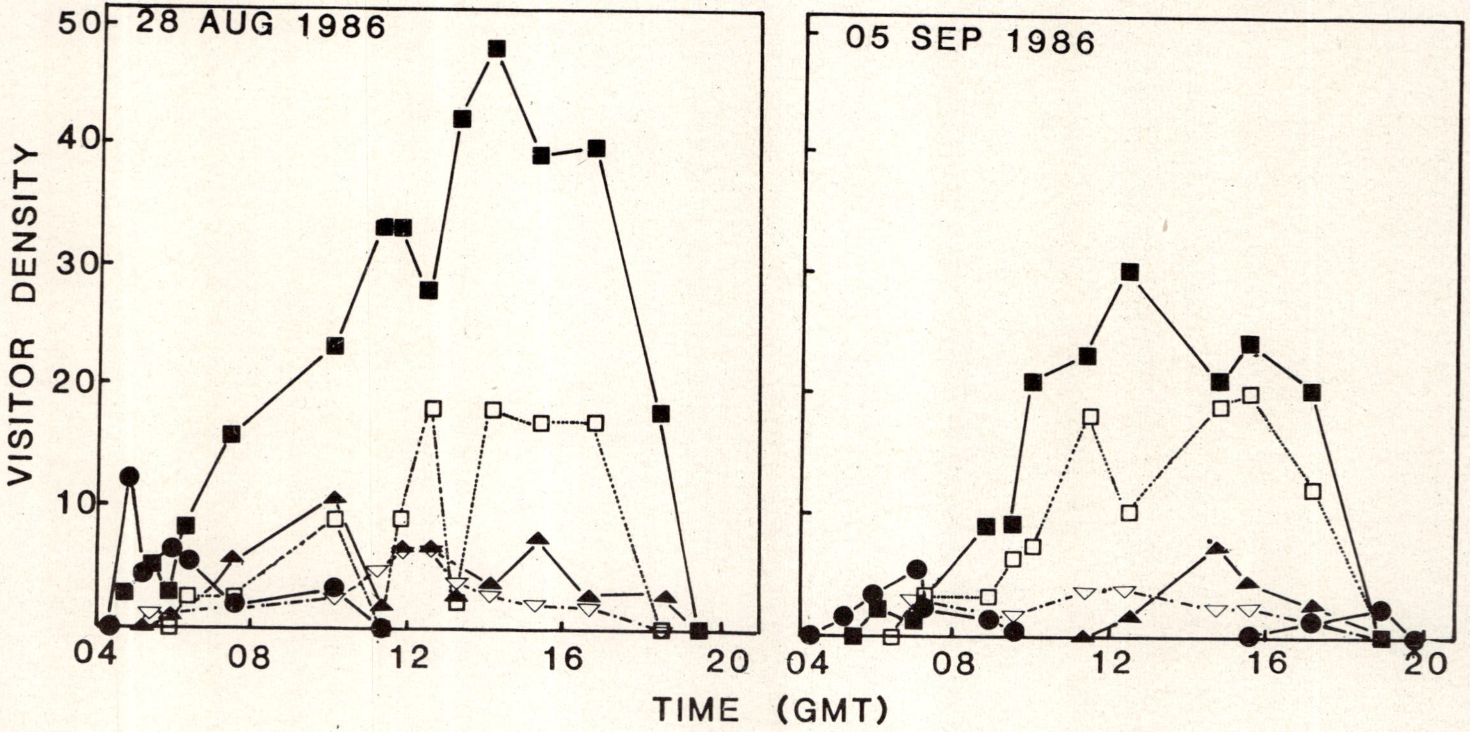

VISITOR DENSITY
50
40
30
20
10
28 AUG 1986
05 SEP 1986
04
08
12
16
20
TIME (GMT)

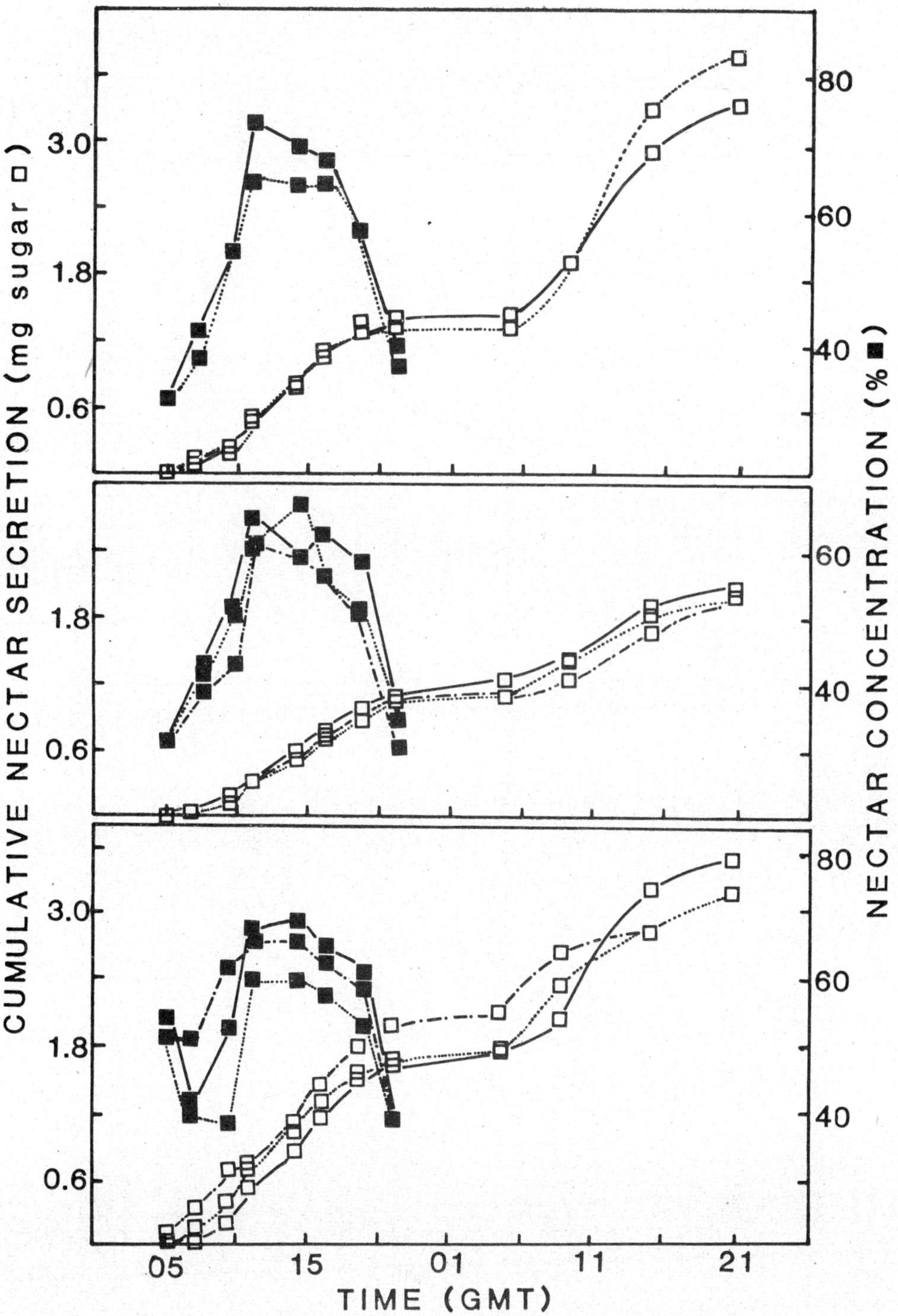

CUMULATIVE NECTAR SECRETION (mg sugar □)
NECTAR CONCENTRATION (% ■)
3.0
1.8
0.6
80
60
40
05
15
01
11
21
TIME (GMT)

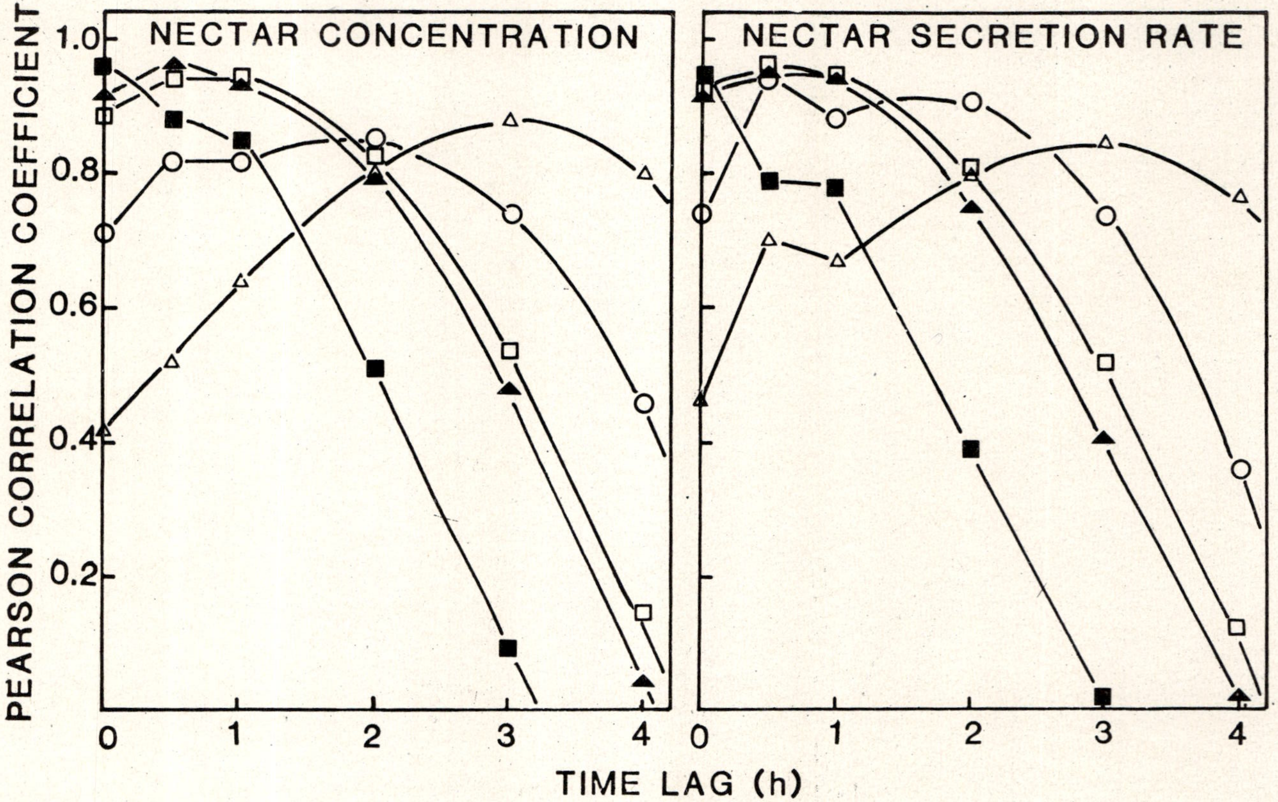
NECTAR CONCENTRATION
NECTAR SECRETION RATE
PEARSON CORRELATION COEFFICIENT
1.0
0.8
0.6
0.4
0.2
0
1
2
3
4
TIME LAG (h)

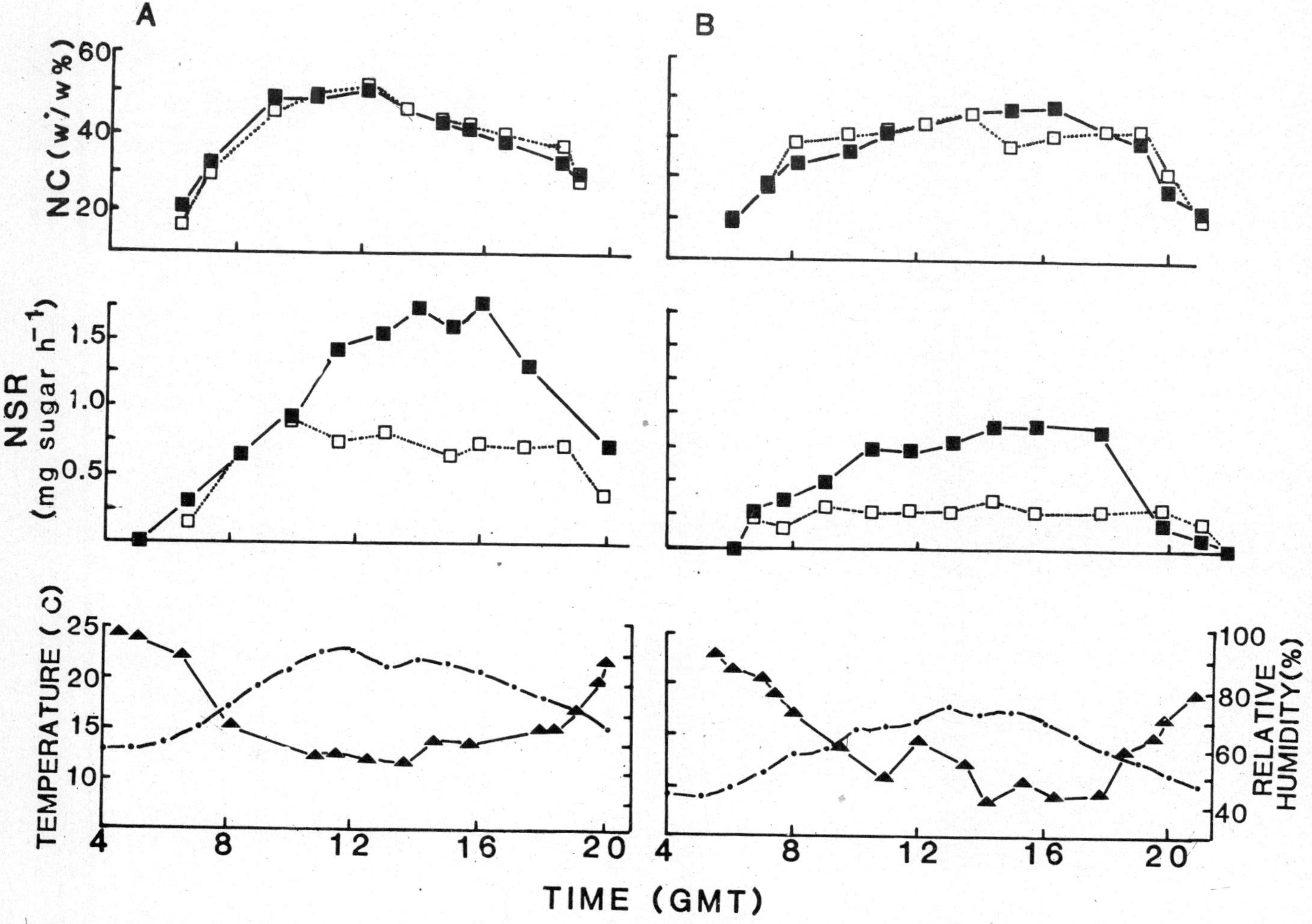
A
B
NC (w/w%)
60
40
20
NSR
(mg sugar h^{-1})
1.5
1.0
0.5
TEMPERATURE (C)
25
20
15
10
4
8
12
16
20
TIME (GMT)
100
80
60
40
RELATIVE
HUMIDITY(%)

FIG. 5. Changes in nectar solute concentration and nectar secretion rate in *Impatiens glandulifera* for two days (A, B) in which environmental factors were very different (closed squares and solid lines). The open squares and dotted lines show the nectar solute concentration and nectar secretion rate changes after total defoliation (B) and defoliation of the branch on which the flowers were sampled (A). Temperature (•) and relative humidity (▲) are shown below. Standard errors of the means are approximately the size of the symbols (n_A = 12; n_B = 12).

Literature Cited

Agthe, C. 1951. Über die physiologische Herkunft des Pflanzennektars. *Ber. schweiz. Bot. Ges., 61* : 240- 274.

Avigad, G. 1982. Sucrose and other disaccharides. In: (eds). F.A. Loews and W. Tammer. *Encyclopedia of Plant Physiology, 13A* : 217-347. Springer Verlag, Berlin.

Bahadur, B., Chaturvedi, A. and Swamy, N.R. 1986. Nectaries in *Impatiens* L. (Balsaminaceae). *J. Swamy Bot. Cl,. 3* : 181-184.

Baker. H.G. 1975 Sugar concentrations in nectars from hummingbird flowers. *Biotropica, 7* : 37-41.

Baker. H.G. and Baker. I. 1975. Studies of nectar- constitution and pollinator-plant coevolution. In: (eds). L.E. Gilbert and P.H. Raven *Coevolution of animals and plants*. Texas Univ. Press. Austin.

Bertsch, A. 1983 Nectar production of *Epilobium angustifolium L. at different air humidities; nectar sugar in individual flowers and the optimal foraging theory.Oecologia, 59* : 40-48.

Boetius, J. 1948. Über den Verlauf der Nektarabsonderung einiger Blutenpflanzen. *Beihefte z. Schweizerichen Bienen-Zeitung, 2* : 258-317.

Bolten, A.B. and Feinsinger, P. 1978. Why do hummingbird flowers secrete dilute nectar?. *Biotropica, 10* : 307-309.

Bonnier. G. 1878. Les nectaries. *Ann. Sci. Nat.* (Bot), *8* : 5-212.

Búrquez. A. 1987. Leaf thickness and water deficit in plants : A tool for field studies *J. Exptl. Bot. 38* : 109-114.

Búrquez, A., Sarukhàn J. and Pedroza, A.L. 1987. Floral biology of a tropical forest palm : *Astrocaryum mexicanum* Liebm. *Bot. J. Linn. Soc.* (in press)

Canny, M.J. 1973. *Phloem Translocation*. Cambridge Univ. Press. Cambridge.

Coombe, D.E. 1956. Notes on some British plants seen in Austria. *Veroff. Geobotan. Inst. Eidgen. Tech. Hoschs. Rubel Zurich, 35* : 128-137.

Corbet, S.A. 1978. Bees and the nectar of *Echium vulgare*. In: (ed). Richards, A.J. *The Pollination of Flowers by Insects*. Linnean Soc. Symp. Series 6. Academic Press. London.

Corbet, S.A. and Delfosse, E.S. 1984. Honeybees and the nectar of *Echium plantagineum* L. in south-eastern Australia. *Aust. J. Ecol., 9* : 125-139.

Corbet, S.A., Unwin, D.M. and Prŷs-Jones, O.E. 1979. Humidity, nectar and insect visits to flowers, with special reference to *Crataegus, Tilia* and *Echium. Ecological Entomology, 4* : 9-22.

Corbet, S.A., Willmer, P.G., Beament, J.W.L., Unwin, D.M., and Prŷs-Jones, O.E. 1979. Post-secretory determinants of sugar concentration in nectar. *Pl. Cell Environ., 2* : 293- 308.

Cruden, R.W., Hermann, S.M. and Peterson, S. 1983. Patterns of nectar production and plant-pollinator coevolution. In: (eds). Elias, T. and Bentley, B. *The Biology of Nectaries*. Columbia Univ. Press. New York.

Czarnowski, C. von 1952. Untersuchungen zur Frage der Nektarabsonderung. *Z. Bienenforsch, 1* : 171-173.

Daumann, E. 1967. Zur Bestaubungs-und Verberitungsokologie dreier *Impatiens-Arten. Preslia, 39* : 43-58.

Eguiarte, L. and Búrquez, A. 1990. Reproductive ecology of *Manfreda brachystachya*, an iteroparous species of Agavaceae. *Southwest. Natur.30* :

Frei, E. 1955. Die innervierung der floren Nektarien dikotyler Pflanzenfamilien. *Ber. Schweiz. Bot . Ges., 70* : 60-114.

Frey-Wyssling, A. 1955. The phloem supply to the nectaries. *Acta Bot. Neerl., 4* : 358-369.

Galil, J. and Zeroni, M. 1965. Nectar system of *Asclepias curassavica. Bot. Gaz., 126* : 144-148.

Gori, D.F. 1983. Post-pollination phenomena and adaptive floral changes. In: (eds). Jones, C.E. and Little, R.J. *Handbook of Experimental Pollination Biology*. p.31-49. Van Nostrand Reinhold Co. Inc. New York.

Harris, R.J. 1975. *A Primer of Multivariate Statistics*. Academic Press. New York.

Heinrich. B. 1976. Resource partitioning among some eusocial insects : bumblebees. *Ecology, 57* : 874-889.

Ho, L.C. 1980. control of import into tomato fruits. *Ber. Deutsch Bot. Ges., 93* : 315-325.

Huber, H. 1956. Die Abhangigkeit der Nektarsekretion von Temperatur, Luft, and Bodenfeuchtigkeit. *Planta, 48* : 47-98.

Kenoyer, L.A. 1917. Environmental influences on nectar secretion. *Bot. Gaz., 63* : 249-265.

Lhotska. M. and Kopecky, K. 1966. Zur Verbreitungsbiologie und Phytozonologie von *Impatiens glandulifera* Royle an den Flussystemen der Svitava, Svratka und oberen Odra. *Preslia, 38* : 376-385.

Luttge, U. 1962. Uber die Zusammensetzung des Nectars und den Mechanismus seiner Secretion III. Mitteilung. Die Rolle der Rukresorption und der specifischen Zuckersekretion. *Planta. 59* : 175-194.

Lüttge, U. and Schnepf, E. 1976. Organic substances. In: (eds). Lüttge, U. and Pitman, M.G. *Encyclopedia of Plant Physiology, 2B* : 244-277. Springer Verlag, Berlin.

Marden, J.H. 1984. Intrapopulation variation in nectar secretion in *Impatiens capensis*. *Oecologia, 63* : 418-422.

Marowitch, J., Richter, C. and Hoddinot, *J.* 1986. the influence of plant temperature on photosynthesis and translocation rates in bean and soybeans. *Can. J. Bot., 64* : 2337-2342.

Martínez del Río, c. and Búrquez, A. 1986. Nectar production and temperature dependent pollination in *Mirabilis jalapa* L. *Biotropica, 18* : 28-31.

Murrell, D.C., Tomes, D.T. and Shuel, R.W. 1982. Inheritance of nectar production in birdsfoot trefoil. *Can. J. Plant Sci., 62* : 101-105.

Nuñez, J. 1977. Nectar flow by melliferous flora and gathering flow by *Apis mellifera ligustica*. *J. Insect. Physiol., 23* : 265-275.

Olesen, J.M. 1985. The Macaronesian bird-flower element and its relation to bird and bee opportunists. *Bot. J. Linn. Soc., 91* : 395-414.

Park. O.W. 1929. The influence of humidity upon sugar concentration in the nectar of various plants. *J. Econom. Entomol., 22* : 534-544.

Pedersen, M.W. 1953. Environmental factors affecting nectar secretion and seed production in alfalfa. *Agronom. J., 45* : 359-361.

Pedersen, M.W., LeFevre, C.W. and Wiebe, H.H. 1958. Absorption of C14 — labeled sucrose by alfalfa nectaries. *Science, 127* : 758-759.

Pleasants, J.M. 1983. Nectar production patterns in *Ipomopsis aggregata* (Polemoniaceae). *Am. J. Bot., 70*: 1468-1475.

Pleasants, J.M. and Chaplin, S.J. 1983. Nectar production rates of *Asclepias quadrifolia* : causes and consequences of individual variation. *Oecologia, 59* : 232- 238.

Plowright, R.C. 1981. Nectar production in the boreal forest lily *Clintonia borealis*. *Can. J. Bot., 59* : 156-160.

Raw, G.R. 1953. The effect on nectar secretion of removing nectar from flowers. *Bee World, 34* : 23-25.

Schaal, B.A. and Leverich, W.J. 1980. Pollination and banner markings in *Lupinus texensis* (Leguminosae). *Southwest. natur., 25* : 280-282.

Scullen, H.A. 1940. Relative humidity and the nectar concentration in fireweed. *J. Econ. Entomol., 33* : 870- 871.

Shuel, r.W. 1961. Influence of reproductive organs on secretion of sugars in flowers of *Streptosolen jamesonii*, Miers. *Pl. Physiol., 36* : 265-271.

Smith, J.A. and Milburn, J.A. 1980. Water stress and phloem loading. *Ber. Deutsch. Bot. Ges., 93* : 269-280.

Southwick, E.A. 1983. Nectar biology and nectar feeders of common milkweed, *Asclepias syriaca* L. *Bull. Torr. Bot. Club, 110* : 324-334.

Southwick, E.E. 1984. Photosynthate allocation to floral nectar : a neglected energy investment. *Ecology, 65* : 1775-1779.

Teuber, L.R. and Barnes, D.K. 1979. Environmental and genetic influences on alfalfa nectar. *Crop Sci., 19* : 874-878.

Toledo, V.M. and Barquez, A. 1980. La danza de has flores : movimientos florales en *Bernullia flammea* (Bombacaceae). Resumenes del VIII congreso Mexicano de Botanica, p. 301-302. Soc. Bot. Mex. Univ. Mich.

Toledo, V.M. and Hernàndez, H.M. 1979. *Erythrina oliviae* : a new case of oriole pollination in Mexico. *Ann. Mo. Bot. Gard., 66* : 503-511.

Unwin, D. 1980. *Microclimate measurements for ecologists*. Academic Press. London.

Valentine, D.H. 1979. The Pollination of introduced species, with special reference to the British Isles and the genus *Impatiens*. In : (ed). Richards, A.J. *The Pollination of Flowers by Insects*. Linnean Soc. Symp. Series 6. Academic Press. London.

Vansell, G.H. 1940. Nectar secretion in *Poinsettia* blossoms. *J. Econ. Bot., 35* : 321-323.

Vogel, S., Westerkamp, C., Thiel, B. and Gessner, K. 1984. Ornithophilie auf den Canarischen Inseln. *Pl. Syst. Evol., 146* : 225-248.

Walker, A.J. and Ho, L.C. 1977. Carbon translocation in the tomato: carbon import and fruit growth. *Ann. Bot., 41* : 813-823.

Wardlaw, I.F. 1967. The effect of water stress on translocation in relation to photosynthesis and growth. *Aust. J. Biol. Sci., 20* : 25-39.

Weber. F. 1951. *Impatiens*-nektar. *Phyton* (Horn), *3* : 110-111.

Willmer, P.G. and Corbet, S.A. 1981. Temporal and microclimatic partitioning of the floral resources of *Justicia aurea* among a concourse of pollen vectors and nectar robbers. *Oecologia, 51* : 67-78.

Wilson, W.P. 1881. The cause of the excretion of water on the surface of nectaries. *Unters. Bot. Inst.* Tubingen, *1* :1-22.

Young, H. Differential effectiveness of beetles pollinating *Dieffenbachia longispatha* (Araceae). MS. in preparation)

Ziegler, H. and Lüttge, U. 1960. Über die Resorption von C14 Glutaminsaure durch sezernierenden Nektarien. *Naturwissenschaften, 47* : 259.

Zimmerman, M. 1983. Plant reproduction and optimal foraging : experimental nectar manipulations in *Delphinium nelsonii. Oikos, 41* : 57-63.

DYNAMICS OF BUTTERFLY NECTARS

C. SUBBA REDDI

Department of Environmental Sciences
Andhra University, Visakhapatnam 530 003, India.

ABSTRACT

The nectars of 42 flower species were analysed for their volume, sugar concentration, 'histidine scale' score and protein presence. The flower species were classified into seven groups based on their flower structure. Each group had different nectar volumes, and in general the volume ranged from traces to 2.8 ul depending on the flower group. There were broadly two ranges in nectar sugar concentrations, 10-48%, and 53-62%, the former being more common with the flowers visited more frequently by butterflies, thus indicating that butterfly flowers are less viscous. Sucrose was predominant in nectars of 12 of the 42 flower species, and these were the flowers frequented more by butterflies, flowers with higher histidine scale score and those with lower score were almost equally sought by the butterflies, thereby indicating that the butterflies need not necessarily feed on aminoacid-rich nectars.

Kew words : Nectar Dynamics, Butterflies.

INTRODUCTION

Floral nectars play an important role in plant-pollinator interactions. The amount of nectar presented to a flower visitor is an important factor in determining the behaviour of that visitor, as well as having important consequences for the breeding system of the plants (Heinrich and Raven, 1972). However, recent studies have shown that the volume of nectar provided by a flower is just a secondary consideration within certain limits and the primary determinant of their preference is the concentration of energy giving chemicals, and quality and quantity of amino acids in nectar (Neff *et al.*, 1977; Baker, 1978). While qualitative nectar sugar spectra of a few Brazilian flowers obtained by Gottsberger *et al.* (1973) did not correlate with pollinator type, Baker (1975) checking sugar concentrations in hummingbird flowers, could show some degree of specialisation in nectar type according to the type of flower visitor or pollinator. Bahadur *et al.* (1986) made a comprehensive study on the nectar composition of 100 plant species of India. They have divided the three common sugars viz., sucrose, fructose and glucose into 6 nectar types and related them to different flower types which are adapted to different pollinator types. The present review examines the nectar characteristics of the flower species commonly visited by butterflies at Visakhapatnam, and discusses the same in the light of existing notions about butterfly nectars.

Flower species examined and their butterfly visitors

The nectars of 42 flower species occurring at Visakhapatnam (17°42'N and 82° 18'E) were studied for their volume in microlitres (μl), sugar concentration (%), 'histidine scale' score, and protein presence (Table 1). the 42 flower species were seen visited by one or the other of 40 butterfly species. The nomenclature adopted for butterflies is after Varshney (1983). On the basis of their structure, the flowers of all the species studied were classified under seven groups as : A– Flowers zygomorphic with the essential organs placed adjacent to or lying on the lower corolla lip; B– Flowers zygomorphic with the essential organs oriented towers the upper lip; C– Flowers open with the essential organs centrally positioned; D– Flowers open with exposed numerous stamens; E– Flowers tubular with the essential organs inserted; F– Flowers tubular with the essential organs exserted, and G– Flowers with the essential organs rather elongated and oriented horizontally.

TABLE 1 : Nectar volume and concentration at 10.00 and 17.00 hr. and predominant sugar, Histidime Scale and presence of proteins in different species.

	Name of the Plant	Flower type	Nectar volume		Nectar concentration		Predominant sugar	Histidime scale	Proteins
	10.00hr	17.00hr	10.00hr	17.00hr					
1.	*Adhatoda vasica*	B	3.80	3.90	21.50	18.00	gsf	1.0	+
2.	*Albizia lebbeck*	D	0.40	0.70	19.00	17.00	gsf	0.3	+
3.	*Anacardium occidentale*	E	0.60	1.30	31.00	26.00	gsf	3.0	+
4.	*Antigonon leptopus*	C	0.02	0.40	58.00	54.00	gsf	0.0	+
5.	*Asystasia gangetica*	E	0.02	0.20	22.00	18.00	gsf	0.0	+
6.	*Borreria hispida*	F	0.02	0.02	28.00	32.00	gsf	4.0	+
7.	*Cadaba fruticosa*	G	2.80	1.60	18.00	20.00	gsf	5.5	+
8.	*Caesalpinia coriaria*	F	0.02	0.06	48.00	26.00	gsf	3.0	+
9.	*C. pulcherrima*	G	0.68	1.22	29.00	18.00	gsf	6.0	+
10.	*Capparis Spinosa*	D	2.00	1.02	26.00	21.00	gsf	6.0	+
11.	*Catharanthus roseus*	E	1.00	2.20	25.00	22.00	gsf	6.0	+
12.	*Citharexylum subserratum*	E	0.08	0.20	24.00	18.00	gsf	4.0	+
13.	*Cleome viscosa*	A	---------- traces of Nectar ----------				gsf	0.0	+
14.	*Clerodendrum infortunatum*	G	0.99	2.25	12.00	20.00	gsf	6.0	+
15.	*C. nerifolium*	G	0.40	0.90	30.00	26.00	gsf	4.0	+
16.	*Duranta repens*	E	0.60	1.00	24.00	19.00	gsf	4.0	+
17.	*Eupatorium triplinerve*	F	0.80	0.40	28.00	23.00	gsf	6.0	+
18.	*Gaillardia picta*	F	1.00 head	1.00	38.00	32.00	gsf	5.0	+
19.	*Hamelia patens*	C	0.90 head	1.30	26.00	21.00	gsf	5.0	+

20.	*Hyptis suaveolens*	B	0.02	2.04	24	19	gsf	1.0	+
21.	*Ixora arborea*	E	2.00	1.60	26	14	gsf	4.0	+
22.	*Jasminum angustifolium*	E&F	0.50	0.61	28	16	gsf	4.0	+
23.	*Jatropha gossypiifolia*	C	1.90	0.20	62	59	gsf	5.0	+
24.	*J. Podagrica*	C	1.40	1.80	56	53	gsf	4.0	+
25.	*Justicia procumbens*	E	0.01	0.04	21	18	gsf	1.0	+
26.	*Lantana camara*	E	0.06	0.04	18	23	gsf	4.0	+
27.	*Moringa oleifera*	A	0.80	1.30	28	10	gsf	1.0	+
28.	*Murraya koenigii*	E	0.06	0.01	23	16	gsf	3.0	+
29.	*Ocimum basilicum*	B	0.01	0.01	18	16	gsf	0.0	+
30.	*Premna latifolia*	E	0.01	0.06	36	33	gsf	2.0	+
31.	*Randia brandisii*	F	0.30	0.40	31	22	gsf	5.0	+
32.	*Santalum album*	C	---------- traces of Nectar ----------				gsf	0.0	+
33.	*Sapindus emarginata*	F	1.30	1.60	39	26	gsf	4.0	+
34.	*Sida acuta*	C	---------- traces of Nectar ----------				gsf	0.0	+
35.	*S. cordifolia*	C	---------- traces of Nectar ----------				gsf	0.0	+
36.	*Stachytarpheta indica*	E	0.90	1.00	27	28	gsf	4.0	+
37.	*Tectona grandis*	E	0.80	0.80	23	19	gsf	3.0	+
38.	*Tithonia rotundifolia*	E	0.80 head	0.60	34	31	gfs	1.0	+
39.	*Tribulus terrestris*	C	0.30	0.90	61	56	gsf	2.0	+
40.	*Tridax procumbens*	F	0.50 head	0.90	29	25	gsf	5.0	+
41.	*Zizyphus mauritiana*	C	0.02	0.02	57	51	gsf	0.0	+
42.	*Z. oenoplia*	C	0.02	0.02	53	49	gsf	0.0	+

Key G = glucose. S = sucrose. F = fructose. Capital letter denotes dominance.

TABLE 2 : The Butterfly species and the flower species visited by them

Butterfly species	*Number of Flower species**
Family Danaidae	
1. *Danaus chrysippus*	4, 6, 8, 9, 11, 12, 13, 16, 17, 18, 22, 26, 27, 28, 30, 33, 36, 38, 40.
2. *Danaus limniace*	3, 4, 11, 17, 18, 33.
3. *Euploea core*	1, 3, 4, 8, 14, 17, 18, 26, 30, 32, 33, 40, 41, 42.
Family Satyridae	
4. *Melanitis ledaismene*	26
Family Nymphalidae	
5. *Euthalia garuda*	4, 8.
6. *Hypolimnas bolina*	4, 12, 17.
7. *H. misippus*	3, 4, 17, 20, 26, 32.
8. *Phalanta phalantha*	4, 8, 12, 16, 17, 26, 30, 32, 33, 37, 41.
9. *Precis almana*	4, 16, 17, 36.
10. *P. hierta*	4, 8, 12, 16, 17, 18, 26, 36, 40.
11. *P. lemonias*	3, 4, 6, 16, 17, 18, 26, 31, 36, 40, 42.
12. *P. orythyia*	4, 6, 17.
Family Acraeidae	
13. *Acraea violae*	4, 6, 8, 16, 17, 18, 26, 36, 37, 40.
Family Lycaenidae	
14. *Apharitis vulcanus*	4.
15. *Castalius rosimon*	4, 6, 13, 25, 29, 40, 41, 42.
16. *Euchrysops cnejus*	13, 23, 25, 29, 40.
17. *Jamides celeno*	4, 23.
18. *Rapala iarbus sorya*	32.
Family Papilionidae	
19. *Atrophaneura aristolochiae*	2, 4, 8, 9, 10, 11, 12, 14, 15, 16, 19, 20, 21, 22, 24, 26, 34, 35, 36, 38, 40, 41, 42.
20. *A. hector*	1, 3, 9, 10, 11, 14, 16, 20, 26, 30, 34, 35, 36, 38, 42.
21. *Graphium agamemnon*	3, 4, 9, 11, 12, 16, 22, 26, 27, 28, 30, 35.
22. *G. doson*	4, 26, 41.
23. *G. nomius*	12, 22.
24. *Papilio demoleus*	4, 5, 8, 11, 12, 14, 19, 21, 22, 28, 31.
25. *P. polymnestor*	4, 11.
26. *P. polytes romulus*	3, 4, 5, 8, 9, 10, 12, 14, 15, 16, 19, 21, 22, 26, 35, 36, 37, 38.

Family Pieridae	
27. *Anaphaeis aurota*	4, 7, 10, 26, 29, 36, 40.
28. *Appias albina darada*	40.
29. *Catopsilia crocale*	4, 15, 17, 26, 31, 34, 35, 36.
30. *C. crocale pomona*	15, 16, 22, 26, 36.
31. *C. pyranthe*	2, 3, 4, 7, 8, 9, 10, 11, 12, 13, 15, 16, 17, 19, 20, 21, 22, 24, 26, 28, 30, 31, 34, 35, 36, 37, 40, 41.
32. *Cepora nerissa*	3, 8, 12, 22; 24, 29, 30, 37, 40.
33. *Colotis danae*	4, 7, 13, 27, 29, 31, 36, 40.
34. *C. eucharis*	4, 7, 20, 24, 25, 26, 29, 31, 40.
35. *C. fausta*	16, 22, 26, 31, 36.
36. *Delias eucharis.*	3, 8, 26.
37. *Eurema hecabe*	4, 6, 16, 17, 20, 26, 29, 30, 36, 39, 40, 41, 42.
38. *Valeria valeria anais*	5, 14.
Family Hesperiidae	
39. *Borbo cinnara*	1, 4, 5, 8, 10, 12, 14, 15, 16, 17, 18, 22, 26, 27, 29, 36, 37, 40.
40. *Pelopidas mathias*	1, 5, 15, 17, 26, 29, 36, 37, 39, 40, 42.

* The numbers relate to the serial number of flower species in Table 1.

Volume of Nectars

The nectar is in traces in four of the 42 plant species, and in the others it was in measurable quantity. The nectar volume in 'A' type flowers ranged from traces to 1.3 μl, that in 'B' type from 0.01 to 0.04 μ, in 'C' type from traces to 1.9 μl, in 'D' type from 0.4 to 2.0 μl, in 'E' type from 0.01 to 2.0 μl, in single flower of 'F' type from 0.02-1.6 μl, and in head inflorescence of 'F' type from 0.4 to 1.0 μl (per head), and in 'G' type from 0.4-2.8 μl. the data suggest that the amount of nectar in one large flower may be equivalent to that in many small flowers and this observation corroborates that of Cruden *et al.* (1983). According to Heinrich (1975), most day-flying Lepidopterans are slow fliers and so have small energy requirements. Nymphalids and Pierids appear to be weak fliers and must be spending little energy in flight, which they obtained by visiting flowers aggregated in heads or other compact inflorescences and secreting small quantity of nectar. Heinrich and Raven (1972) suggested that insects which land on inflorescences are still able to maintain an energy balance despite the minute amounts of nectar per floret, because the energy expended in walking from one floret to another can be 100 times less than an equivalent period of flight, and because the clustered florets can be visited in rapid succession.

Nectar Sugar Concentrations

Some flowers like those of *Sida* species though secreted nectar in traces, the nectar appeared almost in the form of crystals. With other species the sugar concentrations varied from 10% to 62%. Although it is assumed that butterfly nectars can not be very viscous (Baker, 1978), a wide range in nectar sugar concentrations of the flowers utilized by butterflies was reported in the literature : 15-25% (Watt *et al.*, 1974), 13-44% (Baker, 1975), 16-40% (Baker, 1978) and 20-25% (Kingslover and Daniel, 1979), 15-48% (Kevan and Baker, 1983) and the present study. Pivnick and McNiel (1985) observed *Thymelicus lineola* (Hesperiidae) feeding on concentrated nectars (40-65% sucrose) from a variety of flower species. This finding led them to question the recent literature stating that butterflies feed primarily and most effectively on dilute nectars.

The nectars of flowers now examined broadly fall into two ranges : 10-48% and 53-62%. The former concentration range is more common with the flowers receiving frequent visits from butterflies, thereby indicating that butterfly nectars are less viscous. The latter concentration range is encountered with the less often visited flowers indicating that high sugar concentration might not limit butterfly feeding. Probably, as suggested by Pivnick and McNiel (1985), high transport costs and severe stress may shift preferences to higher and lower concentrations respectively. It is likely that the butterflies can imbibe viscuous nectars after diluting them by secreting saliva as is the case with the silver moth (*Plusia gamma*) (Proctor and Yeo, 1972; Kevan and Baker, 1983).

Predominant sugar of Butterfly Nectars

McLean and Ivimey-Cook (1956) stated that butterflies, as they have only themselves to look after, are not so particular about the quality of nectar they obtain. Baker (1978) arranged the sugar composition of nectars for Costa Rican trees and lianes on the basis of predominant pollinator type, and showed that flowers pollinated by butterflies have sucrose dominance. The nectar of *Caesalpinia pulcherrima*, a butterfly flower, is sucrose rich (Cruden and Hermann-Parker, 1979). Present study showed that 14 of the 42 flower species are rich in sucrose, and these are the flowers that are avidly sought and most frequently visited by butterflies. But it also revealed that other nectars with glucose dominance are also utilised by butterflies. Watt *et al.* (1974) found that *Colias* butterflies tended to prefer those flowers that supplied nectars high in monosaccharide content, as opposed to nectars having a predominance of sucrose or larger sugars. The study also indicated that nectars of most tubular flowers contain more of the disaccharide, while those of open flowers its byproducts. Percival (1961), Von Handel *et al.* (1972), Heinrich (1975) and Gottsberger *et al.* (1984) also reported a similar relation between corolla type and predominant sugar.

Amino Acid Presence

Nectars contain from 2 to 24 amino acids according to the flower species concerned (Baker; 1978). Excepting for *Heliconius* butterfly which steeps pollen in nectar; then drinks the nectar with the leached out amino acids (Gilbert, 1972), the nectar amino acids are a potential source for nitrogen nutrition of most butterflies (Faegri and Pijl, 1979). Naturally, butterfly nectars are rich in amino acids Watt *et al.*, 1974) and the 'histidine scale' score reported by Baker and Baker (1973) and Baker (1978) ranged between 4-10, the mean being 6.68. The scores of histidine scale of the nectars of butterfly flowers such as *Cadaba fruticosa* (5.5), *Capparis spinosa* (6.0), *Caesalpinia pulcherrima* (6.0), *Clerodendrum infortunatum* (6.0), and *C. nerifolium* (4.0), and some other tube flowers fall within the range predicted for butterfly nectars. However, the low histidine scale of nectars of *Sida cordifolia* (0.0), *S. acuta* (0.0), *Anacardium occidentale* (3.0), *Caesalpinia coriaria* (3.0), *Albizia lebbeck* (3.0), *Murraya koenigii* (3.0), *Premna latifolia* (2.0), *Hyptis suaveolens* (1.0) and *Santalum album* (0.0), which were found to be commonly visited by butterflies show that butterflies need not necessarily feed on amino acid-rich nectars.

Literature Cited

Bahadur, B., Chaturvedi, A. and Rama Swamy, N. 1986. Nectar types in Indian Plants. *Proc. Indian Acad. Sci.* (Plant Sci.) *96* : 41-48.

Baker, H.G. 1975. Sugar concentrations in nectars from hummingbird flowers. *Biotropica 7* : 37-41.

Baker, H.G. 1978. chemical aspects of the pollination biology of Woody plants in the tropics. In : (eds). P.B. Tomlinson and M.H. Zimmerman *Tropical Trees as Living Systems*. Cambridge University Press, Cambridge/London/New York/Melbourne.

Baker, H.G. and Baker, I. 1973. Amino acids in nectar and their evolutionary significance. *Nature* (London) *241*: 545.

Cruden, R.w. and Hermann-Parker; S.M. 1979. Butterfly pollination of *Caesalpinia pulcherrima* with observations on a psychophilous syndrome. *J. Ecol., 67* : 155-168.

Cruden, R.W., Hermann, S.M. and Peterson, S. 1983. Patterns of nectar production and plant-pollinator coevolution. In : (eds). Barbara Bently and Thomas Elias *The Biology of Nectaries*. Columbia University Press, New York.

Faegri, k. and van der Pijl, L. 1979. *The Principles of Pollination Ecology*, 3rd edn. Pergamon Press, Oxford/New York/Toronto/Sydney/Paris/Franskfort.

Gilbert, L.E. 1972. Pollen feeding and reproductive biology of *Heliconius* butterflies. *Proc. Natl. Acad. Sci* (USA), *69* : 1403-1407.

Gottsberger, G., Schrauwen, J. and Linskens, H.F. 1973. Die Zucker-Bestandeile des Nectars einiger tropischen Bluten. *Protugaliae Acta Biol.* Ser. A *13* : 1-8.

Gottsberger, G., Schrauwen, J. and Linskens, H.F. 1984. Amino acids and sugars in nectar, and their putative evolutionary significance. *Plant Syst. Evol., 145* : 55-77.

Heinrich, B. 1975. Energetics of pollination. *Annu. Rev. Ecol. Syst., 6* : 139-170.

Heinrich, B. and Raven, H.P. 1972. Energetics and pollination ecology. *Science, 176* : 597-602.

Kevan, P.G. and Baker, H.G. 1983. Insects as flower visitors and poilinators. *Ann. Rev. Entomol., 28* : 407-453.

Kingslover, J.G. and Daniel, T.L. 1979. On the mechanics and energetics and energetics of nectar feeding in butterflies. *J. Theor. Biol., 76* : 167-179.

McLean, R.C. and Ivimey-Cook, W.R. 1956. *Text Book of Theoretical Botany*, Vol. II. Longmans Green & Co., London/New York/Toronto.

Neff, J.L., Simpson, B.B. and Moldenke, A.R. 1977. Flowers - flower visitor system. In: (eds). G.H. Onens and O.T. Solbrig *Convergent Evolution in Warm Deserts*. Dowden, Hutchinson and Ross Inc., Stoudsburg.

Percival, M. 1961. Types of nectar in angiosperms. *New Phytol., 60* : 235-281.

Pivnick, K.A. and McNiel, J.N. 1985. Effects of nectar concentration on butterfly feeding : Measured feeding rates for *Thymelicus lineola* (Lepidoptera : Hesperiidae) and a general feeding model for the adult Lepidoptera. *Oecologia* (Berl.), *66* : 226-237.

Proctor, M. and Yeo, P. 1972. *The Pollination of Flowers*. Taplinger Publishing Company, New York.

Varshney, R.K. 1983. Index *Rhopalocera Indica*, Part II. Records of the Zoological Survey of India : Occasional Paper No. 47.

Von Handel, E., Haeger, J.S. and Hauses, C.W. 1972. The sugars of some Florida nectars. *Amer. J. Bot.*, *59* : 1030-1032.

Watt, W.B., Hoch, P.C. and Hills, S.G. 1974. Nectar resource use by *Colias* butterflies : chemical and visual aspects. *Oecologia* (Berl.), *14* : 353-374.

NECTAR UTILIZATION AND POLLINATION POTENTIAL OF THRIPS IN RELATION TO SOME ASTERACEAE

T.N. ANANTHAKRISHNAN and K. GOPINATHAN
Entomology Research Institute
Loyola College, Madras 600 034, India.

ABSTRACT

Flower-insect coadaptations in relation to *Cosmos bipinnatus*, *Wedelia chinensis*, *Synedrella nodiflora* and *Tridax procumbens* (Asteraceae) and their trips pollinators *Microcephalothrips abdominalis*, *Thrips hawaiiensis*, *Frankliniella schultzei* and *Haplothrips tardus* are discussed with special reference to synchronization of thrips biology with flowering phenology, foraging ranges of pollinators, efficiency of pollination and efficient exploitation of nectar resources.

Key words : Nectar utilization; pollination potential; thrips; Asteraceae.

INTRODUCTION

Nectary denotes a highly specialised epidermal gland composed of small, thin-walled secretory cells from which nectar is brought to the surface through modified stomata (Fahn, 1979) that provides a source of attraction to nectar-loving animals. By providing the nectar to the pollinating organisms such as birds, insects and bats, the floral nectaries are directly involved with pollination, while the extrafloral nectaries are concerned more with plant metabolism than with the mechanics of pollination (Schremmer, 1970). Generally, in flowers pollinated by insects or birds, nectar secretion coincides with the pollen maturation and the forging insects in their attempt to collect nectar pick up mature pollen on their body. As a result, the forgers help in the transfer of pollen grains to the stigmas which will be receptive to pollen thus providing an opportunity for fertilization. Secretion of nectar is not a perennial process, since it ceases as soon as the fertilization is completed. In this respect there could be a coordinating mechanism that is normal between the events culminating in pollen maturation and those leading to nectar secretion. Considerable differences between the nectar yield of staminate and pistillate flowers have been noticed (Fahn, 1949), suggesting a possible relationship between the maturation of stamens and pistil and the nectar secretion.

Compared to the well-known hymenopteran and lepidopteran pollinators, information on the role of thrips in pollination has been rather obscure, and has come to be increasingly recognised in recent years, though the early reports of their pollination potential are referable to the observations of Shaw (1914) on thrips flying over sugarbeet fields with considerable pollen loads, and that of Annand (1926) on thrips with pollen in cultivated crops such as sugarbeet, alfalfa, plums and daisey in the United States of America. The active involvement of species of *Taeniothrips* in pollination energetics of *Calluna* (Hagerup, 1950) and *Erica* (Hagerup & Hagerup, 1953), *Frankliniella parvula* in the pollination of Cocoa (Billes, 1941), of *F. occidentalis* in onions (Carlson, 1964), of *Thrips hawaiiensis* in oil-palm pollination (Syed, 1979), and *Heterothrips arisaemae* involved in the pollination of the dioecious aroid *Arisaema triphyllum* (Rust, 1980) well reflect the pollination potential of thrips. The work of Mathur & Mohan Ram (1978) on petal colour change in *Lantana* incidental to pollination by thrips, as well as in *Wedelia chinensis* (Ananthakrishnan *et al.*, 1981) as well as observations of Gopinathan *et al.*, (1981) on the seed viability and germination capacity of *Ageratum conyzoides* with regard to cross pollination by thrips, as well as of seasonal periodicity of thrips infesting some Compositae in relation to pollination (Ananthakrishnan *et al.*, 1981), have further substantiated the role of thrips as efficient pollinators of some plants. Studies on the aspects of pollination in *Elaeis guianensis*, thrips seemed to visit female inflorescence during the time of receptivity and almost 70 percent of the pollen transported was viable, thus enhancing effective cross pollination (Syed, 1978 & 1979). Pollination in some dipterocarps showed that the floral morphology and flowering behaviour of *Shorea* sp. appear to be highly adapted for pollination by thrips as synchronous flowering and clumped distribution of trees allow thrips possibly with the aid of wind drafts, to effect short range pollen transfer between trees to pollinate these self incompatible species (Appanah & Chan, 1981).

Floral adaptations of Asteraceae to Thrips

Pollinators primarily use the floral nectar as a source of sugars which in turn provided energy. Sometimes the minor components of nectar, viz., aminoacids also play a role in attracting the pollinators. Heinrich & Raven (1972) suggested that to attain a maximal cross pollination, a balance must exist, between the energy expended by the flower-visitors and the calorific reward offered by the flowers. Thus the food reward like nectar should be sufficient enough to attract a pollinator, at the same time it should be limited prompting thereby the forager to visit other plants of the same species. Synchronous flowering of a species in a densely populated area enables effective cross pollination with low energy requirement, in spite of high calorific rewards offered by each flower.

To facilitate effective breeding, the most important elements of flowers are pollen and nectar. Nectar and pollen form the main sources of food for thrips pollinators. Thrips suck the contents of pollen out and also feed on the nectar. The asynchronous action of the mouthparts of thrips and the reduction of one mandible has been regarded as an important adaptation to such fluid contents of pollen grains and/or nectar of (Grinfel'd, 1959). In Nature, the disc flowers of Asteraceae are protandrous, and hence when the stigmas emerge through the staminal column they carry pollen grains along their lower surface. The secretion of nectar coincides well with the pollen maturation, the maximal secretion occurring during the stigmatic receptivity, thereby providing an opportunity for fertilization by the foraging insects with mature pollen on their bodies. In *Cosmos bipinnatus*, visits of different groups of insects in the same flower which are almost adapted for the same type of food indicate the high production of food i.e., pollen and nectar. It is estimated that the pollen production in a single disc floret is from 5536 to 5716 and in a capitulum 1, 10, 350 to 2, 17, 208. Starchy pollen grains occur in the outermost row of disc florets and their number gradually decreases towards the innermost row. The nectar secretion also was considerably higher when compared to *Tridax*,

Wedelia and *Synedrella* almost touching half the length of the corolla tube. The flowers, besides providing nectar and pollen as food, provide suitable oviposition sites such as tissues of bracts, corolla as well as pappus and also form a shelter site from the predators. Pappus form suitable ovipositional site for tubuliferan thrips, whereas the terebrantian species lay their eggs in the tissues of bracts, corolla tube and ovarian wall. Apart from this, the protandrous condition, nectar secretion, and the centrepetal developmental pattern of the capitulum appear important adaptations to the biology of thrips. The adaptive significance in terms of the pollinator and flower appears impressive in view of the strategies are evident in species like *Microcephalothrips abdominalis and Wedelia chinensis*. The organisation of the capitural in a corymbose fashion in the homogamous heads helps the pollinators to utilise very little energy for their inter-capitular migration.

Flower-insect coadaptation is a continuing process, since the dynamics of pollen transfer mechanisms are closely related to the behavioural characteristics of the pollinators. In this context an analysis of the 'adaptation spectrum' of thrips would involve aspects such as availability of nectar/pollen as food, stigmatic exudations (generally absent in Asteraceae), nectarine exudations through minute stomatal pores adjacent to the stylar base, favourable micro-environment within the corolla tube providing suitable oviposition sites enabling the emerging larvae to become dusted with pollen grains in their upward and downward movement within the tube, the architecture of the pollen wall coupled with the setal arrangements of the body of thrips, and the synchronisation of the anthesis and the nectar secretion (Ananthakrishnan, 1982).

Morphology, topography and Significance of Stomata on floral Nectaries

Flowers of Asteraceae possess nectary at the bases of their styles, similar to those in flowers of Apiaceae (Fahn, 1949). Intercellular spaces are generally well-developed in the subepidermal nectariferous tissues in instances where nectar 9s exuded through stomata. Such stomata are generally modified in such a way that the guard cells remain open throughout. However some species are able to change the sizes of their apertures, though rarely (Zandonella, 1972). Distinct variations are evident in the structure and topography of the nectary as well as in the mode of secretion of the nectar. In addition to the outward movement of sugars in nectar secretion, reverse movements are also known in which the nectar is reabsorbed by the flowers not only at the end of fertilization but also during the process (Lüttge, 1961; Shuel, 1961). Although the amount of nectar secreted is correlated with the volume of the nectariferous tissues, significant variations in everyday secretion rates of nectar appears to be caused by environmental factors (Marden, 1984). However, the active life of nectary is limited in most of the flowers and the maximum production of nectar being at the time of stigmatic receptivity — a stage when maximum pollinators are attracted to the flowers.

Incidence of nectaries at the stylar bases in species of Asteraceae and Apiaceae, and exudation from these nectaries through stomata is known (Fahn, 1952, 1953, 1979; Frei, 1955; Frey-Wyssling & Hausermann, 1960; Gulyas & Pesti, 1966). Pesti (1976) have provided information on the periodictiy of secretion as well as the daily fluctuations in the sugar contents of nectar in Asteraceae. Studies on the floral nectaries of *Cosmos bipinnatus, Wedelia chinensis, Synedrella nodiflora*, and *Tridax procumbens* with respect to heir morphology, topography and their significance in relation to insect pollination provides an opportunity to understand the closelknit mechanism underlining the pollinator-floral organisation which could reflect the subtle level of coadaptation (Gopinathan & Varatharajan, 1982).

Thrips species move toward the lower regions of the corolla tube to feed on the nectar. In this instance the incidence of stomata in specific patterns on the nectaries appeared impressive. Of the four species examined, *Cosmos bipinnatus* showed large, linear and almost triangular nectaries (Figs. 2B, C; 2, A). The number of stomata ranged from 28-31 along the apical region of the nectary encircling the stylar base, and each stoma is placed equidistally. Nectaries of *W. chinensis* are wider at their apices than at the proximal region nearer the ovary (Figs. 2B; 3C). The stomata occur irrgeularly, 4-6 at the apical region, and the rest are scattered along the sides of the nectary mostly above the mid-region (Fig. 2B). In *Tridax* and nectary is rectangular, encircles the style just above the ovary, and is four lobed at the apex (Fig. 2D). Two of them are large and have four stomata each; the other two are smaller and alternate with the large lobes and have two stomata each.

The stylar region immediately above the nectary is swollen and there is no evidence of any secretory activity (Fig. 2D). The nectary is without cuticle and its cells have large nuclei and granular cytoplasm containing numerous small vacuoles. In *Synedrella* also the nectary is four-lobed but united at the lower regions nearer to the ovary. Unlike the nectaries of *Tridax*, the free lobes cover almost three-fourth of the length of the nectary in *Synedrella*; though the four lobes of the nectary are of similar size, stomatal distribution is characteristic-with three stomata on each of two opposite lobes, and one each at the tip of the other two lbes (Figs. 1A; 2C).

TABLE 1 : Summary of Dimensions of stomata and names of Insect Visitors

Species	*Size of Disc floret mm*		*Number of stomata µm*	*Size of stomatal pore*		*Associated insect visitors*
	Length	*Width*		*Length*	*Width*	
Cosmos bipinnatus	15 ± 3.5	1.4 ± 0.82	29	13.92 ± 3.1	2.32 ± 0.28	Bess, Butterflies, Thrips species such as *Thrips hawaiensis, Microcephalothrips abdominalis,* and *Haplothrips gowdeyi*
Tridax procumbens	10 ± 2.2	0.97 ± 0.25	12	13.92 ± 2.79	2.32 ± 0.85	*Haplothrips tardus, gowdeyi, Microcephalothrips abdominalis* and *Frankliniella schultzei*
Wedelia chinensis	8 ± 1.3	1.00 ± 0.3	11	11.6 ± 3.2	4.64 ± 1.6	*Microcephalothrips abdominalis, Frankliniella schultzei* and *Haplothrips gowdeyi*
Synedrella nodiflora	6 ± 1.8	0.5 ± 0.02	8	20.38 ± 2.46	6.96 ± 1.28	*Microcephalothrips abdominalis* and *Haplothrips gowdeyi*

Values presented are average of 25 replicates

These stomata lack subsidiary cells, remain open throughout the day and night. The stomatal pores continue to be open even after the florets stop producing nectar. Maximum nectar was observed during

6.00-9.00 hr. of the day. Stomata are surrounded by parenchymatous cells of secretary nature, (Fig. 3D & E) and are epistomatic, being elevated from the normal plane of the nectariferous tissue. In *Cosmos* and *Tridax*, stomata are ellipsoidal whereas in *Wedelia* and *Synedrella* they are orbicular. The guard cells are non-chlorophyllous. The presence of starch is more in ellipsoidal types (Figs. 1C and 2A & D) (*Tridax* and *Cosmos*) than in orbicular types (*Wedelia* and *Synedrella*). Dimensions of the disc florets and the stomatal pores as well as the number of stomata (Table 1) reveals that as the number of stomata and size of the pores and the florets increased, a larger number of insect visitors were attracted. The lower number of stomata in *Synedrella* as compared with the other species examined, is compensated by an increase in the size of the pores.

The distribution and topography of the floral stomata suggest the possibility of their functional importance in relation to the foraging behaviour of the pollinating organisms. In other words, larger the floret, greater is the number of stomata, resulting in the regulation or atraction of more insect visitors, diversified qualitatively and quantitatively, to achieve the target function of pollination (Table 1).

Bee-flower interactions depends upon the concentration of available calorific rewards. Observations presented here indicate that stomatal apertures exist in a substrate of highly specialised nectariferous tissues in a characteristic epistomatic fashion, which probably contribute to the evolutionary significance of Compositae (Gopinathan and Varatharajan, 1982). The incidence of floral stomata facilitating the exudation of nectar is strongly contended to be occurring only on nonstructural nectaries which do not possess a specifically differentiated nectariferous tissues (Zimmermann, 1932).

Role of thrips in Pollination

Thrips, inspite of their minute size, play an important role in the pollination of flowers as a result of their tremendous potential in the build up of populations within the flowers, which in turn helps in improving production of viable seeds. The very close interaction between weeds and thrips besides providing a very good example of insect-plant interactions has also served to unravel the adaptive significance of the pollinators in relation to flowers of different weeds and horticultural plants of the natural order Asteraceae in terms of species packing, species dominance, and species succession on the one hand and the population build-up of different species on the other. Thrips population within the flowers shows a remarkable pattern of succession resulting in the displacement of one species by another, a feature primarily dependent upon not only the seasonal periodicity, but also the host range and colonising ability of the respective species of thrips. Infestation by thrips starts at the late bud stage when the corollas of sterile ray floret begin to open. Larval population gradually increases when almost all disc florets are open and the stigmas turn receptive. *Thrips hawaiiensis*, the primary species found in *Cosmos* lay their eggs inside the tissue along the lower parts of the corolla tubes, normally immediately above the nectary. In several cases the eggs are laid encircling the corolla tube, most of them in contact with the nectar secreted. The adults of *T. hawaiiensis* carry the maximum number of pollen grains on their bodies, followed by the larvae. Observations on thrips with pollen load indicate the incidence of pollen grains on 9th and 10th abdominal segments facilitated by the presence of more number of setae than the other body segments (Fig. 3A & B). Besides, *T. hawaiiensis* carry pollen grains in clusters on the legs as well. The emerging larvae coming out of the florets through the staminal column becomes dusted with pollen grains on their body. (Fig. 3F).

Receptivity of the stigma occur when the stigmatic lobes become well-projected and tapering, often touching the lip of the corolla tube, synchronising with the maximum nectar production. Encircling the tapering region of the stigmatic lobes are long papillae, each of which, gradually decreases in length towards the apex. The receptive region occurs along the inner sides of lobes towards the lower portion with closely arranged small papillae. The papillae at the tapering region carry copious amounts of pollen grains during the slow movement of the stigma through the syngenesious anther column. This takes 70-74 hrs. For after the complete curling back and touches the lip of the corolla tube that has numerous minute trichomes on which pollen grains are dusted. Thrips, in their attempt to get into the lower regions of the corolla tube to feed on the nectar, pass along the lips of the corolla, where a large number of pollen grains are accumulated as a result of the shedding of pollen by stigmatic lobes on the surfaces of corolla lobes. During this movement the forelegs and the ventral portions of the bodies of thrips become coated with pollen. Incidentally the wings and the setae along the dorsal sides of thrips also get coated with pollen since thrips brush against the hairs of the stigmatic lobes.

Flower recognition capacity of *T. hawaiiensis* reveals that a majority of thrips are confined to flowers with their ray as well as disc florets of the first two rows open, where generally the maximum amount of nectar and pollen are available, whereas a few thrips prefer the flowers which had just attained senescensce. Abundance of thrips in fully opened flowers of *Cosmos* show their ability to recognise particular stage in floral ontogeny for their development and multiplication (Varatharajan *et al*, 1982). Under natural conditions, in the protandrous disc florets, stigmas with pollen grains along the lower surface emerge through the staminal column. Experiments to confirm any preference for stigmas with pollen indicated that stigmas of *Tridax procumbens* without pollen (mechanically removed in the laboratory) were not recognised. When stigmas of *T. procumbens*, Helianthus annuus and *Wedelia chinensis* with pollen are kept individually as well as in groups, *Haplothrips tardus* showed preference for *T. procumbens* stigmas only (Ananthakrishnan *et al*, 1981). In *Wedelia chinensis*, the terebrantians *Microcephalothrips abdominalis* and *Frankliniella schultzei* oviposit within the ovarian tissues and bracts and enable the larvae to move into the florets on hatching. *Haplothrips tardus*, a tubuliferan, however lays eggs on the petals, bracts, and pappus of Tridax procumbens.

With the blooming of the florets, thrips inhabit the capitula and their population reaches a maximum when the stigmatic lobes gets exposed, during which time the nectar exudation is maximum. Frequent movements of different species of adults and larvae of *M. abdominalis* (the dominant species in the head of *W. chinensis*), *F. schultzei* and *H. tardus* (the dominant species in the heads of *T. procumbens*) form floret to floret occurs. These thrips carry pollen grains on their bodies, particularly within the disc florets, and feed on pollen, nectar, and tender tissues of style and stigma. Longer and larger number of setae of *F. schultzei* enable it to carry pollen grains in clusters on legs, wings, anal setae, and rarely on antennae. The agile movement of *F. schultzei* involving frequent spreading and shaking of wings causes the pollen grains to fall on the stigmas. Pollen grains carried by species of *Haplothrips* on the abdominal region particularly at the region of the anal setae, rub against the stigmatic surface, owing to its large body size, and this process is further facilated by its peculiar backward movements. The frequent combing of the body surface with its hind legs enables shedding of pollen grains on the stigmatic surface when the insect lands on the stigma.

M. abdominalis takes 9-11 days to complete its development. Thrips enter the flower at the late bud stage when the ray florets emerge and become prominent. At this time it lays eggs in the flower, and as soon as the larva emerges from the egg, pollen grains are available to the larvae. When the pollen grain availability declines, nectar is readily available; in the meantime the stigma attains the receptive stage. During the seed formation stage of the flower, transformation into adults of the insect takes place (Ananthakrishnan *et al*, 1981). The flowering phenology with special reference to *W. chinensis* appears well synchronised with the biology of *M. abdominalis* suggesting a possible evolutionary impact made by the pollinator activity on the floral resources. Ecological synchronisation of the pollinating species is facilitated by nectar production providing an inexhaustable supply of nutrients, as well as a vital source of attraction. In *Bidens* and *Coreopsis*, Cronquist (1968) has related the copious nectar secretion to the extensive parallelism between different classes of pollinators and species of Asteraceae. The obvious limitations of these thrips species to the small capitula of *W. chinensis* and *T. procumbens* indicate their profound potential to adapt themselves for an undisturbed living with a substantial supply of food and shelter, safe from the predatory insects, and providing enough space for oviposition.

Anthophilous Thysanoptera seem to be controlled largely by the flowering phenology of host-plants. The continuous build-up of thrips population in a flower leads to inter-, and intraspecific competitions among thrips species which bring about dispersal, ultimately enhancing the possibilities for cross-pollination. Effective cross-pollination mainly depends on the (i) blooming time of the flower, (ii) amount of food reward (nectar/pollen) for the pollinator, and (iii) structures facilitating access to the flowers and food. These facilities are very clearly evident in the examined system, with a characteristic

synchronisation in the relative abundance of thrips as well as the species-packing in the capitula of the plants studied. Incidentally, a limitation of the food reward from the flower to the forager encourages them to visit other plants of the same species. The species living in the heterogamous heads of Asteraceae with solitary inflorescences, seem to spend more energy for their visit to other flowers where the food reward is high. On the contrary, thrips in homogamous capitula spend lesser energy fro their dispersal due to corymbose arrangement where the nectar availability is also less (Gopinathan *et al*, 1981). Thus, a balance as visualised by Heinrich and Raven (1972), exists between the nectar/pollen availability and the incidental calorific reward of a flower on the one hand, and the energy expenditure by the pollinator on the other.

The direct involvement of *T.hawaiiensis* in the pollination of *Cosmos* reveal geitonogamous mode whereas that by other foraging insects such as bees and butterflies show xenogamous mode, resulting in maximum seed production. As far as the food reward to the three different insect groups foraging the inflorescence is concerned, thrips are the major beneficiaries because of their incidence inside the inflorescence throughout. On the contrary, the foraging period of bees and butterflies is restricted to specific timings. Thrips due to their abundance and greater food reward, lead a life with lesser intra-and inter-capitular dispersal resulting in geitonogamy. The ability of thrips to recognise the particular state of the flower ready for pollination appears interesting, even though they are introduced from a different host plant. Synchronisation in terms of infestation by gravid females, Their egg-laying sites where maximum nectar is freely available for the emerging larvae at the receptive stage of stigma, helps in the build-up of population in an inflorescence for pollinators. Thrips can be considered as primary pollinators due to the exclusive presence of *Cosmos* pollen grains. Bees and butterflies are of heterogeneous type since they carry pollen grains other than that of *Cosmos* also.

CONCLUSIONS

The foraging ranges of pollinators are dependent on a number of factors, including resource density and distribution and the density of conspecific and potential competitors. Thysanopteran pollinators associated with Asteraceae are able to synchronise their biology with flowering phenology, being able to recognise particular stages of flowers to infest, localise apt oviposition sites so that the emerging offspring are provided with floral resources without spending much of their energy by searching the food, as also a safe shelter from predatory insects. The centripetal development of the florets of Asteraceae enable a sequential as well as continuous availability of pollen and nectar promoting the development of the pollinator. The intricate biological relationships of the pollinator thrips with the hosts appear fascinating a in view of their efficient exploitation of the natural floral resources for the successful development of the pollinating organism. In composites and a plants with umber inflorescence the pattern of arrangement of flowers facilitates the flower-to-flower movement of foraging thrips as compared with solitary floral arrangements. The preference of flower thrips to hosts with this kind of floral arrangement not only reveals the adaptive significance of the flowers for feeding and breeding of thrips but also the enabling of thrips to spend minimal energy for flower to flower dispersal. As the flowers are arranged in close proximity in these floral systems, the pattern of flower organisation facilitates interfloral dispersal and inter-capitular dispersal of thrips resulting in successful cross pollination-geitonogamy with minimal energy expenditure. The distance between the flowers being an important factor related to the energy balance of the pollinator (Heinrich & Raven, 1972; Heinrich, 1975), thrips probably colonise flowers arranged in such a manner.

Colonisation by sucking insects may increase the rate of secretion by nectaries (Mound, 1962) and this increase is positively correlated with increased infestation level. This is well compatible to the observation of thysanopteran pollinators infesting in different composites with floral nectaries. Sucking insects reduce the "Source pressure" of an organ (and may even cause to become a sink), and yet nectar secretion increases with increasing infestation. High infestation of insects and demand for nectar induces the flowers for increased nectar production. This eventhough increases the cost of nectar production as nectar secretion requires metabolic energy, and nectar itself is composed of metabollically useful compounds — will be compensated by the production of more number of seeds through effective cross pollination.

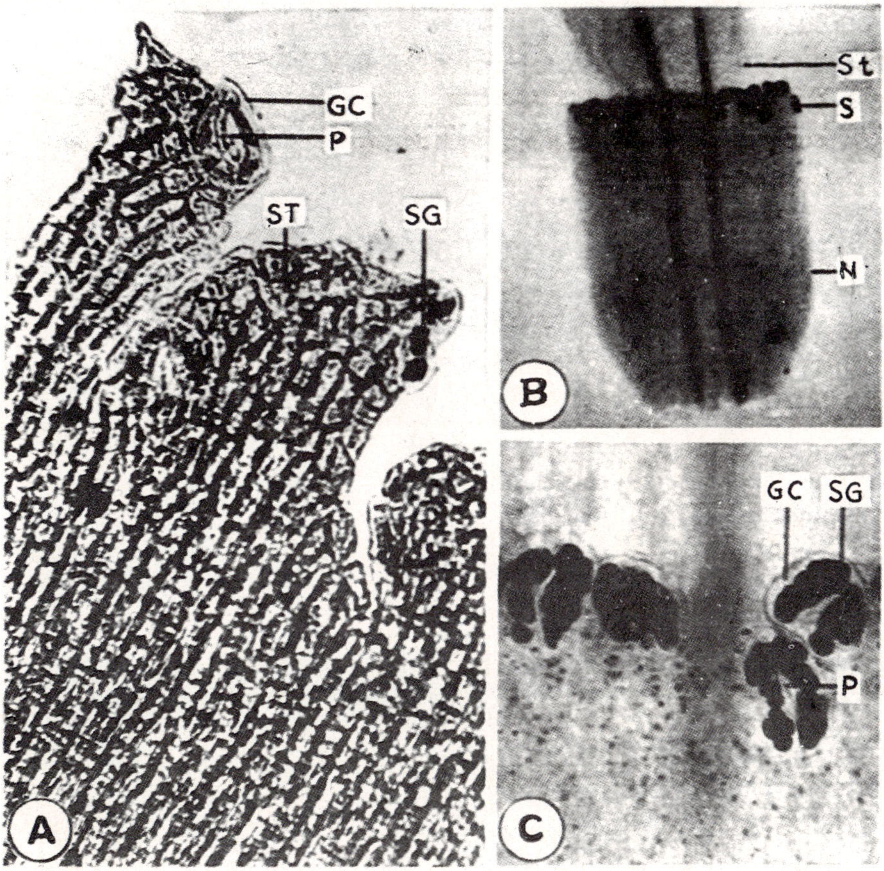
GC
P
ST
SG
A
St
S
N
B
GC
SG
P
C

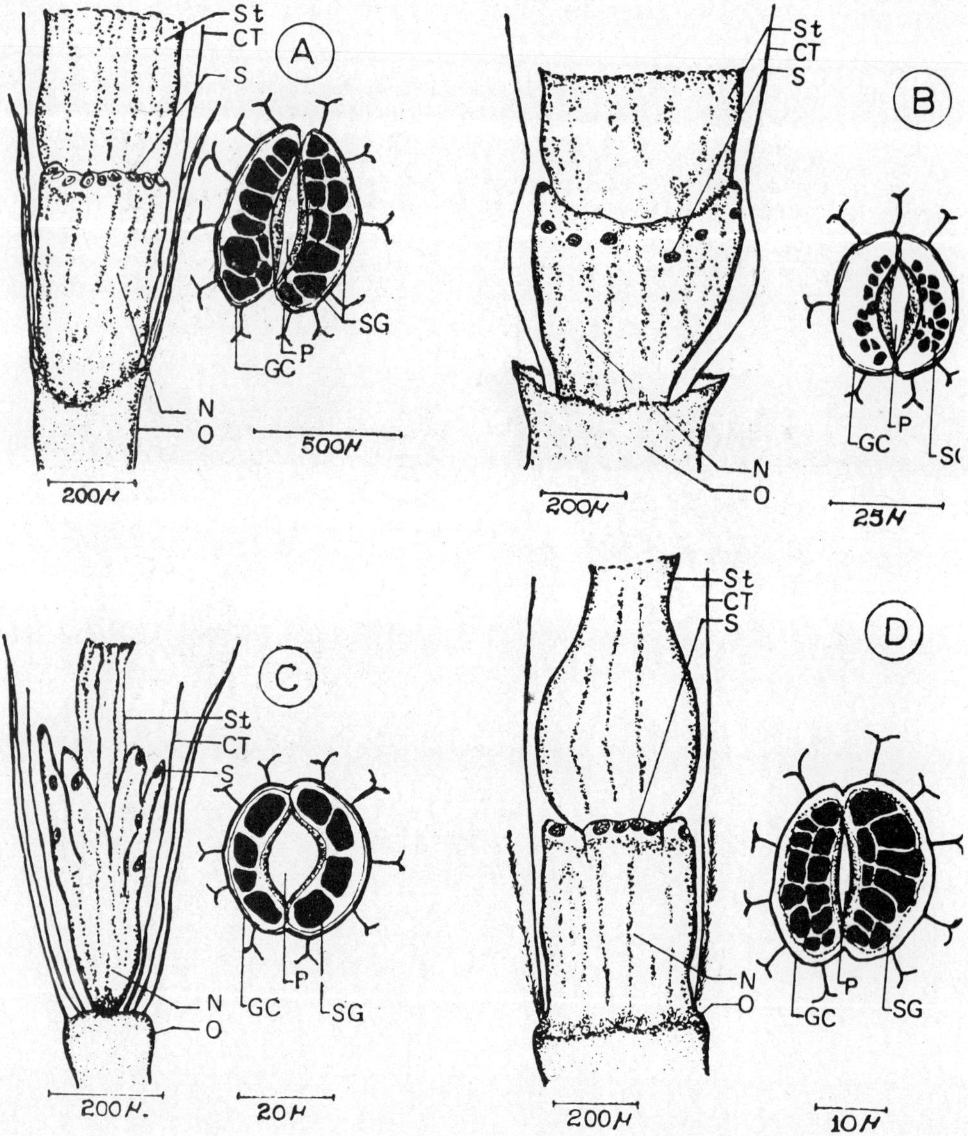

A
St
CT
S
SG
P
GC
N
O
200µ
500µ
B
St
CT
S
GC
P
N
O
200µ
25µ
C
St
CT
S
GC
P
SG
N
O
200µ.
20µ
D
St
CT
S
N
O
GC
P
SG
200µ
10µ

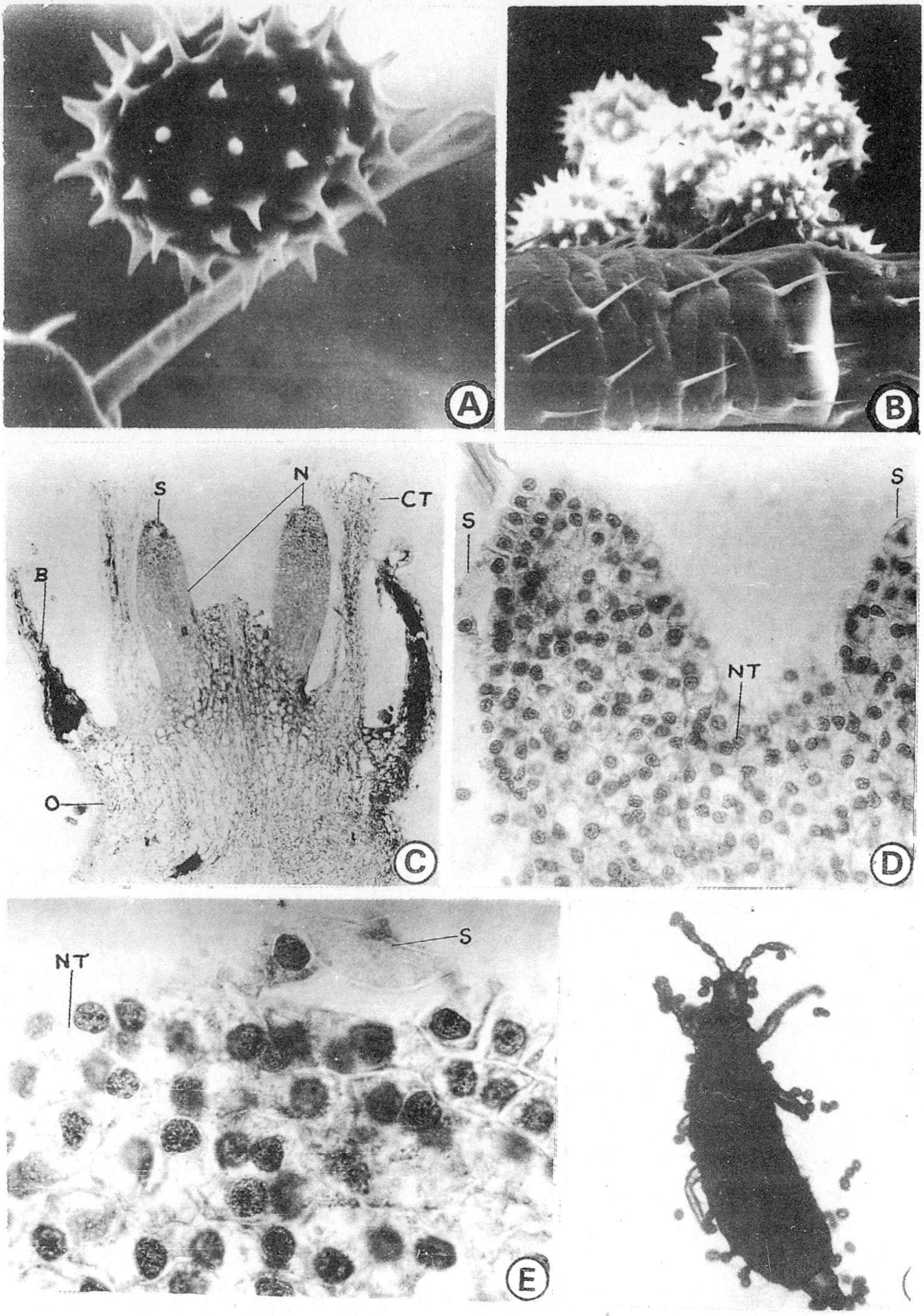
A
B
S
N
CT
B
O
C
S
S
NT
D
S
NT
E

Explanation to Figures

FIGURE I

A—C : (GC, guard cell; N, nectary; P, pore; S, stoma; SG, starch grain; St, secretary tissue; St, style); A. *Synedrella nodiflora.* Apical portion of nectary showing stomata with starch grains. X 1000; B & C. *Cosmos bipinnatus*; B. Nectary at stylar base showing stoma arranged on top. x 35; C. Enlarged view of stomata. X 2800.

FIGURE 2

A—D : (CT, corolla tube; GC, guard cell; N, nectary; O, ovary; P, pore; S, stoma; Sg, starch grain) Nectary and enlarged view of stoma; A. *Cosmos bipinnatus*; B. *Wedelia chinensis*; C. *Synedrella nodiflora*; D. *Tridax procumbens*

FIGURE 3

A—F : (B, bract; CT, corolla tube; N, nectary; NT, nectariferous tissues; O, ovary; S, stomata); A. Pollen attached on the thoracic seta; B. Leg region with a cluster of pollen grains of *Tridax procumbens*; C. Flower L.S. showing nectary attached to ovary surrounding the style; D. Nectary C.S showing secretory tissues; E. Nectary C.S. showing secretory tissues and stomata; F. Thrips larva having pollen grains on its body.

Literature Cited

Ananthakrishnan, T.N. 1982. Thrips and pollination biology; *Curr. Sci., 51* : 168-172.

Ananthakrishnan, T.N. Varatharajan, R. and Gopinathan, K. 1981. Pollination in *Wedelia chinensis* (Osbeck) Merr. and *Tridax procumbens* L. (Compositae) by thrips (Thysanoptera : Insecta); *Proc. Indian natn. Sci. Acad., B47* : 159-165.

Ananthakrishnan. T.N, Varatharajan, R. and Gopinathan, K. 1981 Seasonal periodicity of thrips infesting some Compositae in relation to pollination; *Proc. Indian natn. Sci. Acad., B47* : 811-815.

Annand. P.N. 1926. Thysanoptera and the pollination of flowers; *Am. Nat., 60* : 177-182.

Appanah, S. and Chan, H.T. 1981. Thrips : the pollinators of some Dipterocarps; *Malaysian Forester, 44* : 234-252.

Billes, D.J. 1941. Pollination of *Theobroma cacao* L. in Trinidad, B.W.I., *Trop. Agric. Trin., 18* : 151-156.

Carlson, E.C. 1964. Effect of flower thrips on onion seed plants and as study of their control; *J.Econ. Entomol., 57* : 735-741.

Cronquist, A. 1968. *The Evolution and Classification of Flowering Plants*. Boston : Houghton Mifflin Company, pp.396.

Fahn, A. 1949. Studies on the ecology of nectar secretion; *Palest. J.Bot. Jerusalem Ser., 4* : 207-224.

Fahn, A. 1952. On the structure of floral nectaries; *Bot. Gaz., 113* : 464-470.

Fahn, A.1953. The topography of the nectary in the flower and its phylogenetical trend; *Phytomorphology, 3* : 424-426.

Fahn, A. 1979. *Secretory Tissues in Plants.* Academic Press London.

Frei, E. 1955. Die Innervierung der Floralen Nektarien dikotyler Pflan-zentamilien; *Ber. schweiz. bot. Ges., 65* : 60-114.

Frey-Wyssling, A. and Hausermann, E. 1960 Deutung der Gestaltlosen Nektarien; *Ber. schweiz. bot. Ges., 70* : 150-162.

Gopinathan, K. and Varatharajan, R. 1982. On the morphology, topography and the significance of stomata on floral nectaries of some Compositae; *Phytomorphology., 32* : 265-269.

Gopinathan, K. Varatharajan, R. and Ananthakrishnan, T.N. 1981. Incidence of *Microcephalothrips abdominalis* (Crawford) (Thysanoptera : Insecta) in relation to the pollination biology of the weed *Ageratum conyzoides* Linn. (Compositae) *Proc. Indian natn. Sci. Acad., B47* : 505-509.

Grinfel'd, E.K. 1959. The feeding of thrips (Thysanoptera) on pollen of flowers and the origin of asymmetry in their mouthparts; *Ent. Obozr., 38 : 789-804.*

Gulyas, S. and Pesti, J. 1966. Angaben zur Anatomie der Nektarien der Centaureae; *Acta biol. Szeged., 12* : 17-24.

Hagerup, O. 1950. Thrips pollination in *Calluna; D. Kgl. Danske Vidensk. Selsk. Biol. Medd., 18* : 1-116.

Hagerup and Hagerup, O 1953. Thrips pollination of *Erica tetralix; New Phytol.,* 52 : 17.

Heinrich, B. 1975. Energetics of Pollination. : *Annu. Rev. Ecol. and Syst.*, *6* : 139-170.

Heinrich, B and Raven, P.H. 1972. Energetics and pollination ecology; *Science, 176* : 597-602.

Luttge, U. 1961. Uber die Zusammensetzung des Nektars und den Mechanisums seiner sekretion; *I. Planta., 56* : 189-212.

Marden, J.H. 1984. Intra population variation in nectar secretion in *Impatiens capensis; Oecologia* (Berlin), *63* : 418-422.

Mathur, G. and Mohan Ram, H.Y. 1978. Significance of petal colour in thrips pollinated *Lantana camara* L. *Ann. Bot., 42* : 1473-1476.

Mound, L.A. 1962. Extra floral nectaries of cotton and their secretions; *Emp. Cotton. Grow. Rev., 39* : 254-261.

Pesti, J. 1976. Daily fluctuations in the sugar content of nectar and periodicity of secretion in the compositae; *Acta Agron. Acad. Sci. Hung., 25* : 5-17.

Rust, R.W. 1980. Pollen movement and reproduction in *Arisoema triphyllum; Bull. Torrey. Bot. Club., 107* : 539-542.

Schremmer, F. 1970 Extra nuptiale nektarien : Beobachtungen an *Salix eleagnos* und *Pteridium aquilinum*; *Oesterr. Bot. Z., 117* : 205-222.

Shaw, 1914. Thrips as pollinators of beet flowers; *Bull. U.S. Dept. Agric.* p.104.

Shuel, R.W. 1961. Influence of reproductive organs on the secretion of sugar in flowers of *Streptosolen jamesonii; Pl. Physiol.*, 36 : 265-271.

Syed, R.A. 1978. Thrips pollination of oil palm in West Malysia. Commonwealth Institute of Biological Control rèport. Comm. Agric. bureau. Slough.

Syed, R.A. 1979. Studies on oil palm pollination by insects; *Bull. Ent. Res., 69* : 213-224.

Varatharajan, R., Gopinathan, K. and Ananthakrishnan, T.N. 1982. Comparative efficiency of thrips in relation to other foraging insects in the pollination of *Cosmos bipinnatus* Cav. (Compositae); *Proc. Indian natn. Sci. Acad., B48* : 735-739.

Zandonella, P. 1972. Le nectaire floral des Centrospermales, localisation, morphologies, anatomie, histologie, cytologie; these *Univ. Claude Bernard*, Lyon, 2 Vols.

Zimmermann, J.G. 1932. Uber die extrafloralen Nektarien der Angiospermen; *Beih. bot. Zbl., 49A* : 99-196.

SPECULATION ON NECTAR PRODUCTION AND ADVERTISEMENT BY FOSSIL PLANTS

J.H.J. PENNY

Department of Earth Sciences, Cambridge University
Downing Street, Cambridge, CB2 3EQ, U.K.

ABSTRACT

The reductions in productivity and dispersal of female reproductive cells associated with the adoption of the seed habit created pressure for the protection of ovules against herbivory, leading to enclosure of the ovules by cupulate structures during the Devonian and Carboniferous. This paper examines possible evidence for the subsequent development of plant-pollinator relationships, with particular emphasis on entomophily and beginning with a brief overview of insect evolution.

It would appear that palynophagous arthropods were the earliest opportunistic pollinators, insect involvement possibly beginning as early as the Carboniferous. Earliest pollinator attraction may have been stimulated by structural modifications of the reproductive organs and the use of scent, while pollen was probably the first pollinator reward. The first use of nectar-like secretions possibly involved the micropylar fluid, while male Bennettite flowers could provide evidence of the oldest nectary structures. With the appearance of the angiosperms nectar might have replaced pollen as the main reward and simple use of colour for target-type nectar guides could have been in use by the Albian. Faithful insect pollinators and associated advanced floral structures had appeared by the early Tertiary.

Key words : Nectar production; speculation, advertisement; fossil plants.

INTRODUCTION

In extant angiosperms nectar is the main food reward received by pollination vectors. The production and advertisement of the nectar reward differs from plant to plant, depending on the particular pollinator which is involved. Variations in the site and quantity of nectar production lead to highly complex interactions, where the reward of the pollinator must be balanced against the need for the numerous separate visits required for pollination. If the reward from one flower is too great the pollinator will visit fewer flowers and pollination will be reduced; if the reward is too small the pollinator will learn to visit another species instead (Heinrich, 1975, 1976; Heinrich and Raven, 1972).

The question I should like to discuss here is whether it might be possible to identify fossil evidence to suggest that extinct plants used nectar or similar secretions as pollinator rewards. Clearly this question is not easily addressed, since nectar and scent are not available in the fossil record and colour is only preserved under exceptional conditions. Nevertheless, there is some evidence to be gained from the investigation of plant mega- and microfossils which suggests the possibility of the existence of nectiferous secretions in fossil angiosperms and gymnosperms.

Evidence for Pollinator availability and involvement

Vector pollination can be viewed as the controlled exploitation of animals for pollen transport. I use the word controlled deliberately, since the earliest interactions between plants and pollinators were almost certainly not altruistic.

Spores, pollen and ovules have a significant nutritional value and plants must have been under early pressure to protect their reproductive structures from predators. Thus the earliest evidence of associations might be expected to take the form of defensive structures, while the development of specific controlling features would follow more slowly in response to originaly fortuitous advantages gained from the attentions of visiting predators.

Among the earliest associations were interactions between terrestrial arthropods and pteridophyte plants, such as the association of trigonotarbid arachnids with sporangia of *Rhynia major* (Rolfe, pers. comm. in Chaloner and Saville, 1975). Such relationships might have had a significance in spore dispersal, particularly as the spores themselves show a resistance to digestion (Chaloner, 1976).

With the evolution of the seed habit, particularly of dioecism, much greater emphasis must have been placed on vector involvement, since successful reproduction now depended on pollen transfer between male and female organs and was no longer a question of simple spore dissemination. Many plants must have relied on the wind for pollen dispersal, but there is compelling evidence that this was not the case in all. For example the prepollen *Monoletes*, which is of pteridosperm origin, is significantly in excess of the typical size range associated with wind dispersal (Whitehead, 1969; Taylor, 1981), reaching 600um in the Medullosaceae.

Crepet (1983) suggests that the medullosans might not have been anemophilous. He points out that if medullosans were of patchy distribution on floodplains or grew as understory plants in coal swamp forests (as suggested by Phillips and DiMichele 1981), then they would either not approach the dense populations often associated with anemophily (Whitehead, 1969) or would suffer from unfavorable wind conditions in the understory whereby the large pollen could not be effectively distributed on the available air currents. Crepet (1983) further suggest that pollen organs such as *Dolerotheca* might have influenced the attraction of pollinators by concentrating and advertising the pollen reward. The pollinator in this instance might have been a segmented arthropod such as *Arthropleura*, which has been found with *Monoletes* type prepollen attached to appendages (Scott and Taylor, 1983).

The earliest insect involvement may have been in the Carboniferous, where the first insects appear in the Namurian (Carpenter, 1976). By the end of the Carboniferous eleven order of insects had appeared, of which seven died out in the Permian. There is some evidence of insect-plant interactions among these early forms, the three palaeopteran (non wing-folding) orders Palaeodictyoptera, Megasecoptera and Diaphanopterodea having the piercing mouthparts of sap feeders. Pollen was also predated by these early insects, being indicated by the predominance of pollen in insect coprolites of this age (Taylor and Millay, 1979), while some insects even appear to mimic pteridosperm pinnule venation suggesting a camouflage function (Scott and Taylor, 1983) which would be associated with extended residence on these plants. However, Jarzembowski (1987) has suggested that this similarity might be the result of convergent evolution rather than specific adaptation. It is likely that many of the early insects were litter feeders, cockroaches (Blattodea) accounting for some eighty percent of the Late Carboniferous insects collected (Carpenter and Burnham, 1985).

The most important feature of the Late Carboniferous insect fauna is the existence of wings in most groups. Since mobility is a major prerequisite for the efficiency of pollination vectors this development was to be of undoubted importance in the subsequent development of entomophilous associations, especially as the insects were the only animals capable of flight in the Late Palaeozoic (Jarzembowski, 1987).

Insect diversity increased greatly through the Permian and Early Mesozoic, so that by the end of the Jurassic most of the major extant orders were represented. Of particular importance from the point of view of pollination were the appearances of the four major Recent orders of pollinators, the Coleoptera, Diptera, Hymenoptera and Lepidoptera.

The Coleoptera appear first in the Artinskian (Early Permian, Carpenter, 1976), being represented only by the extinct order Protelytroptera. These had modified hind wings resembling elytra, but also possessed features that suggest the equal possibility of a relationship with the Dermaptera (earwigs) (Carpenter and Burnham 1985). The Triassic saw the appearance of both the Diptera and the Hymenoptera (Carpenter and Burnham, 1985). Triassic Dipterans included eight families, possibly in the suborder Nematocera, which is the least specialised in the order today, or possibly representing an extinct suborder (Rohdendorf, 1964). The Hymenoptera of this period included fifty nine genera in two families, both of which are in the relatively unspecialised suborder Symphyta (Carpenter and Burnham, 1985).

The Diptera and Hymenoptera diversified during the Jurassic, important Hymenoptera including wasps of the family Aculeata which today include active predators that sometimes feed on plant exudates and nectar (Riek, 1970) and which may have been among the earliest angiosperm pollinators (Jarzembowski, 1984). Indeed, the radiation of the angiosperms during the Early Cretaceous may well have stimulated the appearance of important hymenopteran pollinators, this period also providing the earliest evidence of social insects (ants) (Carpenter and Burnham, 1985).

The most diverse of the Late Palaeozoic to Early Mesozoic insects were the Coleopterans (Carpenter and Burnham, 1985), which are therefore likely to have been among the most important of early pollinators. This, together with the relatively unspecialised nature of the Diptera and Hymenoptera may suggest that opportunistic pollination by palynophagous beetles could have been the main entomophilous strategy of Permian to Jurassic times.

The Lepidoptera were possibly present during the Jurassic (Whalley, 1986), where they are represented by only two specimens, one from the upper Jurassic of Russia (Rasnitsyn, 1983) and the other from the lower Lias of Dorset (Whalley, 1985). Whalley (1986) also discusses possible Triassic Lepidopterans, but these are of uncertain taxonomic affinity because of the difficulties associated with the distinction of Lepidopterans from the very similar Trichoptera when only fragments are available.

The possible Jurassic appearance of Lepidoptera and the appearance of important Hymenopteran pollinator groups in the Early Cretaceous suggests the possibility of a significant improvement in entomophily, the relatively clumsy Coleoptera becoming less important than the more specialised Lepidoptera and Hymenoptera during the Late Jurassic and Early Cretaceous.

The greater specialisation of entomophily in the Cretaceous in reflected not only by increased diversity of pollinating insect diversity but also by the appearance of the oldest available fossil angiosperm flowers, some of which possess definite nectaries (Friis, 1984a, 1985a; Friis, Crane and Pedersen, 1986). The subsequent rapid floral diversification resulted in the appearance of most of the important pollinators by the Early Tertiary. These included faithful Hymenopteran pollinators (Crepet and Friis, 1987) associated with actinomorphic bell, bowl, funnel and brush flowers (Crepet, 1979; Friis & Crepet, 1987). Psycophilous (butterfly pollinated) and Phalaenophilous (moth pollinated) flowers of tubular structure with well hidden nectar also appear by the Eocene (Crepet, 1979) together with typically Coleopteran pollinated flowers and even spadices and traps indicating sapromyophilous associations (Crepet, 1979).

Botanical evidence for pollinator involvement

The adoption of the seed habit must have been accompanied by a reduction in the rate of production of female reproductive cells, such cells being produced in specialised structures on the parent plant. The parental investment in each female cell is consequently higher than that for a free sporing plant and it might therefore be expected that the plants were under greater pressure to protect their ovules, particularly in view of the relative accessability of undispersed female cells to herbivores.

Studies of Early Carboniferous ovules have revealed a possible sequence of enclosure of the ovules by the integuments (Andrews, 1963), which vary from being entirely free, eg. *Genomosperma kidstoni* or basally fused, eg. *G.latens* to being virtually completely fused, eg. *Eurystoma angulare*. In these ovules the apex of the nucellus was extended to form a specialised pollen trapping structure, the salpinx, and it is thought that movements of the floor of the pollen chamber might have drawn pollen down through the aperture in a fluid drop (Rothwell, 1977).

A further feature of some of these pteridosperm seeds is the possession of densely-packed hairs and projections on the integument lobes, eg. *Salpingostoma dasu*. It has been suggested that these hair might have been secretory, for example in *Physostoma elegans*. It is possible that secretory hairs of this kind might have assisted in the deterrance of potential herbivore activity, which in view of the small size of many of these structures may mainly have involved insects. In *Lagenostoma ovoides* there are particularly well developed capitate hairs which cover not only the cupule but also the stems and foliage of the plant, reinflorcing the suggestion of their possibly protective function.

However, in addition to protecting the ovules it was vital that these plants develop a reliable mechanism for pollen transfer. A pollen drop mechanism seems likely, both for the salpinx-bearing forms and for those where the integuments had fused completely with each other and with the nucellus, rendering the salpinx redundant and leaving micropyle for pollen access. Pollen would presumably arrive at the pollen drop on the wind. This mechanism is inherently inefficient, since it is open to indiscriminate pollen reception with consequent clogging of the pollen chamber (Taylor and Millay, 1979). Some of the cupulate forms have ovules which possess long filaments arising from around the micropyle eg. *Gnetopsis* (Taylor and Millay, 1979). These filaments are sometimes hairy and may have acted like stigmas for trapping pollen.

In those species which did use a pollination droplet it can be seen that there would be a considerable advantage in direct pollen transfer, thus avoiding clogging of the pollen chamber by foreign grains.

Many early insects, in particular the Coleoptera, had orthoghathic chewing mouthparts, ideally suited to palynophagy. Indeed, observations of probable insect coprolites have revealed a palynophagous diet (Taylor and Millay, 1979). Could it be possible that such insects also visited the female organs, perhaps in order to feed on sweet exudates from glandular structures or perhaps on the micropylar fluid itself, which could have been one of the earliest nectar-like secretions? If such visits did occur pollen might have been transferred directly from the mandibles to the pollen drop. In such a situation an adaptive significance could be envisaged for the fusion of the integuments to form a long micropyle, since this would direct the insect's feeding activities away from the ovules. In fact the development of the micropyle is very marked in some plants, for example *Umkomasia* and *Pilophorosperma*, while in the Triassic to Cretaceous *Caytonia* the long micropyles are extended into a canal running though the fused cupule lobes (Reymanowna, 1973). In addition to *Caytonia* the Mesozoic saw a great diversification of seed plants, some of which still survive today. One of these, the Gnetales, includes three genera which have become severely restricted in their Recent distribution. These again show the development of very long micropyles and may in some cases be insect pollinated. Fossil pollen grains assigned to this group, such as the genus *Ephedripites*, are often extremely large, reaching lengths of more than 100μm in some Cretaceous examples and suggesting the improbability of effective wind transfer, but the gnetalean megafossil record is still incomplete.

Furthermore, Recent *Ephedra* often has coloured bracts, suggesting a possible function for insect attraction. Although the use of colour by fossil plants cannot be ruled out, it seems more likely that scent could have been used in primary attraction of pollinators, perhaps influencing pollinator habituation which is, of course, vital for optimally efficient pollination.

Of particular interest in the Mesozoic is the extinct group Bennettitales. It is in this group that the earliest flower-like structures have been observed and which seems likely to have been insect pollinated.

Early examples of the flowers of the Bennettites include genera such as *Williamsoniella* (bisexual), *Weltrichia* (male) and *Williamsonia* (female), these being freely borne on the branching axes of the plant.

The microsporangiate *Weltrichia* consisted of whorls of microsporophylls bearing capsular sporangia, the microsporophylls often being fused basally to form a cup (eg. *W. sol* Harris 1969. *W. santalensis* Sitholey and Bose, 1971). Harris (1969) reconstucted *W. sol* as an open cup-like structure dividing at the top into about thirty ray-like segments on the inner surfaces of which sporangia were borne. The inner basal part of the surface of the cup did not bear sporangia but had numerous resinous bodies.

The female flower *Williamsonia* was also reconstructed by Harris (1969) and was comprised of a central columella bearing tightly-packed sterile interseminal scales around ovules with extended micropyles. The slightly expanded heads of the interseminal scales produce a characteristic tesselated pattern on the outside of the gynoecium and the long micropyles project slightly between encircling groups of interseminal scales. Harris (1971) suggested that the outer bracts of *Williamsonia* were often detached and that the gynoecia might have been invested with a sticky coating of sugary fluid originating from the micropyles.

Taking these observations into account it might be suggested that the flower-like structures are showing direct adaptation for the exploitation of insects such as beetles as pollination vectors. The sporangia on the rays of *Weltrichia* are ideally placed for contact with the underside of a crawling insect which could have been induced to visit the flower by the presence of the resin bodies, which might represent nectary-like structures, or by a pool of sugary fluid in the cup of the flower. Later visits to the gynoecium would dislodge pollen from the underside of the insect directly into the micropylar openings. Crowson (1975) suggested that the sterile scales would protect the ovules from insect predation, but the crevices between them might have allowed eggs to be deposited by females with typical Coleopteran boring ovipositors. If such activities occurred it might explain the extensive insect damage to gynoecia observed by Crowson (1975) and Crepet (1974). This damage has been suggested to be Coleopteran with a consequent relevance in pollination, although no remains of boring organisms have been found (Crepet, 1972). the absence of boring organisms and the observations of Crowson (1975) lead me to suggest that these borings are more likely to represent the feeding activities of Coleopteran larvae, the holes bored to the gynoecial surface being imago exit holes.

Pressure from larval predation of this kind might have contributed to the subsequent gradual changes which led to the withdrawal of the openly-borne flowers to the later *Cycadeoidea* forms, where the flowers were protected by being produced among the persistent leaf bases of the stem. This was at the expense of entomophily, *Cycadeoidea* probably being autogamous (Crepet, 1974) and may consequently have contributed to the later extinction of the group through the lack of outbreeding and consequent loss of genetic fitness.

The angiosperms, which are the plants most associated with entomophily today, first appear in the Early Cretaceous. The earliest evidence for angiosperms lies in the palynological record, where angiospermid pollen is distinguished by its tectate to semitectate columellate exine structure.

Heslop-Harrison (1976) suggested that the tectate structure of the angiosperm pollen exine might be related to the production and storage of stigma recognition factors. It has also been suggested that tectate structure might aid the coherence of pollen grains for insect transport (Heslop-Harrison, 1971; Faegri and van der Pijl, 1979), while it is also possible that chemical compounds in the pollen wall might have a phagostimulatory or olfactory attractiveness to insects.

If the view that this exine structure is associated with entomophilous angiosperms is accepted, then fossil pollen of this kind will be useful for inferring the existence of plants with angiospermous reproduction. It may not, however, be a reliable indicator of events such as the first appearance of angiosperms, since this morphology represents a secondary specialisation to entomophily.

The earliest angiospermid pollen, based on the above criteria, occur in England (Hughes and McDougall, 1987), where the oldest are of Hauterivian age. Records of such angiosperm pollen have repeatedly demonstrated a typical sequence of morphological advancement related to aperture modification and proliferation.

The rarity of many of these early forms in comparison to be contemporary gymnosperm (presumably anemophilous) pollen forms could be indicative of reduced pollen output by the parent plants. The repetition of this rarity at successive geographical locations reduces the possibility of this being associated with sample failure or peripheral populations. This not only provides further reinforcement for the interpretation of such pollen in terms of entomophily but raises the additional question of the extent to which such pollen was involved in the reward of insect pollinators.

During the early history of pollinator involvement there seems little doubt that pollen was the main reward, consequently being produced at a greater rate to accomodate predation. This is still the case in some Recent plants, some of which even produce sterile pollen for that explicit purpose (Thomas and Spicer, 1987). In most angiosperms however, nectar is the dominant reward and surplus pollen production is not seen. It is therefore interesting to speculate that the apparently lower pollen output by some of the Early Cretaceous angiosperms might indicate that nectar production was already established as a pollinator reward.

Megafossil evidence is, of course, vital if this argument is to be borne out. At present there is, albeit sparse, evidence of definite angiosperm flowers which appear for the first time in Albian and Cenomanian deposits. One of the earliest of these is *Hyrcantha* Krassilov, Shilin and Vachrameev 1983, a paniculate inflorescence from Kazachstan. Like the slightly later example *Archaeanthus* (Dilcher and Crane, 1984) from the Cenomanian of Kansas, *Hyrcantha* has a morphology which is suggestive of the actinomorphic disk or bowl-shaped floral organisation which Faegri and van der Pijl (1979) consider to be visually attractive to insects and which Arber and Parkin (1907) suggested might be the structure expected in the earliest flowers. Although the structure of these flowers implies probable insect pollinator association, there is no evidence of developed nectaries in the fossils currently available.

The quality of the record of fossil flowers increases greatly in the Late Cretaceous. In Sweden Friis (1984a) and Friis and Skarbya (1982) have recorded a range of mainly actinomorphic flowers with well developed disk-shaped corollas, again suggesting adaptation for entomophily and associated nectar production, while further specimens from the Late Cretaceaous of Germany show the remains of the nectaries themselves (Friis, 1984b). Friis also records a tubular flower from the Swedish deposits. This flower, *Actinocalyx*, has a construction below the corolla lobes which suggests nectar production at the bottom of the flower (Friis, 1985).

The development of the actinomorphic disc-shaped flower might have been accompanied by the earliest use of colour as an advertising mechanism. It is likely that earlier advertisement mechanisms had involved structural modifications to increase the prominence of the reproductive structures, for example the conspicuous pollen organs of the Medullosaceae and flowers of the Bennettitales. In these early plants odour was probably the primary long distance attractant, but when open disk-shaped petaloid flowers appeared plants may quickly have seized the opportunity to develop the use of colour in the attraction and secondary orientation of flying insects.

Studies of Recent flowers have repeatedly demonstrated the colourimetric specialisation of flowers for entomophily. Colour patterns of "nectar guides" were first noted by Sprengel (1793) and Richtmayer (1923) made the first photographic observations of the UV component in flower colours. Nectar guides have been shown to influence foraging behaviour (Knoll, 1922), which may depend on the colour patterns (Scora, 1964).

Insect colour vision is good. The sensitive spectral range extends from UV to green or yellow, but with the exception of certain Heliconid butterflies, insects are insensitive to red light (Mazochin-Porshnyakov, 1969; Goldsmith and Bernard, 1974 and others). Daumer (1956) showed that contrast boundaries caused proboscis extension in visiting insects, while Waser and Price (1983) showed that insects became disoriented on flowers with lower contrasts than normal. These and other studies indicate that it is contrast boundaries rather than colour which specifically influence insects. Indeed, the insect eye has been shown to be well adapted to code contrast information (Laughlin, 1976a, b).

Penny (1983) used quantitative photographic techniques to measure the specific reflectances by corollas of both the human visible primary colours (red, blue and green) and the insect visible primaries (UV, blue and green). A subsequent comparison between nectar guide/petal contrasts in the human and insect visible spectra showed that contrasts were apparently greater in the insect visible spectrum, confirming that flowers are adapted to utilise contrast information for the orientation of visiting insects. In addition it would appear that the high contrast which is evident between flowers and the background foliage is of primary importance in long-range insect attraction, insects tending to land at the edges of flowers where the contrast between petals and foliage is greatest and then move towards the centre of the flower guided by lines on the petals (Manning, 1956).

All the contrasts measured by Penny (1983) were more apparent in colour than black and white, because colour contrasts are the product of both luminosity and hue, whereas black and white contrasts are solely the result of luminosity differences. This suggests that it is the influence of colour on insects that is of primary importance. If this is the case then before it is possible to assert an early use of colour by flowers it is necessary to consider whether fossil insects had a developed sense of colour vision. Once again is largely circumstantial.

Many of the early insects are likely to have been active flying predators, for example members of the Odonata, Neuroptera, Diptera and Hymenoptera. Such insects would benefit greatly from colour vision because of the concomitant advantages associated with the detection of hue as well as luminosity differences in picking out their prey, many of which might have had cryptic camouflage; eg. the apparent mimicking of Pteridosperm pinnule venation by certain Carboniferous insects which was noted by Taylor and Scott (1983) might have been associated with cryptic colouration.

Other evidence suggests that colours were being used for display purposes. For example, Jarzembowski (1984) has discovered

Neuropteran wing fossils in the Wealden deposits of southern England which show large eyespots. Thus it would appear that there was indeed a well developed insect fauna with colour vision and, in some causes, a possible predelection for nectar or honeydew (eg. Aculeate wasps, Jarzembowski, 1984) which were available for early exploitation by coloured flowers.

Penny (1983) recognised three types of nectar guide, involving petalcentre "target" type contrasts, petal-petal marking contrasts and petal-reproductive organ contrasts (Plate 1), while all flowers had strong contrast with the associated background foliage. The most important of these were the petal-centre "target" contrasts, which were mainly associated with actinomorphic disk or bowl-shaped flowers. Looking again at the fossil evidence we can see that, as prdicted by Arber and Parkin (1907) the earliest probably entomophilous fossil flowers currently available appear to be of this organisation (Krassilov *et al.*, 1983; Dilcher and Crane, 1984; Crane, Friis and Pedersen, 1986), and may well have operated as coloured targets in the attraction of pollinators.

Subsequent refinements in the use of colour, scent and floral structure would have enabled the flowers of different species to attain the individuality necessary for insect habituation with the consequent evolution of faithful insect pollinators and advanced floral structures such a those associated with zygomorphy, both of which are evident by the Early Tertiary (Crepet, 1979).

Explanation of Plate 1

Flowers photographed under natural (left) and ultraviolet (right) illumination. Three types of nectar guide are shown.

1, 2 : *Ranunculus lingua* (petal-centre + petal- reproductive organs)

3, 4 : *Josseia reptans* (petal-reproductive organs)

5, 6 : *Geranium sanguineum* (petal-centre + petal - petal markings)

Literature Cited

Andrews, H.N. 1963. Early seed plants. *Science, 142* : 925-931.

Arber, E.A.N. & Parkin, J. 1907. On the origin of the angiosperms. *Bot. Jour. Linn. Soc., 38* : 29-80.

Bassinger, J. and Dilcher, D.L. 1984. *Science, 224* : 511-513.

1
2
3
4
5
6

Carpenter, F.M. 1976. Geological history and the evolution of the insects. *Proc. 15th. Int. Congr. Entomol.*, 1976: pp. 63-70.

Carpenter, F.M. & Burnham, L. 1985. The geological record of insects. *Annu. Rev. Ecol. and Systemat., 13* : 297-314.

Chaloner, W.G. 1976. The evolution of adaptive features in fossil exines. In: (eds.) I.K. Fergusun & J. Muller. *The Evolutionary Significance of the Exine*, pp. 1-14. Academic Press, London.

Crepet, W.L. 1972. Investigation of North American cycadeoids : pollination mechanisms in *Cycadeoidea. Am. J. Bot., 59* : 1048-1056.

Crepet, W.L. 1974. Investigations of North American cycadeoids : the reproductive biology of *Cycadeoidea. Palaeontographica, 148B* : 144-169.

Crepet, W.L. 1979. Some aspects of the pollination biology of Middle Eocene angiosperms. *Rev. Palaeobot. and Palynol., 27* : 213-238.

Crepet, W.L. 1983. The role of insect pollination in the evolution of the angiosperms. In: (ed.) L. Real. *Pollination Biology*, pp.31-50, Academic Press, London.

Crepet, W.L. and Friss, E.M. 1987. The evolution of insect pollination. In: *The Origins of Angiosperms and their Biological Consequences*, (eds.) Friss, E.M., Chaloner, W.G. and Crane. P.R. pp. 181-202.

Crowson, R.A. 1975. The evolutionary history of Coleoptera, as documented by fossil and comparative evidence. *Atti Congresso Nazionale Italiano di Entomologica.* Bologna (1974.) *10* : 47-90.

Daumer, K. 1956. Reizmetrische untersuchung des farbensehens der bienen. *Zeitschrift fur vergleischende Physiologie. 38* : 413-478.

Diane. E.M., Pferfferkorn, H.W. and Alleman, V.A. 1992. *Amer. J. Bot.*

Dilcher, D.L. & Crane, P.R. 1984. *Archaeanthus* : an early angiosperm from the Cenomanian of the Western Interior of North America. *Ann. Mo. Bot. Gard., 71* : 351-383.

Faegri, K. & Van Der Pijl, L. 1979. *The Principles of Pollination Ecology* 22nd Edition, 244 pp., Pergamon Press, Oxford.

Friis, E.M. 1984a. Preliminary report of upper Cretaceous angiosperm reproductive organs from Sweden and their level of organisation. *Ann. Mo. Bot. Gard., 71* : 403-418.

Friis, E.M. 1984b. Dakfroede planter fra Ovre Kridt. *Fauna och Flora, 72* : 169-180.

Friis, E.M. 1985. *Actinocalyx* gen.nov., sympetalous angiosperm flowers from the upper Cretaceous of southern Sweden. *Rev. Palaeobot. and Palynol, 45* : 171-183.

Friis, E.M., Crane, P.R. and Pedersen, K.R. 1986. Floral evidence for Cretaceous chloranthoid angiosperms. *Nature, 320* : 163-164.

Friis, E.M. and Crepet, W.L. 1987. Time of appearance of floral features. In: (eds.) Friis, E.M., Chaloner, W.G. and Crane, P.R. *The Origins of Angiosperms and their Biological consequences*, pp. 145-170.

Friis, E.M. and Skarbya, A. 1982. *Scandianthus* gen. nov., angiosperm flowers of Saxifragalean affinity from the upper Cretaceous of southen Sweden. *Ann. Bot., 50* : 569-583.

Friis, E.M. and Endress, P.K. 1994. Origin and evolution of angiosperm flower, In: (ed.) Callow, J.A. *Adv. Bot. Res., 17* : 100-162. Academic Press, London.

Goldsmith, T.H. & Bernard, G.D. 1974. The visual system of insects. In: (ed.) M. Rockstein. *The Physiology of Insecta*, pp.165-272. Academic Press, London.

Harris, T.M. 1969. *The Yorkshire Jurassic Flora III Bennettitales*. British Museum (Natural History) London, publication no. 675.

Harris, T.M. 1971. The strange Bennetitales. 19th. Sir Albert Charles Seward Memorial Lecture, (issued 1973).

Heinrich, B. 1975. Energetics of pollination. *Annu. Rev. Ecol. and Systemat., 6* : 139-179.

Heinrich, B. 1976. Resource partitioning among some social insects : Bumblebees. *Ecology, 57* : 874-889.

Heinrich, B. & Raven, P.H. 1972. Energetics and pollination ecology. *Science, 176* : 597-602.

Heslop-Harrison, J. 1971. Sporopollenin in the biological context. In *Sporopollenin* : (eds.) J. Brooks, P.R. Grant, M. Muir, P. van Gijzel, G. Shaw, pp. 1-30. New York, Academic Press.

Heslop-Harrison, J. 1976. The adaptive significance of the exine. In: *The Evolutionary Significance of the Exine* (eds.) I.K. Ferguson & J. Muller. Linnean Society Symposia 1, pp. 27-38. Academic Press, London.

Hughes, N.F. & McDougall, A.B. 1987. Records of angiospermid pollen entry into the English early Cretaceous succession. *Rev. Palaeobot. and Palynol., 50* : 255-272.

Jarzembowski, E.A. 1984. Early Cretaceous insects from southern England. *Modern Geol., 9* : 71-93.

Jarzembowski, E.A. 1987. The occurrence and diversity of Coal Measure insects. *Jour Geol. Soc., Lond., 144* : 507-511.

Kevan, P.G. Chaloner, W.G. & Saville, D.B.O.1975. Interrelationships of early terrestrial arthropods and plants. *Palaentology, 18* : 391-417.

Knoll, F. 1922. Insekten und blumen. Experimentale arbeiten zur vertiefung unserer kenntnisse uber die wechselbeziehungen zwischen pflanzen und tieren. III. Lichsinn und blumemnbesuch der falters von *Macroglossum stellatarum. Abhandlungen der Zoologisch-botanischen Gesellschaft in Wien, 12* : 127-378.

Krassilov, V.A., Shilin, P.V. & Vachrameev, V.A. 1983. Cretaceous flowers from Kazackstan. *Rev. Palaeobot. and Palynol., 40* : 91-113.

Laughlin, S.B. 1976a. Neural intergration in the firs optic neuropile of dragonflies. IV. Interneuron spectral sensitivity and contrast coding. *Jour. Comparat. Physiol., 112* : 199-211.

Laughlin, S.B. 1976b. Adaptations of the dragonfly retina fro contrast detection and the elucidation of neural principles in the peripheral visual system. In: *Neural Principles in Vision* (eds.) F. Zettler & R. Wieler, Springer-Verlag, Berlin.

Mamay, S.H. 1976. Palacozoie origin of Cyeads. *U.S. Geof Swn. Prof. Paper., 934* : 1-48.

Manning, A. 1956. The effect of honey guides. *Behaviour, 9* : 114-139.

Mazokhin-Porshnyakov, G.A. 1969. *Insect vision.* (Translated from the Russian by R. and L. Masironi, (ed.) T.H. Goldsmith, Plenum, New York.

Penny, J.H.J. 1983. Nectar guide colour contrast : a possible relationship with pollination strategy. *New Phytol, 95* : 707-721.

Phillips, T.L. & DiMichele, W.A. 1981. Paleoecology of middle Pennsylvanian age coal swamps in the southern Illinois/Herrin coal member at Sahara Mine No. 6. In: (ed.) K. Niklas. *Paleobotany, Paleoecology and Evolution*, vol. 1, pp. 231-284. Praeger, New York.

Rasnitsyn, A.P. 1983. Pervaya nakhodka babochki yourskogo vozrasta. [First find of a moth from the Jurassic]. *Doklady Akademii Nauk SSSR, 269* : 467-471.

Retallack, G. & Dilcher, D.L. 1981. Early angiosperm reproduction : *Prisca raynoldsii* gen. et sp. nov. from mid-Cretaceous coastal deposits in Kansas USA. *Palaentographia, 179B* : 103-137.

Raymanowna, M. 1973. The Jurassic flora from Grojec near Krakow in Poland. Part II. Caytoniales and anatomy of *Caytonia. Acta Palaeobot, 14 : 45-84.*

Richtmayer, F.K. 1923. The reflection of ultraviolet by flowers. *Jour. Optic. Soc. America, 7* : 151-168.

Riek, E.F. 1970. Hymenotera. In : *The Insects of Australia*, pp. 867-959. Melbourne Univesity Press, Carlton, Victoria.

Rohdendorf, B.B. 1962. [Arthropoda, Tracheata and Chalicerata]. Osanovy Palenontologii, Moscow. (in Russian).

Rothwell, G.w. 1977. Evidence for a pollination drop mechanism in Paleozoic pteridosperms. *Science, 198* : 1251-1252.

Scora, R.W. 1964. Dependency of pollination on patterns in *Monarda* (Labiateae). *Nature, 204* : 1011-1012.

Scott, A.C. & Taylor, T.N. 1983. Plant/animal interactions during the upper Carboniferous. *Bot. Rev., 49* : 259-307.

Sitholey, R.V. & Bose, M.N. 1971. *Weltrichia santalensis* Sitholey and Bose and other Bennettitalean male fructifications from India. *Palaentographica, 131B* : 156-159.

Sprengel. C.K. 1793. *Das Entdeckte Geheimniss der Nature in Bau and in der Befruchtung der Blumen.* 4 Band. Herausg von P. Knuth. Wilhelm Engelmann. Leipzig 1894.

Shukla. R.K. 1958. *J. Palaentol. Soc. India, 3* : 114-118.

Shukla, V.B. 1944. *Proc. Natl. Acad. Sci. India, 24* : 1-39.

Taylor, T.N. 1981. Pollen and pollen organ evolution in early seed plants. In: (ed.) K. Niklas. *Paleobotany, Paleoecology and Evolution*,. Praeger, New York.

Taylor, T.N. & Millay, M.A. 1979. Pollination biology and reproduction in early seed plants. *Rev. Palaeobot. and Palynol, 27* : 329-355.

Thomas, B.A. & Spicer, R.A. 197. *The Evolution and Palaebiology of Land Plants.* Croom Helm, London and Sydney.

Waser, N.M. & Price, M.V. 1983. Pollinator behaviour and natural selection for flower colour in *Delphinium nelsonii. Nature, 302* : 422-424.

Whalley, P.E.S. 1985. the systematics and palaeogeographgy of the lower Jurassic insects of Dorset, England. *Bull Brit. Mus. (Natur. Hist.), Geology, 39* : 107-189.

Whalley, P.E.S. 1986. A review of the current fossil evidence of Lepidoptera in the Mesozoic. *Bot. Jour. Linn. Soc., 28* : 253-271.

Whitehead, D.R. 1969. Wind pollination in the angiosperms : evolutionary and environmental considerations. *Evolution, 23* : 28-35.

Addendum (Editor)

Since the submission of the manuscript some old and new literature on fossil nectaries has come to light hence included. Nectaries have been recorded in variety of late Cretaceous flowers. Bassinger and Dilcher (1984) reconstructed the lobed nectary disc of Early Cenomanian Nebraskan flower but the earliest evidence of nectaries are afforded by the Santonian/Companian flowers from Scania. Apart from the occurrence of nectaries in *Scandianthus* (Rosidean affinity), nectaries in flowers from the early Companian of Aachen has been reported. (Fries and Endress, 1994). One sided fossil nectaries from Decean intratrappean reported in *Sahnianthus* are characterised by a single scale or two lobed bodies (Shukla, 1944; Shukla, 1958). Nectaries are also reported from Early Tertiary malpighiaceous flower. *Eoglandulosa warmanensis* (Taylor and Crept, 1987), Diane *et al.* (1992) reported ovuliferous remains of cupuliferous branch from Carboniferous of Peru. The cupules has 5-9 lobes measuring 0.4 to 0.8 mm long; the lobed margins with 0,3 mm narrow projections representing either trichomes/glands. These structures resemble *Lagenospermum inparirameum* and *L. sinclairi*. Likewise the reconstructed megasporophyll of *Phasmatocycas* with glands suggest entomophily (Mamay, 1976).

INDIAN HONEYS : AN EVALUATION OF QUALITATIVE POLLEN ANALYSIS

MITHILESH CHATURVEDI
Palynology Laboratory
National Botanical Research Institute, Lucknow, India.

ABSTRACT

The present review is aimed at consolidating information on the plant sources of honeys originated from different regions of India. The qualitative pollen analysis of honeys, made from time to time by different workers forms the basis of this review.

Key words : Indian honeys, qualitative pollen analysis.

INTRODUCTION

During the course of coevolution of plants and insects, hermaphrodite condition in plants appeared, and with that a state of self-incompatibility evolved and scope for selection of cross-pollination emerged, resulting in the concurrent evolution of the bees. The occurrence of bees has been related to the lower Oligocene. However, the inter-relationship of angiosperms with bees may be recognised from lower Cretaceous onwards, when the angiosperm fossils first appeared. The culmination of the evolution of bees resulting in their sucking type of mouth parts, synchronised with the evolution of angiosperm flower containing nectar producing part — the nectary, which together with associated incompatibility system are all interrelated phenomena. The dependence of bee on flowers for nectar and pollen results in its probing the flower and in the process it reciprocates by effecting pollination. The pollen is also deliberately collected by bees in the form of pellets (loads) for feeding their larvae.

The bees work the flowers for the reward of nectar, which is processed by them into honey and deposited in the honey comb.

In an angiosperm flower, nectary is located at various places viz. on the perianth, on the receptacle, between the sepals and petals, between the petals and stamens, between the bases of the stamens, on the stamens, between the stamens and the ovary, or it forms a disc on the receptacle between the sepals and ovary (Fahn, 1953). While nectar is being collected, pollen produced by the flowers tends to mix with it in different proportions and is disseminated in honey. Since honey is the product of one or several plants visited by bees, it is important to know the plant sources.

Thus, the pollen contained in honey are recognised as perhaps the only tool for the identification of the plant sources from which the honey has originated. The exine of the pollen is endowed with characteristic features at various taxonomic levels, which to a large extent can be successfully employed in the qualitative analysis of honey for determining its floral components (Figs. 1-16). The quantity of pollen and its ratio with nectar depends upon the orientation of nectary vis-a-vis anthers, number of pollen grains produced per anther, size of the pollen grains, and also in case of unisexual flowers, if female flowers are also visited by bees, however, the pollen components of a honey can lead to the identification of geographical region and also climatic and biotic zone, from which it has originated. It is also helpful in identifying poisonous pollen (Chaubal & Deodikar, 1963) and detecting the misrepresentation and adulteration of honeys. Deodikar and Thakar (1953) made a pioneer effort in India to study the major honey yielding plants of Mahabaleshwar hills. The work on similar lines was extended to the unifloral honeys from the Western Ghat forests alongwith the presentation of morphological descriptions of the pollen of bee plants (Chaubal and Deodikar, 1965).

Method for Qualitative analysis of Indian Honeys

Various workers have carried out qualitative pollen analysis of commercial/regional honeys in India. In these studies methods of pollen preparations have been the same as followed for pollen morphological studies. According to the recommendations of the International Commission for Bee Botany (1970), pollen preparations are made by dissolving 10 g of honey in 20ml of hot water, centrifuged and again washed with distilled water and centrifuged for complete removal of sugars. The sediment is mounted with stained or unstained glycerine jelly. However, the palynological basis for the identification of plant sources in honeys warrants the identification of pollen without limitations, as Indian honeys are essentially floral honeys. As compared to the temperate regions, tropical and subtropical regions are richer in plant material and therefore identification of pollen contained in honeys presents a challenging task. Therefore, in almost all the melissopalynological works in India which have been done by palynologists, pollen sediment was acetolysed (Erdtman, 1952) to remove protoplast so that the exine characters could be made discernible in order to facilitate better identification of pollen. Lieux (1980) and Moar (1985) have also stressed on the importance of acetolysis in the pollen analysis of honeys. According to the ICBB, in the qualitative pollen analysis, honeys with 45% or above of any single pollen type are termed as unifloral and those honeys which have several pollen types represented are termed as multifloral.

QUALITATIVE POLLEN ANALYSIS

Commercial Honeys

The initiation of the pioneer work goes to the credit of Sen and Banerjee (1956) who analysed a honey sample from Calcutta and reported the occurrence of anemophilous pollen in large number. Further, Vishnu Mittre (1958) analysed some commercial honey samples named as Almora honey, Haridwar honey, Kashmir honey, Lucknow honey, Lotus honey and Sunderbans honey, and reported mixing of several types of honeys in these samples.

Nair (1964) published a comprehensive account of qualitative microscopical analysis of 76 commercial Indian honey samples. The honeys originated from several states, were categorised broadly into five regions namely, Peninsular region, Western region, Indogangetic region, Eastern region and the Himalayan region. In the pollen spectra of Peninsular, Western and Indogangetic regions, pollen grains of *Syzygium* (*Eugenia*) dominated. However, in the Peninsular region, out of 58 pollen types several other plants were represented by their pollen in varying percentages e.g. *Sapindus, Holoptelea, Cocos, Pongamia*, Labiatae, *Emblica* and *Mangifera*. In the honeys of the

Western region, the total number of pollen types were 21 and other important types were *Brassica*, *Sapindus* and *Bombax*. In those samples which originated from the Indogangetic region, 45 pollen types were recorded and *Litchi*, *Citrus*, *Putranjiva*, Asteraceae, *Mimosa*, *Cedrela*, *Barringtonia*, *Azadirachta*, Solanaceae and *Butea* were represented by considerable percentages of their pollen. The Eastern region samples showed a clear dominance of *Litchi* pollen followed by those of *Brassica* pollen.

The honeys which originated from the Himalayan region had the pollen spectra of temperate plants. *Plectranthus* was observed to be the most important scurce out of 54 pollen types followed by *Alnus*, *Rumex hastata*, *Rosaceae*, *Syzygium (Eugenia)*, *Ligustrum*, *Carthamus*, and *Grewia*.

Regional Honeys

Considering the vastness of Indian subcontinent, the attempts made by various workers to analyse localized honeys at district levels are too meagre. The apicultural work initiated at the Central Bee Research Institute, Pune, advanced in the direction of documenting bee forage plants of Coorg (Suryanarayana, 1966) and Mahabaleshwar hills (Thakar *et al.*, 1962). Further, Chaubal and Deodikar (1965) identified the pollen sources of honeys of Western Ghats and reported seasonal variation in pollen components of honeys collected at the intervals of 15 days. The pollen analysis of honeys of several districts of Uttar Pradesh, including hill regions (Sharma and Nair, 1965; Chaturvedi, 1983, 1989), and of Kerala, Karnataka, Andhra Pradesh, West Bengal, and Orissa (Chanda and Ganguly, 1981) presented, to some extent, identifiable characteristic features of pollen spectra of honeys originated from various localities, as under :

(i) ***Uttar Pradesh honeys***

Honey samples collected from Almora, Pithoragarh, Tehri Garhwal and Ramgarh, among the hill regions and Dehra Dun (foot-hill) and Lucknow (plains) were determined for their pollen contents. The sample from Almora was unifloral with the pollen of the Euphorbiaceae as its dominant type. Three samples from Pithoragarh were also unifloral, but their dominant types were different, being *Smilax*, Rosaceae and Meliaceae, respectively. Out of three samples from Tehri Garhwal-another hill resort, one sample was unifloral with pollen of *Rumex* as its dominant type (53.4%) followed by those of Rosaceae (22.44%), the former being anemophilous and the latter entomophilous. The other two samples were multifloral with the pollen of Cruciferae and Rosaceae in the highest frequencies in both the samples, respectively, and the pollen of *Rumex* was next in the order of dominance in both the samples. Besides, the pollen grains of *Juglans*, Melastomaceae, Berberidaceae, *Polygonum* and Styraceae were also recorded in these samples, indicating the temperate origin of the samples.

The sample from Ramgarh was unifloral comprising mainly the pollen of Cruciferae, most probably of *Brassica*.

The sample which originated from Dehra Dun was named as 'Litchi' Honey, and it also showed a predominance of *Litchi* pollen. Dehra Dun is a city of 'Litchi' orchards. The presence of such orchards facilitates the production of unifloral honeys.

The honey samples of Lucknow exhibited well marked characteristic pollen spectra having the pollen of *Syzygium* in all the four samples analysed, of which one spectrum was defined as unifloral, two spectra had these grains in the highest frequencies and in one spectrum these grains found second place after the pollen of Leguminosae. There are many 'Jamun' (*Syzygium*) trees in Lucknow and it appears that these honeys formed during spring season when these trees came to flower. It is further substantiated by the presence of pollen grains of *Holoptelea, Bombax, Ailanthus* etc. which also flower during spring season. According to Suryanarayana *et al.* (1981) the 'Litchi' and 'Jamun' honeys which originated from other places showed different pollen spectra. The samples of 'Litchi' honeys collected from Sitakundu and Hooghly (West Bengal), Muzuffarpur (Bihar), Haldwani (Uttar Pradesh), and Pathankot (Punjab) and the 'Jamun' honeys collected from the localities of W. Bengal, Bihar, Maharashtra, Karnataka and Tamilnadu had their characteristic pollen types representing the local floras. Regional and seasonal variation in the absolute pollen count of the same type of honey were also reported. Also, absolute pollen counts of 'Jamun' and 'Litchi' honeys were reported to be higher than those in the unifloral honeys from temperate regions. Apparently 'Litchi' and 'Jamun' are important honey sources in most part of India.

Seasonal Honeys of Uttar Pradesh : The knowledge of harvesting time gives a seasonal identity to honeys, as their floral sources are variable in different seasons. In the hill regions of Uttar Pradesh, honey is harvested in spring and autumn seasons. The studies in qualitative pollen analysis of 13 samples of autumn honeys collected from seven localities situated in Kumaon region, namely, Kausani-Chanoda, Kausani-proper, Almora, Ranikhet, Bhowali, Jeolikote and Haldwani (foot-hill) determined the floral sources of autumn honeys of this region (Chaturvedi, 1983). The honey spectra from these localities were variable, and the influence of the local flora was distinctly visible, however, the presence of the characteristic pollen types of the temperate plants gave these samples a geographical and seasonal identity. A comparative account of autumn honey samples with respect to their floral patterns is provided in Table-I. Out of 13 samples six samples were unifloral and seven were multifloral, and a total of 86 pollen types occurred in these samples. Among the unifloral samples, pollen of *Eucalyptus, Myrica* and *Brassica* were the major types. The samples from Almora and Haldwani were characterised by 53% and 55% pollen of *Brassica;* respectively, the one from Kausani-Chanoda had 47% pollen of *Eucalyptus*, and in the sample of Kausani-proper, pollen of *Myrica* dominated with 65% pollen and one sample from Bhowali had 76.6% pollen of Asteraceae —*Anaphalis* group. All the four samples collected from Ranikhet were multifloral and almost similar, the pollen of *Alnus, Eucalyptus* and *Rumex* occurring in all the four samples. The two multifloral samples from Bhowali had pollen of Labiatae — *Plectranthus rugosus* type, *Brassica* and Poaceae in common, although these samples had the highest percentages of Asteraceae-*Anaphalis* group and Asteraceae-*Bidens* group, respectively. The multifloral honey sample originated from Jeolikote was characterised by 37% pollen of Labiatae-*Origanum vulgare* type showing the highest percentage of pollen followed by Rosaceae-*Prunus* type, Asteraceae — *Bidens* and *Anaphalis groups, Strobilanthes* and *Brassica*, each representing more than 5% pollen, besides other pollen components in smaller percentages.

TABLE 1 : A comparative account of various autumn honey samples of Kumaon region with respect to their floral patterns (from Chaturvedi, 1983).

Locality		*Type of honey*	*Total number of taxa represented*	*Main floral components (above 5 percent pollen in case of multifloral honeys)*
Kausani :	Chanoda	Unifloral	29	*Eucalyptus*
Kausani :	proper	Unifloral	25	*Myrica*
Almora :	Sample—1	Unifloral	41	*Brassica*
	Sample—2	Unifloral	28	*Brassica*
Ranikhet :	1. North	Multifloral	33	*Eucalyptus, Alnus, Clematis, Rumex*, Asteraceae-*Helianthus* group, *Myrica.*
	2. South	–do–	27	*Alnus*, Asteraceae-*Helianthus* group, Rosaceae-*Prunus* type, *Eucalyptus, Gentiana, Rumex, Clematis.*
	3. South	–do–	21	Asteraceae-*Helianthus* group, *Alnus, Eucalyptus, Rumex, Myrica*, Rosaceae-*Prunus* type, Labiatae-*Plectranthus* type.
	4. East	–do–	14	*Myrica*, Asteraceae-*Helianthus* group, *Eucalyptus*, Rosaceae-*Prunus* type, Ranunculaceae, *Alnus, Rumex.*
Bhowali :	Sample—1	–do–	21	Asteraceae-*Anaphalis* group, Poaceae, Labiatae-*Plectranthus rugosus* type, *Brassica.*
	Sample—2	Unifloral	11	Asteraceae-*Anaphalis* group.
	Sample—3	Multifloral	12	Asteraceae-*Bidens* group, *Alnus*, Poaceae, Labiatae-*Plectranthus rugosus* type, Rosaceae-*Rubus* type, *Brassica.*
Jeolikote		–do–	23	Labiatae-*Origanum vulgare* type, Rosaceae-*Prunus* type, Asteraceae-*Bidens* and *Anaphalis* groups, *Strobilanthes, Brassica.*
Haldwani		Unifloral	19	*Brassica.*

TABLE 2 : A comparative account of some spring honey samples from the western Himalayan region of Uttar Pradesh. (From Chaturvedi, 1989).

Locality	*Type of honey*	*Total No. of taxa represented*	*Main floral components**	*Remarks*
Kausani-Chanoda (Kumaon hills)	Unifloral	17	Rosaceae-*Prunus* type (52%)	
Kausani-proper (Kumaon hills)	Multifloral	15	*Salix* (39%), *Brassica* (31%), Rosaceae-*Prunus* type (18.4%)	
Haldwani (Kumaon foot hills)				
Sample-I	Unifloral	1	Rosaceae-*Prunus* type (100%)	Pure unifloral sample
Sample-II	Unifloral	10	*Syzygium* (72.5%)	
Uttarkashi (Garhwal hills)				
Sample-I	Unifloral	3	*Brassica* (100%)	Pure unifloral sample; *Bombax*, Pisum as stray grains
Sample-II	Unifloral	1	*Brassica* (100%)	Pure unifloral sample
Sample-III	Unifloral	16	*Brassica* (67%)	
Sample-IV	Multifloral	20	*Rumex* (39%), *Brassica* (18%), *Quercus* (11.8%), *Eucalyptus* (9.2%), *Lagerstroemia* (6%)	Main entomophilous types: *Brassica, Eucalyptus, Lagerstroemia*
Sample-V	Unifloral	31	*Brassica* (61%)	Main entomophilious types:
Sample-VI	Unifloral	20	*Alnus* (56%)	Labiatae, Rosaceae-*Prunus* type
Sample-VII	Unifloral	30	*Rumex* (54.3%)	Main entomophilous type *Brassica*
Sample-VIII	Unifloral	22	*Alnus* (61.2%)	Entomophilious types under-represented.

*only those taxa, which showed more than 5% counts, included in multifloral honey samples.

The spring samples of Kausani-Chanoda, Kausani-proper, and Haldwani were also analysed (Chaturvedi, 1989) and it was observed that these samples were markedly different from autumn samples in their pollen components. The sample from chanoda was unifloral with

52% pollen of Rosaceae-*Prunus* type, and Umbelliferae-*Coriandrum* type, *Brassica, Eucalyptus*, *Rumex* and *Citrus* were the other important types. The honey collected from Kausani-proper was multifloral with *Salix* (39%), *Brassica* (31%) and Rosaceae-*Prunus* type (18.4%), as its main components. Two spring samples from Haldwani were unifloral, one of them being a pure sample of Rosaceae-*Prunus* type and seems to have originated from an orchard. The other sample was characterised by 72.5% pollen of *Syzygium* ('Jamun'). It may be inferred that in the spring season, rosaceous fruit crops and *Syzygium* are good sources of honey in Haldwani, as against *Brassica* recorded earlier in autumn samples. Among these samples the pollen frequency of cultivated plants is much higher than that of the naturalised plants. The unifloral spring samples of Garhwal region (Uttarkashi) show a predominance of *Brassica* pollen among the entomophilous plants. *Eucalyptus, Lagerstroemia*, Labiatae and Rosaceae-*Prunus* type are the other entomophilous nectar sources of the region (Table 2).

(ii) ***Kerala honeys***

A sample from Rubber states showed pollen of *Barringtonia* (25%), and *Moraceae* (20%) in higher frequencies, while the sample from Palghat exhibited pollen of *Zizyphus jujuba* (43%) and *Cordia* (17%) besides other types.

(iii) ***Karnataka honeys***

A sample collected from Kumtha was characterised by five pollen types with *Michelia champaca* (24%) and *Mangifera indica* (22%) in higher frequencies.

(iv) ***West Bengal honeys***

The pollen spectra of honeys of the three localities were variable. Sundarban sample showed the characteristic pollen of mangrove and associated plants. *Sonneratia apetala* dominated the spectrum with 42.5% pollen. In Bashirhat sample pollen of *Zizyphus jujuba* dominated with 30% pollen. In Baruipur sample, pollen grains of *Ipomoea* and *Barringtonia* were in high frequencies.

(v) *Andhra Pradesh honeys*

In the sample from Narsipatnam, *Euphrasia* and *Datura* species were represented by 32.5% and 12.5% pollen, respectively.

Recently, additional information has emanated on the honey sources of Andhra Pradesh. Unifloral honey samples of *Prosopis juliflora* (Ramanujam and Kalpana, 1990-91), *Carum copticum* and *Guizotia abyssinica* (Kalpana and Ramanujam, 1991) have been reported from Ranga Reddy district of the state. In the unifloral honey samples from the agricultural tracts of Guntur district, pollen grains of *Mimosa pudica*, *Sapindus emarginatus* and *Capsicum frutescens* were predominant, besides those of *Prosopis juliflora* (Ramanujam and Khatija, 1991). Jhansi *et al.* (1991) enumerated important honey sources from the deciduous forest tracts of Prakasam district viz. *Cassia fistula, Terminalia alata, Bauhinia racemosa, Feronia elephantum, Lagerstroemia parviflora, Strychnos potatorum, Zizyphus zylopyrus, Phyllanthus* sp., *Soymida febrifuga, Syzygium cumini, Dalbergia latifolia* and *Caesalpinia bonduc*.

A seasonal analysis of honeys originated from the coastal belt of East Godavari district shows that *Sapindus emarginatus* and *Eucalyptus globulus* are the major sources of winter honey, and *Borassus flabellifer* and *Syzygium cumini*, of summer honey (Ramanujam *et al.*, 1992).

(vi) *Orissa honeys*

In Orissa sample, pollen grains of *Euphrasia* (27%) *Zizyphus jujuba* (22.5%) and *Citrus* (20%) were the important components of honey.

In the investigations of these honey samples Chanda and Ganguly (1981) enumerated various pollen grains belonging to anemophilous plants. In other investigations also several anemophilous pollen types were recorded (Sen and Banerjee, 1956; Nair, 1964; Sharma and Nair, 1965; Suryanarayana *et al.*, 1981; Chaturvedi, 1983, 1989). Adams *et al.* (1976) reported that honey bees were seen collecting pollen from anemophilous plant *Plantago lanceolata* and then visiting *Trifolium repens* nearby for nectar. Such deliberate collection of anemophilous pollen, though alters the pollen spectrum of a honey, but at the same time gives it a characteristic feature.

CONCLUSIONS

Honey is a supplement of food and with the increasing awareness and awakening towards health and nutrition, its importance has greatly enhanced. In India, the practice of bee-keeping has been followed in the areas of naturalised assemblage of plants and therefore, the honey, thus produced has the representation of such natural flora. In the last two decades, due to the expansion of agricultural and horticultural practices, a large number of naturalised plants have been slowly been replaced by the agricultural crops and orchards, and therefore the pollen spectra of honeys in various floral units ought to be different from each other. Simultaneously, under the social forestry programmes, there have been extensive plantations of trees of which *Eucalyptus* has come to be established as most prominent, all over India. This is also evident by the presence of air-borne pollen of this tree reported in the atmospheric surveys from all over India (Nair *et al.*, 1986). In Australia, *Eucalyptus* is reported to be a major honey yielding plant, while in India, it is still to be exploited for major yield of nectar. The occurrence of pollen of *Eucalyptus* in the autumn samples of honeys collected from Kausani and Ranikhet and from Andhra Pradesh in the South, is indicative of the growing important of the plant as a honey source, and if properly exploited it might turn out to be an importance honey plant of India.

Among other trees, the pollen of *Syzygium* has been widely represented in many pollen spectra of Indian honeys, especially those from northern India. Similarly, pollen of *Litchi* dominates in the samples of North-West region. In most of the investigations on the analysis of honeys, the information on the harvesting season of the honeys has not been provided, and therefore, the possibility of drawing generalised conclusions regarding the seasonal honey plants is limited. However judging by the pollen spectra of various honeys, *Syzygium* and *Litchi* could be considered the main nectar yielding plants of spring season in the plains of the northern India. Pollen associations contained in 'Jamun' and 'Litchi' honeys, representing cultivated and naturalised plants surrounding the chief honey sources may lead to the identification of the region from which these honeys originate (Suryanarayana *et al.*, 1981).

In the Himalayan region, the pollen grains of *Plectranthus* have been reported to occur in several honey samples and also in the autumn samples of Kumaon hill region of Uttar Pradesh. Asteraceae-*Anaphalis* group, *Eucalyptus* and *Myrica* have also formed unifloral samples in Kumaon hills, in autumn. However, the rosaceous fruit plants (peaches, plums, apples) are among the main sources of spring honeys in these regions. The importance of honey plant depends upon its regional concentration and for this reason the annual single crop like *Brassica* is a major component of many honey samples of North India originated from both hills and plains.

Citrus, Sapindus and *Zizyphus jujuba* are some other plants represented in several honey samples in considerable frequencies of which pollen grains of *Zizyphus jujuba* have been found to occur in the samples of Kerala, Orissa and West Bengal.

In the identification of the geographical region from which the honeys originate, the anemophilous pollen types may be used as markers. The pollen grains of *Alnus, Corylus, Juglans* and *Rumex hastatus* frequently occur in the samples of the Himalayan regions. The presence of pollen of *Cocos* indicates the origin of honey from the coastal region. The pollen grains of *Holoptelea* may be used as the markers of honeys originated from Indogangetic plains, to a large extent.

The determination of seasonal plant sources of honeys with their phenological records will also help in detecting mixing of seasonal honeys and such studies if undertaken for different localities will help in indexing their seasonal plant sources.

In various investigations of Indian honeys, the information regarding the origin of the samples is very vague and therefore, closer systematic studies in Melissopalynology for the identification of floral zones and the zonal honey plants, the standardisation of Indian honeys vis-a-vis major honey plants by both qualitative and quantitative methods, establishment of relative nutritive values of unifloral honeys produced under controlled conditions are some of the aspects which need much attention.

Explanations of Figures

FIGS. 1—16 : Some pollen types contained in various honeys. Figs. 1. *Alnus*, 2. *Borassus*, 3. *Brassica*, 4. *Citrus*, 5. *Cocos*, 6. *Coriandrum*, 7. *Eucalyptus*, 8. *Holoptelea*, 9. *Lagerstroemia*, 10. *Myrica*, 11. *Phyllanthus*, 12. *Plectranthus*, 13. *Prunus*, 14. *Rumex*, 15. *Salix*, 16. *Syzygium* (X1000)

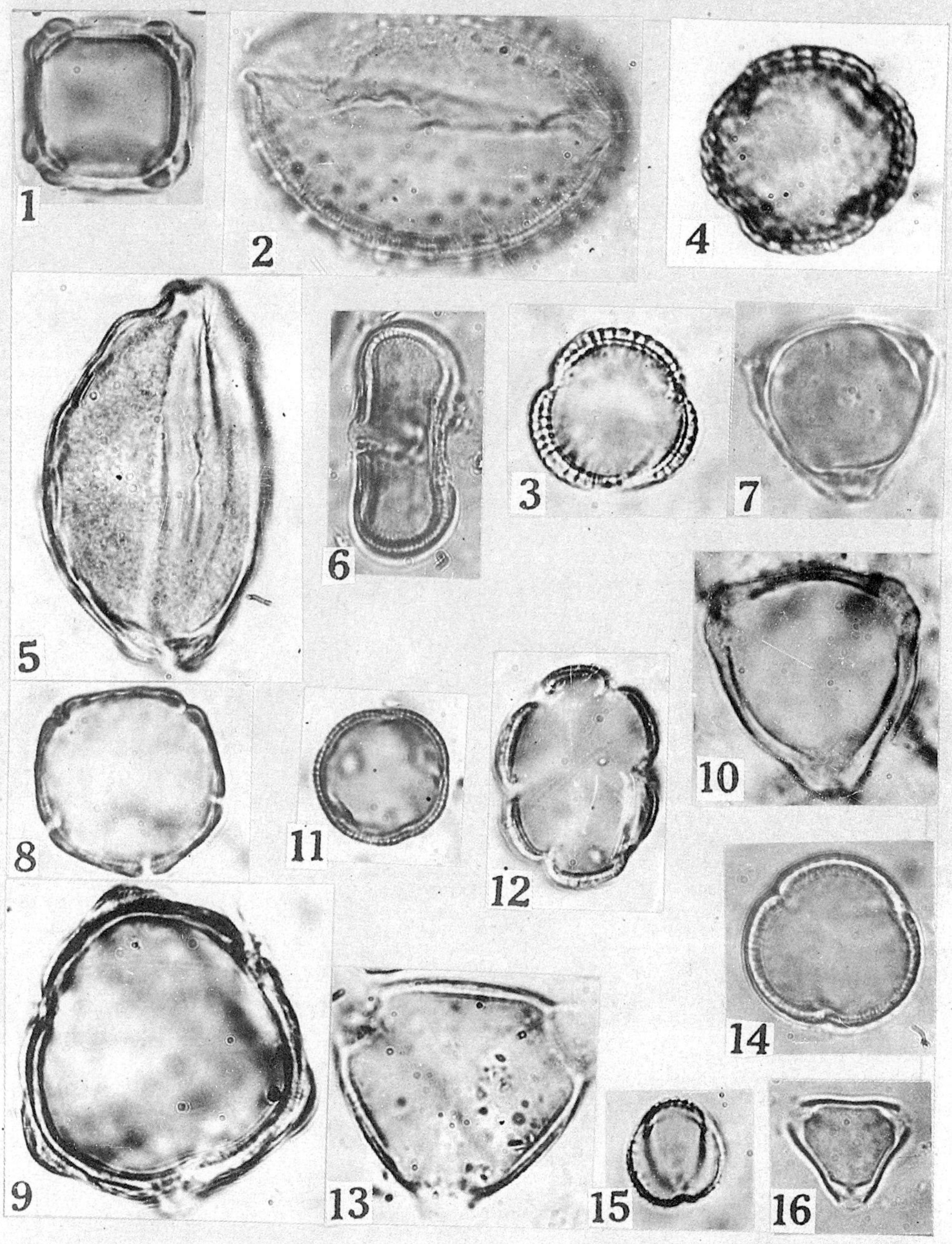
1
2
4
5
6
3
7
8
11
12
10
9
13
14
15
16

Literature Cited

Adams, R.J., Smith, M.V. and Townsend, G.F. 1979. Identification of honey sources by pollen analysis of nectar from hive. *J. apic. Res., 18* : 292-297.

Chanda, S. and Ganguly, P. 1981. Comparative analysis of the pollen content of Indian honeys with reference to entomophily and anemophily. *Proc. 4th Int. Palynol. Conf. Lucknow* (1976-77), *3* : 485-490.

Chaturvedi, M. 1983. Pollen analysis of autumn honeys of Kumaon region. *Proc. Indian natn. Sci. Acad., B49* : 125-133.

Chaturvedi, M. 1989. Pollen analysis of some spring honeys from the western Himalayan region of Uttar Pradesh, India. *Proc. Indian Acad. Sci.* (Plant Sciences), *99* : 241-246.

Chaubal, P.D. and Deodikar, G.B. 1963. Pollen grains of poisonous plants. *Grana Palynol., 4* : 393-397.

Chaubal, P.D. and Deodikar, G.B. 1965. Morphological characterisation of pollen grains of some major honey yielding plants of the Western Ghats. *Indian Bee J., 27* : 1-28.

Deodikar, G.B. and Thakar, C.V. 1953. A pollen study of major honey yielding plants of Mahabaleshwar hills. *Bulletin* I. Apicultural Laboratory, Mahabal Eshwar.

Erdtman, G. 1952. *Pollen Morphology and Plant Taxonomy Angiosperms.* Almqvist and Wiksell, Stockholm.

Fahn, A. 1953. The topography of the nectary in the flower and its phylogenetic trend. *Phytomorphology, 3* : 424-426.

ICBB 1970. Methods of Melissopalynology. *Bee Wld., 51* : 125-138.

Lieux, M.H. 1980. Acetolysis applied to microscopical honey analysis. *Grana, 19* : 57-61.

Jhansi, P., Kalpana, T.P. and Ramanujam, C.G.K. 1991. Pollen analysis of rock bee summer honeys from the Prakasam district of the Andhra Pradesh, India. *J. apicult. Res., 30* : 33-40.

Kalpana, T.P. and Ramanujam, C.G.K. 1991. A melittopalynological investigation of honeys from *Apis florea* and *Apis dorsata* hives. *Biovigyanam, 17* : 12-23.

Moar, N.T. 1985. Pollen analysis of New Zealand honey. *New Zealand J. agr. Res., 28* : 39-70.

Nair, P.K.K. 1964. A pollen analytical study of Indian honeys. *J. Indian bot. Soc., 43* : 179-191.

Nair, P.K.K.; Joshi, A.P. and Gangal, S.V. (eds.). 1986. *Airborne pollen, spores and other plant materials of India. A Survey* (C.S.I.R. Centre for Biochemicals, Delhi and National Botanical Research Institute, Lucknow).

Ramanujam, C.G.K. and Kalpana, T.P. 1990-91. Pollen analysis of *Prosopis juliflora* honeys from Ranga Reddy dist., A.P. and its relevance to apiculture and social forestry. *Current Perspectives in Palynological Research* (Silver Jubilee Commemoration Volume of the *Journal of Palynology* 1990-91), pp. 345-368.

Ramanujam, C.G.K. and Khatija, F. 1991. Melittopalynology of the agricultural tracts in Guntur district, Andhra Pradesh. *J. Indian Inst. Sci., 71* : 25-34.

Ramanujam, C.G.K., Reddy, P.R. and Kalpana, T.P. 1992. Pollen analysis of apiary honeys from East Godavari district, AP. *J. Indian Inst. Sci., 72* : 289-299.

Sen, J. and Banerjee, D. 1956. A pollen analysis of Indian honey. *Bee Wld., 37* : 52-54.

Sharma, M. and Nair, P.K.K. 1965. Pollen analysis of some honeys from Uttar Pradesh. *Indian J. Hort., 22* : 46- 51.

Suryanarayana, M.C. 1966. Studies on flora of Coorg with emphasis on bee-forage plants. 1. General ecological and botanical features. *Indian Bee J., 28* : 59-75.

Suryanarayana, M.C., Seethalakshmi, T.S. and Phadke, R.P. 1981. Pollen analysis of Indian honeys. 1. Honeys from Litchi (*Nephelium litchi*) and jamun (*Syzygium cumini*). *Proc. 4th Int. Palynol. Conf. Lucknow* (1976-77), *3* : 491-498.

Thakar, C.V., Diwan, V.V. and Salvi, S.R. 1962. Floral calendar of major and minor bee-forage plants in Mahabaleshwar hills (Western Ghats). *Indian Bee J., 24* : 35-48.

Vishnu Mittre. 1958. Pollen content of some Indian honeys. *J. sci. industr. Res., C17* : 123-124.

HONEYS FROM ANDHRA PRADESH. A CRITICAL APPRAISAL OF THEIR SOURCE AND CHEMICAL CHARACTERIZATION

C.G.K. RAMANUJAM, T.P. KALPANA and F. KHATIJA

Department of Botany, P.G. College of Science
Saifabad, Hyderabad 500 004, India.

ABSTRACT

The paper provides critical survey of the overall data generated during the last ten years on the pollen analysis of 300 honey samples collected from five districts of Andhra Pradesh viz., East and West Godavari, Guntur, Ranga Reddy and Mahboobnagar in order to recognize the chief and alternate sources of nectar in honey production. 98 of these honeys (84 unifloral and 14 multifloral) were subjected to chemical analysis.

Two honey flow periods (HFP) could be recognised in East Godavari and Ranga Reddy districts, which provided the maximum number of honeys in this study. HFP I spans from November to February and HFP II, from March to June. The former is the principal honey flow period in both the districts. July to October constitutes the dearth period with inadequate sources of nectar resulting in little or no surplus honey in both these districts.

In all the honeys studied, the levulose/dextrose ratios were found to be more than 1 indicating that these honeys seldom granulate under storage.

Key words : Pollen and chemical analysis, apiary and squeezed honey, chief and alternate sources of nectar, Andhra Pradesh.

INTRODUCTION

The food of honey bees consists exclusively of two discrete plant products, the nectar and pollen. Nectar, a sugary syrup normally with a high concentration of sucrose is converted into honey through two chemical changes and one physical change. The chemical changes involve the activity of two enzymes viz., invertase and glucose-oxidase, the former converting sucrose into glucose and fructose and the latter bringing about the conversion of a small amount of glucose to gluconic acid, which incidentally makes the honey slightly acidic. The physical change leads to reduction of moisture content of the honey. The nectar essentially provides the energy source or the carbohydrates and the pollen provides proteins, lipids and minerals so imperative for body building in the brood. Sources of nectar rich in sugars and pollen rich in proteins are, as a rule, preferred by the honey bees.

A plant species may provide either nectar or pollen, or both. As adequate source of both nectar and pollen within the foraging range of the bees is of prime importance for the survival and growth of bee colonies, only such areas with a more or less unhindered supply of both these raw materials are earmarked for successful bee-keeping ventures. Therefore, identification and proper demarcation of all such areas which have the potential for the healthy sustenance of bee colonies through major part of the year, is the most important pre-requisite for launching apiary industry involved in commercial honey production. This information can be obtained by melittopalynological studies, as the pollen encountered in honeys and pollen loads constitute the only reliable source of recognition of bee forage plants.

Melittopalynology encompasses a critical microscopic and field study involving qualitative and quantitative analysis of the myriad pollen contents of honeys and pollen loads from diverse floristic and geographical regions (Ramanujam, 1991). Pollen analysis of honeys furnishes information of the plants constituting the nectar source for the bees, as the nectar of a plant always contains some pollen of that plant (anthesis facilitates this). Analysis of pollen loads, on the other hand, helps in identifying and evaluating the pollen sources for the bees. If a plant is preferred for both nectar and pollen, its pollen would then be encountered in both the honey and pollen loads. Pollen analytical studies in conjunction with field observations provide reliable data on the relative preferences of the bees for nectar and pollen among the alternative plant sources flowering synchronously. Because of perceptible diversity in floristic complexes in the context of dominance or otherwise of a taxon or a group of taxa coupled with the occurrence of strictly local floral elements, the pollen spectrum of a honey is also an expression of its geographical origin.

Melittopalynology is a grossly neglected aspect of bee-botany in the Indian context in general and Andhra Pradesh in particular. It is only during the last ten years that indepth studies on pollen analysis of honeys have been undertaken in Andhra Pradesh in a well planned and organised way (Jhansi & Ramanujam, 1986, 1990; Kalpana & Ramanujam, 1989, 1991; Ramanujam, Khatija & Kalpana, 1990; Ramanujam & Kalpana, 1990-91, 1992, 1993; Ramanujam & Khatija, 1991; Kalpana, 1992; Khatija, 1992; Ramanujam, Kalpana & Khatija, 1992; Ramanujam, Reddy & Kalpana, 1992).

This overview is primarily designed to collate and critically analyse the information obtained from a study of 300 honey samples (127 apiary; 173 squeezed) by the senior author and his associates over the last ten years from five districts of Andhra Pradesh viz., East and West Godavari, Guntur, Ranga Reddy and Mahboobnagar (Fig. 1). The honeys representing the products of all the three species of Indian honey bees viz., *Apis cerana*, *A. dorsata* and *A. florea* were collected mostly during the winter and summer seasons. Table 1 provides the

TABLE 1 : Inventory of the Honey Samples

District	*Collection Period*	*No. of honey samples*	*Honey bee species*		
			A. cerana	*A. florea*	*A. dorsata*
East Godavari	Nov.—Feb. (winter)	43	42	—	1
	Mar.—June (summer)	37	34	3	—
West Godavari	Apr.—July (summer)	12	3	—	9
Guntur	Sept. (monsoon)	8	8	—	—
	Dec.—Jan. (winter)	6	6	—	—
	Mar.—July (summer)	14	14	—	—
Ranga Reddy	Nov.—Feb. (winter)	119	14	95	10
	Mar.—June (summer)	29	6	23	—
Mahboobnagar	Mar.—June (summer)	32	—	—	32
Total number of samples		300	—	—	—

broad inventory of the honey samples utilised in this analysis. The methodology recommended by International Commission for Bee Botany (Louveaux *et al.*, 1978) was followed for the analysis of the honey samples.

OBSERVATIONS

Pollen analysis

East Godavari district : A total of 80 honeys viz., 43 winter and 37 summer samples have been investigated from this district. Of the 43 winter honeys 31 were found to be unifloral and 12, multifloral. *Sapindus emarginatus* (47.67-85.33%) in 16 samples *Eucalyptus globulus* (47.0-80.0%) 10 samples, *Mollugo cerviana* (62.0 %, 67.67%) 2 samples and, *Mimosa pudica* (73.0%), *Capparis grandis* (47.33 %) and *Hygrophila auriculata* (52.67 %) 1 sample each represent the predominant pollen types in the unifloral honeys. The multifloral honeys are the composite (mixed) honeys of *Eucalyptus globulus*. *Cocos nucifera, Sapindus emarginatus, Phoenix sylvestris, Borassus flabellifer, Prosopis juliflora, Feronia elephantum, Anacardium occidentale, Citrus* sp. and *Croton bonplandianum*. *Sapindus emarginatus* (soapnut) and *Eucalyptus globulus* honeys may be considered as representative of the winter honeys of East Godavari district.

30 of the 37 summer honeys were found to be unifloral and the rest, multifloral. *Borassus flabellifer* (46.0-77.33 %) in 13 samples, *Cocos nucifera* (48.0-72.33%) 7 samples, *Syzygium cumini* (70.67-83.33%) 5 samples, *Phoenix sylvestris* (57.33 %) and *Anacardium occidentale* (54.67 %, 59.33 %) 2 samples each and, *Mollugo cerviana* (80.33 %) 1 sample constitute the predominant pollen types in the summer unifloral honeys. The multifloral honeys are the composite honeys of *Capparis grandis, Borassus flabellifer, Syzygium cumini, Morinda citrifolia, Cocos nucifera, Eucalyptus globulus* and *Citrus* sp. *Borassus flabellifer, Cocos nucifera* and *Syzygium cumini* honeys may be considered as characteristic of the summer honeys.

West Godavari district

12 honeys, all obtained during the summer months were studied from this district. Of these, 9 originated from the agency forests and

3 from the agricultural tracts. *Aspidopterys indica* (55.66-66.33 %) in 6 samples and *Lagerstroemia parviflora* (67.33 %) and *Phyllanthus* sp. (53.66 %) 1 sample each are the predominant pollen types in the 8 unifloral forest honeys. All the 3 honeys from the agricultural tracts were unifloral *Cocos nucifera* honeys with the pollen of this taxon as the predominant type (51.33-57.0 %). *Aspidopterys indica* honeys are considered as characteristic of summer honeys in the agency forests.

Guntur district

28 honey samples studied from this district were obtained during monsoon, winter and summer months. Of the 8 samples collected from the monsoon September month, 4 were found to be unifloral with *Mimosa pudica* (49.6-53.6 %) as the predominant pollen. The 4 multifloral honeys are the composite honeys of *Phoenix sylvestris, Hygrophila auriculata, Cleome viscosa* and *Cucumis* sp. *Mimosa pudica* honey is considered as representative of the September month.

5 of the 6 honeys obtained during December-January (winter) were found to be unifloral with *Sapindus emarginatus* (63.0 %, 70.2 %) in 2 samples and *Capsicum frutescens* (60.27 %), *Prosopis juliflora* (58.2 %) and *Hygrophila auriculata* (59.67 %) 1 sample each forming the predominant pollen types. Soapnut (*Sapindus emarginatus*) honeys may be considered as commonly encountered honeys in the winter months of Guntur district.

Of the 14 summer honeys from this district, 6 were found to be unifloral and the rest multifloral. *Borassus flabellifer* (56.67-87.12 %) in 3 samples, *Hygrophila auriculata* (46.0- 49.5 %) 2 samples and *Brassica nigra* (53.33 %) 1 sample represent the predominant pollen types of the unifloral honeys. The multifloral honeys are the composite honeys of *Hygrophila auriculata, Borassus flabellifer, Helianthus annuus, Brassica nigra, Cocos nucifera, Phoenix sylvestris, Phyla nodiflora, Crotalaria juncea, Cucumis* sp. and *Momordica charantia. Borassus flabellifer* honey may be considered as the characteristic summer honey of Guntur district as evidenced by the significant proportion of the pollen of this plant in the majority of honey samples.

Ranga Reddy district

A total of 148 honeys were investigated from the agricultural tracts of this district. Of these, 119 samples were obtained during the winter season and 29 samples, during the summer season. In the winter honeys, 102 samples were found to be unifloral and 17, multifloral. The predominant pollen types encountered in the unifloral honeys are viz., *Carum copticum* (46.0-89.67 %) in 38 samples, *Prosopis juliflora* (49.33-95.92 %) 19 samples, *Phoenix sylvestris* (46.67-87.67 %) 9 samples, *Guizotia abyssinica* (46.33-67.33%) 8 samples, *Ageratum conyzoides* (52.33-84.0 %) 7 samples, *Coriandrum sativum* (53.0-63.67 %) 5 samples, *Mangifera indica* (54.0 %, 69.67 %), *Eucalyptus globulus* (52.33 %, 84.67 %), *Ailanthus excelsa* (49.67 %, 77.33 %), *Memecylon edule* (56.33 %, 70.67 %) 2 samples each and, *Sphaeranthus indicus* (57.33 %), *Allium cepa* (52.0 %), *Syzygium cumini* (54.67 %), *Helianthus annuus* (82.0 %), *Evolvulus alsinoides* (50.33 %), *Capsicum frutescens* (59.67 %), *Justicia procumbens* (63.0 %) and *Croton bonplandianum* (75.33 %) 1 sample each. *Carum copticum, Prosopis juliflora, Phoenix sylvestris* and *Guizotia abyssinica* honeys may be considered as characteristic of the winter honeys of Ranga Reddy district. The winter multifloral honeys represent essentially mixed honeys of *Sphaeranthus indicus, Guizotia abyssinica, Tridax procumbens, Justicia procumbens, Ageratum conyzoides, Carum copticum, Cleome gynandra, Phoenix sylvestris, Prosopis juliflora, Eucalyptus globulus, Capsicum frutescens, Derris* sp. and *Punica granatum.*

26 of the 29 summer honeys were found to be unifloral and the rest, multifloral. *Ageratum conyzoides* (55.33-86.33 %) in 7 samples, *Punica granatum* (58.67-74.67 %) 4 samples, *Tamarindus indica* (50.67-88.0 %)and *Prosopis juliflora* (63.33-88.67 %) 3 samples each, *Terminalia arjuna* (47.0 %, 84.33 %) 2 samples and, *Tridax procumbens* (49.33 %), *Casearia elliptica* (51.0 %), *Capparis grandis* (62.67 %), *Pongamia pinnata* (63.67 %), *Mimosa rubicaulis* (60.0 %), *Syzygium cumini* (55.0 %) and *Psidium guajava* (78.67 %) 1 sample each represent the predominant pollen types of the unifloral summer honeys. We consider *Ageratum conyzoides* and *Tamarindus indica* honeys as the characteristic summer honeys of Ranga Reddy district in view of the significant representation of the pollen of these taxa in a number of honey samples. The summer multifloral honeys are found to be the composite honeys of *Ageratum conyzoides, Tamarindus indica, Dodonaea viscosa, Ailanthus excelsa, Tridax procumbens* and *Borreria hispida.*

Mahboobnagar district

Of the 32 summer honeys obtained from the deciduous forests of Mahboobnagar district (no winter honeys were available for study) 24 were found to be unifloral and the rest, multifloral. *Sterculia urens* (58.0-73.33 %) in 7 samples, *Aegle marmelos* (51.33-60.33 %), *Adina cordifolia* (46.67-68.67 %) 4 samples each, *Lagerstroemia parviflora* (50.33 %, 56.33 %), *Crataeva magna* (54.0 %, 58.33 %) 2 samples each and *Spondias pinnata* (51.33 %), *Soymida febrifuga* (50.33 %), *Prosopis juliflora* (76.67 %), *Schleichera oleosa* (53.0 %) and *Syzygium cumini* (51.0 %) 1 sample each were encountered as predominant pollen types in the unifloral honeys. Sterculia urens, Aegle marmelos and *Adina cordifolia* honeys may be considered as representative of the summer season in Mahboobnagar deciduous forests. The summer multifloral honeys of these forests constitute the composite honeys of *Terminalia arjuna, Mimosa rubicaulis, Phyllanthus* sp., *Loranthus longiflorus, Ziziphus xylopyrus, Premna tomentosa, Capparis grandis, Caesalpinia bonduc, Crataeva magna, Grewia* sp *Lannea coromandelica* and *Adina cordifolia.*

CHEMICAL ANALYSIS

A total of 98 honey samples (84 unifloral and 14 multifloral) were subjected to chemical analysis employing Indian Standard Specification (IS : 4941 1974, IS : 8464 1977). Of the 84 unifloral honeys, 50 were of *Apis cerana* (7 from Guntur and 43 from East Godavari district), 22 of *A florea* (from Ranga Reddy district) and 12 of *A. dorsata* (from Mahboobnagar district). All the 14 multifloral honeys analysed chemically were of *A. cerana* from East Godavari district. The honey samples were analysed for 1. Moisture, 2. Total Reducing Sugars, 3. Levulose (Fructose), 4. Dextrose (Glucose), 5. Levulose/Dextrose (L/D) Ratio, 6. Sucrose and 7. Acidity. The average values of the analysis of honeys from the four districts are provided in Tables 2a and 2b.

A. dorsata honeys (squeezed) from Mahboobnagar forests showed higher percentage of reducing sugars. The L/D ratio of these honeys is higher than that of *A. cerana* but lower than that of *A. florea.* The average value for total reducing sugars in *A. florea honeys of Ranga Reddu district is higher than that of A. cerana* honeys of Guntur and

TABLE 2a : Average Analytical Values of Unifloral Honeys

Parameter	*Apis cerana*		*Apis florea*	*Apis dorsata*
	Guntur dist.	*East Godavari dist.*	*Ranga Reddy dist*	*hboobnagar dist.*
Moisture %	20.54 (20.0—22.0)	21.605 (20.0—23.0)	20.683 (18.2—24.0)	20.63 (20.0—22.0)
Total reducing sugars %	74.906 (72.660—76.226)	70.990 (67.953—72.698)	75.227 (67.989—78.864)	75.766 (73.118—76.844)
Levulose or Fructose %	40.976 (37.320—42.461)	38.529 (36.247—0.501)	41.429 (35.320—45.660)	41.630 (39.604—42.864)
Dextrose or Glucose %	33.927 (32.639—35.340)	32.461 (31.064—34.440)	33.798 (30.839—37.292)	34.136 (32.228—35.388)
L/D ratio	1.207 (1.056—1.266)	1.188 (1.059—1.276)	1.232 (1.013—1.439)	1.219 (1.140—1.298)
Sucrose %	1.905 (1.413—2.706)	1.502 (0.69—2.935)	1.579 (0.422—3.942)	1.793 (1.336—2.463)
Acidity %	0.110 (0.069—0.1794)	0.0373 (0.0115—0.0736)	0.0488 (0.0276—0.0782)	0.055 (0.023—0.069)

TABLE 2b : Average Analytical Values of Multifloral Honeys

Parameter	*East Godavari dist.*
Moisture %	21.5 (20.6—23.0)
Total reduction sugars %	70.482 (68.155—72.013)
Leveulose or Fructose %	38.486 (36.562—40.049)
Dextrose or Glucose %	31.996 (31.064—33.765)
L/D ratio	1.203 (1.128—1.266)
Sucrose %	1.568 (0.911—2.265)
Acidity %	0.041 (O.0184—0.0805)

East Godavari districts. The squeezed honeys of the Ranga Reddy and Mahboobnagar districts showed higher percentage of total reducing sugars than the apiary honeys of Guntur and East Godavari districts.

Similarly levulose is in higher percentage in the squeezed than in apiary honeys. It may further be highlighted that the average values of total reducing sugars and sucrose are perceptibly lower in the coastal honeys of East Godavari district when compared to the honeys of other districts; the same applies to average L/D ratio of the former. The L/D ratios in all the honeys studied were consistently more than 1 which clearly indicates that these honeys seldom granulate under storage. No significant differences are noted between uni-and multifloral honeys of the East Godavari district.

A comparison of the multifloral honeys of the East Godavari district with those of the south zone (Phadke 1967) shows that the latter had higher percentages of the total reducing sugars (72.88 %) and acidity (0.159 %) but lower values of moisture (20.34 %) and L/D ratio (1.137).

DISCUSSION

Melittopalynological study of 300 samples of honey (apiary 127; squeezed 173) obtained from the colonies of *Apis cerana, A. florea* and *A. dorsata* in five districts of Andhra Pradesh viz., East Godavari, West Godavari, Guntur, Ranga Reddy and Mahboobnagar has brought to light 239 unifloral and 61 multifloral honeys. Honeys from different seasons and floristic regimes highlight different sources of nectar for the honey bees. We have considered all such taxa contributing predominant pollen types in the unifloral honeys of a district as chief sources of nectar and those represented by atleast 10 % of the pollen spectrum of each honey sample as alternate sources of nectar in that district.

Table 3 provides details of the chief and alternate sources of nectar for the honey bees in all the above five districts. We have further recognised major chief sources of nectar in each district on the basis of relative extensiveness of spatial coverage and the frequency of occurrence of each taxon of the predominant pollen type in the total contingent of honeys of that district. Accordingly, in the coastal East Godavari district, *Sapindus emarginatus and Eucalyptus globulus* in winter and, *Borassus flabellifer*, *Cocos nucifera* and *Syzygium cumini* in summer are considered as major chief sources of nectar for honey production. In West Godavari district where information is available

TABLE 3 : Chief and Alternate Sources of Nectar for Honey Bees

District			*Taxa*
EAST GODAVARI			
	Winter :	CS —	*Sapindus emarginatus, Eucalyptus globulus, Mollugo cerviana, Mimosa pudica, Capparis grandis, Hygrophila auriculata*
		AS —	*Phoenix sylvestris, Cocos nucifera, Prosopis juliflora, Borassus, flabellifer, Allium cepa, Croton bonplandianum, Syzygium cumini, Cleome viscosa, Phyla nodiflora, Feronia elephantum, Anacardium occidentale, Parkinsonia aculeata, Citrus* sp., *Ziziphus mauritiana*
	Summer :	CS —	*Borassus flabellifer, Cocos nucifera, Syzygium cumini, Phoenix sylvestris, Anacardium occidentale, Mollugo cerviana*
		AS —	*Capparis grandis, Morinda citrifolia, Mimosa pudica, Barringtonia acutangula, Eucalyptus globulus, Sesbania* sp., *Citrus* sp., *Feronia elephantum, Guazuma ulmifolia*
WEST GODAVARI AGENCY FOREST			
	Summer :	CS —	*Aspidopterys indica, Lagerstroemia parviflora, Phyllanthus* sp.
		AS —	*Terminalia* sp., *Mimosa rubicaulis*
AGRICULTURAL TRACTS			
	Summer :	CS —	*Cocos nucifera*
		AS —	*Cleome gynandra, Phyllanthus emblica*
GUNTUR	Monsoon :	CS —	*Mimosa pudica*
		AS —	*Phoenix sylvestris, Hygrophila auriculata, Sopubia delphinifolia, Cocos nucifera, Brassica nigra, Cleome viscosa, Cucumis* sp., *Eucalyptus globulus*
	Winter :	CS —	*Sapindus emarginatus, Capsicum frutescens, Prosopis juliflora, Hygrophila auriculata*
		AS —	*Phoenix sylvestris, Brassica nigra, Ricinus communis*
	Summer :	CS —	*Borassus flabellifer, Hygrophila auriculata, Brassica nigra*
		AS —	*Helianthus annuus, Cocos nucifera, Syzygium cumini, Phoenix sylvestris, Phyla nodiflora, Crotalaria juncea, Cucumis* sp., *Momordica charantia, Citrus limon*

RANGA REDDY			
	Winter :	CS —	*Carum copticum, Prosopis juliflora, Phoenix sylvestris, Guizotia abyssinica, Ageratum conyzoides, Coriandrum sativum, Mangifera indica, Eucalyptus globulus, Ailanthus excelsa, Memecylon edule, Sphaeranthus indicus, Allium cepa, Syzygium cumini, Helianthus annuus, Evolvulus alsinoides, Capsicum frutescens, Justicia procumbens, Croton bonplandianum*
		AS —	*Tridax procumbens, Rungia repens, Cleome gynandra, Cocos nucifera, Dodonaea viscosa, Cajanus cajan, Derris* sp., *Punica granatum, Ricinus communis, Brassica nigra, Sopubia delphinifolia, Buchanania lanzan, Spinacia oleracea, Hyptis suaveolens*
	Summer :	CS —	*Ageratum conyzoides, Punica granatum, Tamarindus indica, Prosopis juliflora, Terminalia arjuna, Tridax procumbens, Casearia elliptica, Capparis grandis, Pongamia pinnata, Mimosa rubicaulis, Syzygium cumini, Psidium guajava*
		AS —	*Ailanthus excelsa, Borreria hispida, Arachis hypogaea, Acacia nilotica, Parkinsonia aculeata, Cocos nucifera*
MAHBOOBNAGAR			
	Summer :	CS —	*Sterculia urens, Adina cordifolia, Aegle marmelos, Lagerstroemia parviflora, Crataeva magna, Spondias pinnata, Soymida febrifuga, Prosopis juliflora, Schleichera oleosa, Syzygium cumini*
		AS —	*Terminalia arjuna, Terminalia alata, Mimosa rubicaulis, Phyllanthus* sp., *Loranthus longiflorus, Premna tomentosa, Capparis grandis, Caesalpinia bonduc, Grewia salvifolia, Lannea coromandelica, Phoenix sylvestris, Mitragyna parvifolia, Dichrostachys cinerea, Gardenia latifolia*

Key : **CS** — Chief source of nectar; **AS** — Alternate source of nectar

only on summer honeys, *Aspidopterys indica* in the deciduous forests and *Cocos nucifera* in the agricultural tracts represent the major chief sources of nectar. In Guntur district *Mimosa pudica* during monsoon, *Sapindus emarginatus* during winter and *Borassus flabellifer* during summer represent the major chief sources of nectar. *Carum copticum, Prosopis juliflora, Phoenix sylvestris* and *Guizotia abyssinica* during winter and *Ageratum conyzoides* and *Tamarindus indica* during summer constitute the major chief sources of nectar in the agricultural tracts of Ranga Reddy district. In the deciduous forests of Mahboobnagar district *Sterculia urens, Aegle marmelos* and *Adina cordifolia* contribute to the major chief sources of nectar.

The coastal East Godavari and the inland Ranga Reddy districts, where it has been possible to collect an appreciably high number of honey samples harvested in various months of the year, we have been able to recognise month-wise chief and alternate sources of nectar for the honey bees. Further, on the basis of our studies in the laboratory coupled with field observations of the bee colonies and bee flora, it has been possible to demarcate the honey flow and dearth periods. Figs. 2 and 3 furnish information on the nectar calendar for the honey bees in these two districts. highlighting the honey flow and dearth periods.

Two honey flow periods (HFP I; HFP II) could be recognised in the East Godavari district, the first spanning November to February (winter) and the second, March to June (summer). The former constitutes the principal or main flow period providing maximum honey production and the latter, the secondary flow period with reduced honey production. The copious secretion of nectar by *Sapindus emarginatus* and *Eucalyptus globulus* is responsible for the maximum harvest of honey during the principal honey flow period. On the other hand, *Borassus flabellifer, Cocos nucifera, Syzygium cumini* along with *Phoenix sylvestris* and *Anacardium occidentale* provide ample source of nectar for the secondary honey flow period. July to October constituting essentially the monsoon season furnishes inadequate or poor sources of nectar (as well as pollen) preferred by the bees and the supers of the bee hives during this period are with little or no surplus honey. We consider this season as the dearth period.

In the agricultural tracts of the Ranga Reddy district we could again recognise two honey flow periods, the first during November to February (winter) and the second from March to June (summer). The former is the principal or main honey flow period facilitating maximum honey production and the latter, the secondary flow period during which the honey production gets considerably reduced. *Carum copticum, Prosopis juliflora, Phoenix sylvestris* and *Guizotia abyssinica* provide the major source of nectar during principal honey flow period. *Ageratum conyzoides* and *Tamarindus indica* along with *Punica granatum* and *Pongamia pinnata* contribute to the major source of nectar during the secondary honey flow period. As in the East Godavari district, July to October, the monsoon season, represents the dearth period.

Lastly, in facilitating recognition and prediction of specific kinds of honeys, chief and alternate sources of nectar for the honey bees and honey flow and dearth periods, this study would be of immense utilitarian value to the bee-keepers in the efficient and successful management of their apiaries resulting in enhanced honey production.

ACKNOWLEDGEMENTS

The authors express their deep appreciation to Messers K. Venkateswara Rao, bee-keeper, Guntur district and, B.V. Narayana, G. Appa Rao, G. Venkata Rao, U. Talupula Rao and Sesha Rao, bee-keepers, East Godavari district for the supply of apiary honeys. To Shri Sultan Mohiuddin of Forest department, A.P., we are thankful for his help in the collection of squeezed honeys from the deciduous forests of Mahboobnagar district. The financial help received from CSIR and UGC, New Delhi for undertaking this study is gratefully acknowledged.

Explanation to Figures

FIG. 1 : Map showing the districts which provided honey samples

FIG. 2 : Nectar calendar for the honey bees in East Godavari district.

FIG. 3 : Nectar calendar for the honey bees in Ranga Reddy district.

Literature Cited

IS : 4941 1974. Indian standard specification for extracted honey; Indian standards Institution, New Delhi, 1-16.

IS : 8464 1977. Indian standard specification for squeezed honey; Indian standards Institution, New Delhi, 1-7.

Jhansi, P. & Ramanujam, C.G.K. 1986. Pollen analysis of unifloral honeys from Andhra Pradesh; *Proc. Spl. Gec. Conv., Poona,* 69-72.

Jhansi, P. & Ramanujam, C.G.K. 1990. Pollen analysis of some honey samples from Andhra Pradesh; *Asian Jour. Pl. Sci., 2 :* 19-26.

Kalpana, T.P. 1992. Melittopalynology of Ranga Reddy district and its relevance to apiary industry; Ph.D. thesis, Osmania University, Hyderabad, India.

Kalpana, T.P. & Ramanujam, C.G.K. 1989. A melittopalynological investigation of Nawabpet mandal of Ranga Reddy district, A.P.; *J. Swamy Bot. Cl., 6* : 57-64.

Kalpana, T.P. & Ramanujam, C.G.K. 1991. A melittopalynological investigation of honeys from *Apis florea* and *Apis dorsata* hives; *Biovigyanam, 17* : 12-23.

Khatija, F. 1992. Melittopalynology of diverse floristic regions of Andhra Pradesh; Ph.D. thesis, Osmania University, Hyderabad, India.

Louveaux, J., Maurizio, A. & Vorwohl, G. 1978 Methods of melissopalynology; *Bee World, 59* : 139-157.

Phadke, R.P. 1967. Studies on Indian honeys. 1. Proximate composition and physico-chemical characteristics of Indian multiflcral apiary honeys from *Apis indica* bees; *Indian Bee Journal, 29* : 14-26.

Ramanujam, C.G.K. 1991. Beekeeping and melittopalynology — perspectives and prospects; *Prof. T. Navaneeth Rao Commemoration Volume, Osmania University, Hyderabad,* 74-79.

Ramanujam, C.G.K. & Kalpana, T.P. 1990-91. Pollen analysis of *Prosopis juliflora* honeys from Ranga Reddy dist., A.P., and its relevance to apiculture and social forestry; *Silver Jubilee Commemoration Volume of the Journal of Palynology, 26-27* : 345-368.

Ramanujam, C.G.K. & Kalpana, T.P. 1992. *Tamarindus indica* L an important forage plant for *Apis florea* F in south central India; *Apidologie, 23* : 403-413.

Ramanujam, C.G.K. & Kalpana, T.P. 1993. Pollen analysis of honeys from Kondevaram apiaries of East Godavari district, Andhra Pradesh; *Biovigyanam,* 19 : 11-19.

Ramanujam, C.G.K. & Khatija, F. 1991 Melittopalynology of the agriculture tracts in Guntur district, Andhra Pradesh; *J. Indian Inst. Sci., 71* : 25-34.

Ramanujam, C.G.K., Kalpana, T.P. & Khatija, F. 1992. Melittopalynology and recognition of major nectar and pollen sources for honey bees in some districts of Andhra Pradesh; *Geophytology, 22* : 261-271.

Ramanujam, C.G.K., Khatija, F & Kalpana, T.P. 1990. Significance of *Borassus flabellifer* L. pollen in apiary honeys of Guntur district, Andhra Pradesh; *Geophytology, 20* :119-123.

Ramanujam, C.G.K., Reddy, P.R. & Kalpana, T.P. 1992. Pollen analysis of apiary honeys from East Godavari district, A.P; *J. Indian Inst. Sci., 72* : 289-299.

ANDHRA PRADESH

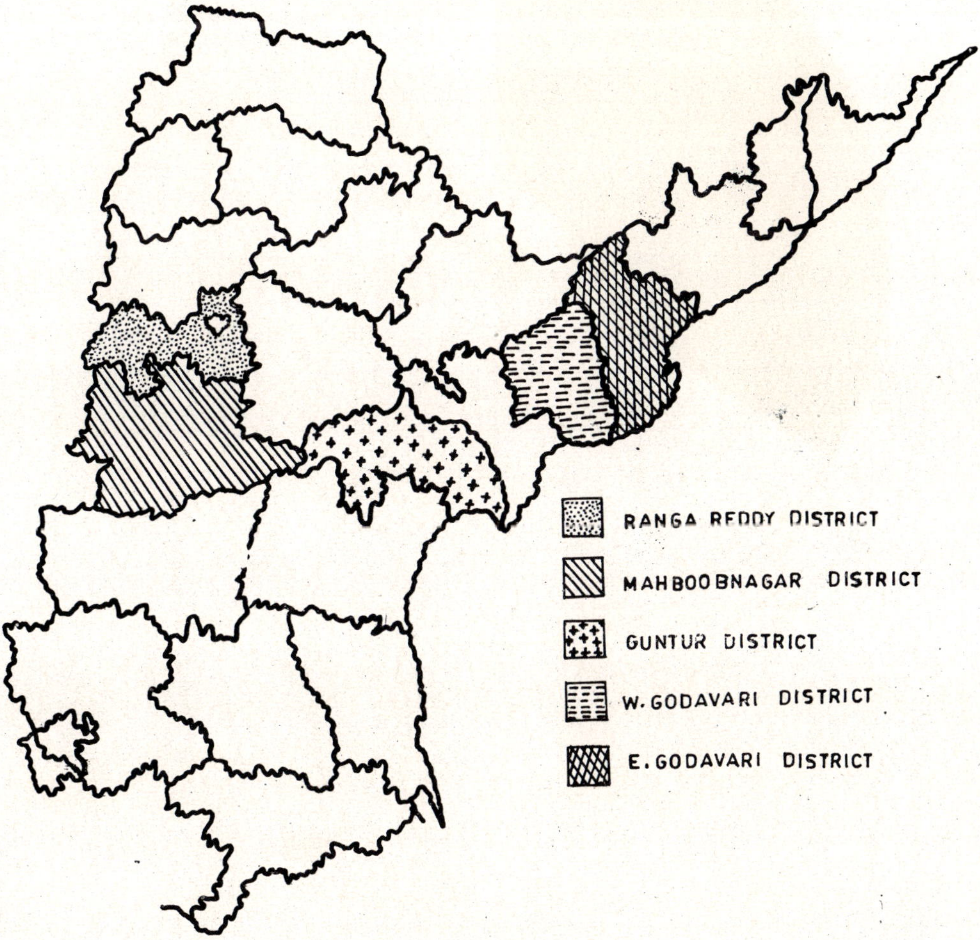

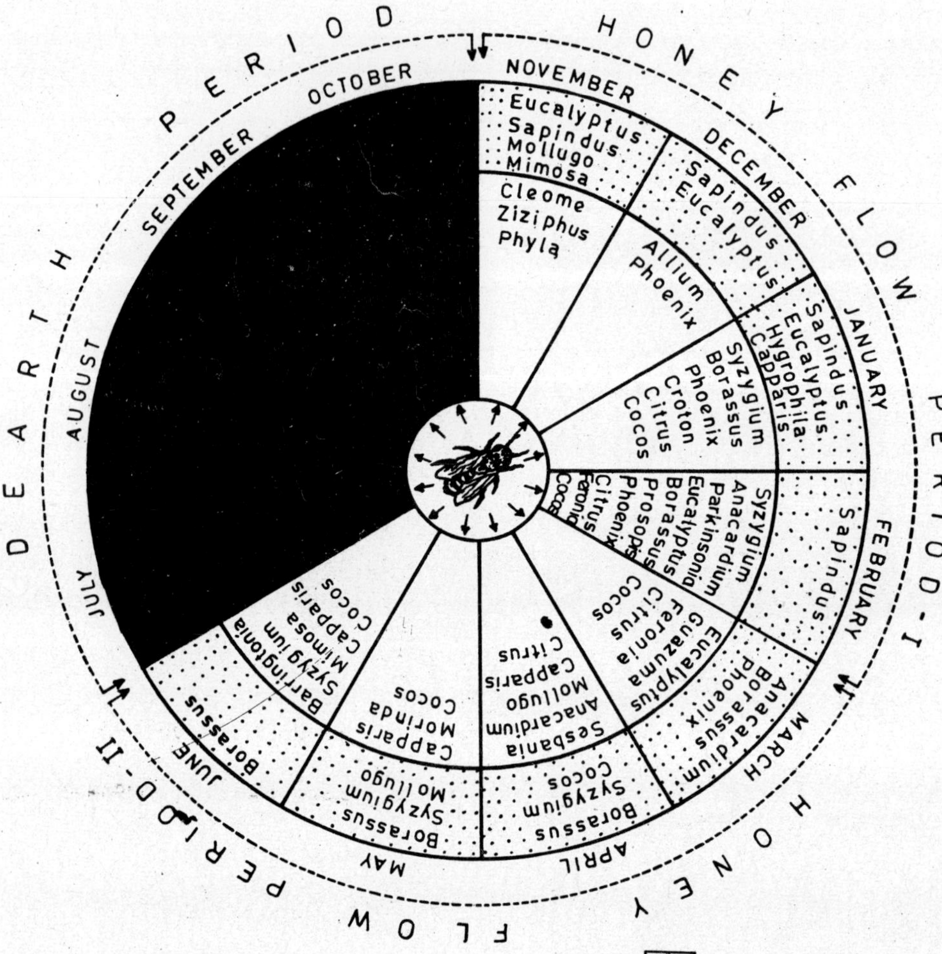

Chief nectar source
Alternate nectar source
Dearth period

Fig. 2

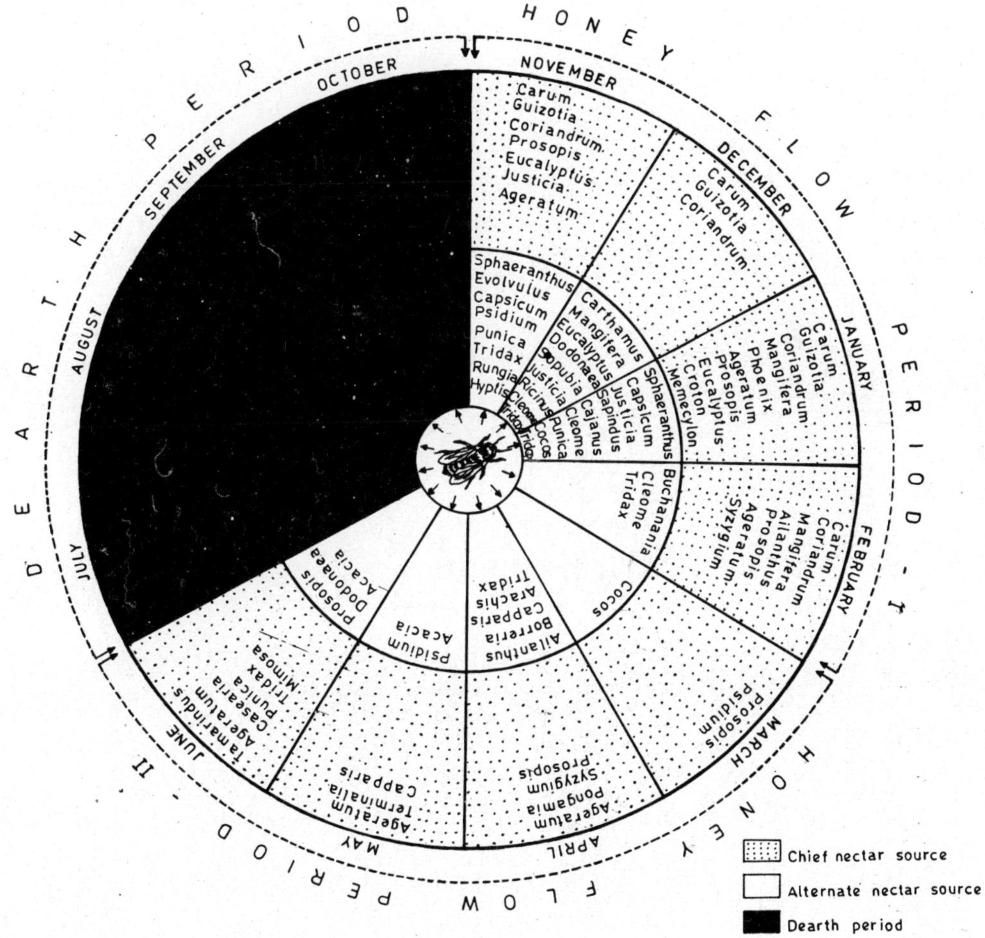
DEARTH PERIOD
HONEY FLOW PERIOD - I
HONEY FLOW PERIOD - II
OCTOBER
SEPTEMBER
AUGUST
JULY
NOVEMBER
Carum
Guizotia
Coriandrum
Prosopis
Eucalyptus
Justicia
Ageratum
Sphaeranthus
Evolvulus
Capsicum
Psidium
Punica
Tridax
Rungia
Hyptis
DECEMBER
Carum
Guizotia
Coriandrum
Carthamus
Mangifera
Eucalyptus
Dodonaea
Justicia
Ricinus
Cleome
Tridax
JANUARY
Carum
Guizotia
Coriandrum
Mangifera
Phoenix
Ageratum
Prosopis
Eucalyptus
Croton
Memecylon
Sphaeranthus
Capsicum
Justicia
Sapindus
Cajanus
Cleome
Punica
Cocos
FEBRUARY
Carum
Coriandrum
Mangifera
Ailanthus
Prosopis
Ageratum
Syzygium
Buchanania
Cleome
Tridax
MARCH
Prosopis
Psidium
Cocos
APRIL
Ageratum
Pongamia
Syzygium
Prosopis
Ailanthus
Borreria
Capparis
Arachis
Tridax
MAY
Ageratum
Terminalia
Capparis
Psidium
Acacia
JUNE
Tamarindus
Ageratum
Casearia
Punica
Tridax
Mimosa
Prosopis
Dodonaea
Acacia
Chief nectar source
Alternate nectar source
Dearth period

Fig.3

NECTAR IN BEE BIOLOGY AND BEE-KEEPING

M.C. SURYANARAYANA*

Central Bee Research Institute

Khadi & Village Industries Commission, Pune 411 016, India.

ABSTRACT

The evolution of pleomorphic flowers during the early Tertiary period marked the introduction of nectar as a food in the entomophilous flower syndrome. Among the anthophils honey bees depend exclusively on nectar for their carbohydrate and energy requirement. The basis of beekeeping is the behaviour of the bees of storing honey in excess of their immediate requirement.

Foraging for nectar, its conversion into honey and storage as a food reserve have been major factors that instigated and regulated the evolution of these highly developed social insects, even as they participated and encouraged in the evolution of flowering plants. For the bees nectar comes mostly from floral or extrafloral nectaries of plants, the latter being common in tropical and sub-tropical regions. Honey bees show a high degree of adaptation to anthophily that includes special body structure and physiology that facilities food search, identifying and selective foraging for food. In discriminating a food source honey bees use their highly developed tactile, optical, olfactory and gustatory senses. Bee dances constitute a fairly accurate system of communication that helps in exploiting only good and useful sources of food, and in competing successfully with other flower visitors. The decision to accept or reject a sweet liquid depends on the concentration, types and proportion of sugars in the liquid and in the intensity of requirement of nectars in the

* Present address : 7, GURUKRUPA, 365/2, Ekbote Colony, Pune 411042, India.

colony. The higher the sugar content in the nectar, the better would be the energy economy for the bees. The quantity of nectar produced in a flower too is a determinant of the energy requirement in a foraging trip. Nectars with sucrose alone, or in combination with fructose and glucose, are preferred to those with other pure or mixed sugars. Mannose, galactose and a few other sugars are sometimes toxic to bees.

In active growth season, a bee colony may collect nectar to meet its requirement of water, besides the carbohydrates, minerals and other nutrients. Foraging for nectar is affected by several factors, both outside and inside the hive, either directly affecting the bee biology or indirectly through their effect on nectar secretion in plants. Bees suck the nectar from nectaries into their honey stomach by using their proboscis. In the hive the nectar load is regurgitated and passed on to the house bees. In the processes, digestive enzymes of bees are added that convert sucrose in the nectar into hexoses. Bees remove the excess water in it by evaporation in an elaborate process of ripening. Ripened or mature honey contains about 20 per cent water. All honeys contain osmophilic yeasts that may cause fermentation of honey under conditions of high humidity and temperature.

An understanding of the biology of nectars and foraging behaviour of honey bees is useful in improving productivity of bee colonies in beekeeping as also in augmenting crop yields through bee pollination.

Key words : Nectar, Bee Biology and Beekeeping

INTRODUCTION

Nectar, the golden liquid of packed radiant solar energy in the form of sugar molecules, is the gift of nature to a variety of animal forms from insects to human beings. Produced in the nectaries, as a result of active metabolism of the plants, it is believed to help in regulating their internal osmotic pressure. In this context, the nectaries are considered to function as sugar valves that regulate translocation of sugar in the plant body to areas where they are needed. Even so the precise methods and functioning of both the nectaries and nectar are not yet well understood. In any case, nectar constitutes the source of energy for several anthophilous animals, which in the process of collection of this as food, incidentally bring about pollination in flowers. Nectar, thus, helps the plants in reproduction and continuation of the species.

Nectar is the exclusive source of carbohydrates to the honey bees, which represent a highly developed social organisation. This society, known commonly as a colony, has a fertile female individual — the queen bee, that ensures development and reproduction of the colony; a few hundred male bees, called drones that have almost the only function of fertilizing young queen bees; and several thousand sterile females, the worker bees, which as the name indicates, perform a variety of duties within and outside the hive, depending on their physiological state of growth. The young bees nurse the larvae and brood in the colony, attend upon the queen bee, produce beeswax and construct combs, clean the combs and the hive, maintain the hive temperature and regulate its microclimate, defend the colony and finally take to the outdoor duty of foraging. Honey bees forage for water, propolis, pollen and nectar.

Nectar is converted into honey by the bees which store it in that form for use during adverse conditions of scarcity or absence of food. Beekeeping is based on this behaviour of the bees of storing honey which is in excess of their immediate requirement. Until recently honey production used to be the sole purpose of beekeeping. Modern beekeeping involves a wider spectrum of using bees for production of other valuable materials like beeswax, pollen, royal jelly, bee venom, propolis and most importantly, for pollination and improving the yields of legume, pulse, oilseed, vegetable, spice, fodder, fibre and fruit crops. Nectar, however, remains to be the basis for using bees for all these purposes, for, it plays an important and unique role in the biology of the honey bees and their colony.

EVOLUTION OF BEE-FLOWER RELATIONSHIP

The name 'nectar' was first given by Virgil to the liquid sucked by the bees from flowers (Butler, 1953). Honey bees are obligatory phytophags and depend entirely on the nectar and pollen produced by plants. while on the one hand this dependence on plants for food is the result of evolution of a synagonistic relationship between flowering plants and insects (Leppik, 1957, 1977; Deodikar, 1961), it is on the other hand, and more particularly, the result of evolution of one of the highly successful social organisations among insects. The mutual interdependence of the anthophilous insects and entomophilous angiosperms led to the co-evolution of highly advanced insect groups and highly developed flower structures. The successful association between plants and insects resulted in the rapid spread of flowering plants. Among the extant insects, the aculeate hymenoptera, with their highly developed sensory capabilities emerged as pre-dominant pollinators. It is believed that bees have co-evolved during the middle Cretaceous period along with the then already dominant angiosperms (Michener, 1974). The evolution of pleomorphic flowers (Leppik, 1977) during the early Tertiary period marked the introduction of nectar as a food in the entomophilous flower syndrome.

An important aspect of the social behaviour is honey bees is the distribution of work among the adult individuals. In a honey bee colony the queen bee has the reproductive function while the workers do all the other work of the colony, including the raring of the young. For this purpose the bees collect and store food in large quantities.

Honey bees constitute the second link in the food chain, directly after the plants which are the primary manufactures of food. Apoidea, or the bees, are known to collectively visit more flowers than all other groups of anthophilous insects (Percival, 1965). They show a high degree of adaptation to anthophily. They have plumose hairs all over the body, and special structures on their legs to collect pollen. Their mouth parts can be made into a tubular proboscis to suck nectar. They have a specialised sac in the alimentary system to store and carry nectar. Their optical, olfactory and gustatory senses are well developed. They can distinguish colours, shapes and scents of flowers and can learn intricate floral structures and reach the concealed nectaries. Further, they have well-developed time-sense, and can forage for food as it is produced in the flowers (Kevan and Baker, 1983). They can perceive variations in altitude and magnetic field. This enables them to orientate themselves to the food source with reference to their hive.

Pollen provides the honey bees the protein food required for their body growth and for various vital physiological functions. A strong colony of the European hive bee, *Apis mellifera* L., is estimated to require over 20 kg of pollen in a growing season. Nectar provides the energy required for all their metabolic functions. A strong colony collects upwards of 800 kg of nectar often converted into 200 kg of honey, in a growing season.

Source of Nectar

From the bees point of view nectar, as the raw material to prepare honey, comes mostly from the nectaries of plants and rarely from the sweet excretions of aphids and other plant-sap sucking insects. Since we are concerned here with the nectaries, these sweet liquids albeit of plant origin, but produced by animal mediation, will not be considered further.

Honey bees also collect the sweet plant sap which flows out when the plant is injured exposing the phloem tubes in the vascular bundles. Thus, when the spadices of certain palms like *Borassus flabellifer* L., *Phoenix sylvestris* Roxb. and *Cocos nucifera* L. are cut to 'tap' the sap or when sugarcane is harvested the sweet liquids oozing out are eagerly collected by bees. The sap so produced differs from nectar in chemical composition. Being chance occurrences, normally such liquids are not of importance to honey bees.

Nectaries are normally found inside flowers when they are called floral nectaries. In the temperate climates most of the raw material for production of honey comes from flowers of the higher plants (Maurizio, 1962, 1975). In the tropical and sub-tropical regions there is an additional source in the form of a variety of extrafloral nectaries (e.g., *Hevea brasiliensis* Muell.- Arg.). Honey bees also collect sweet secretions and exudations from leaves and other parts of plants. Though not strictly originating from the nectaries, these liquids hardly differ from the normal nectars. Exudations from leaves and tender parts of *Mangifera indica* L. often prompted by infestation of jassids, and from tender leaves of *Syzygium cumini* Skeels are examples of this type of nectar. Since these are exposed to the atmosphere like those produced by the extrafloral nectaries they are similar to the latter for all practical purposes.

Some important and peculiar sources of nectar are listed in Table I.

TABLE 1 : Some sources of nectar used by honey bees in India

Botanical Name	*Family*	*Common/Local Name*	*Importance to bee-keeping Characteristics*
Actinodaphne aungustifolia Nees	Lauraceae	Pisa	In moist evergreen or montane evergreen forests. Honey dark amber, rich in minerals.
Ailanthus excelsa Roxb	Simarou-baceae	Tree of Heaven	Cultivated. Favoured particularly by the dwarf bee.
Anacardium occidentale L.	Anacardia-ceae	Cashew tree	Cultivated mainly along coastal districts. A very good source of thin, fine flavoured and light coloured honey.
Antigonon lepto-pus Hk. & Arn.	Polygon-aceae	Coral creeper	Cultivated, often running wild. Attractive source to all honey bees.
Azadirachta indica A. Juss	Meliaceae	Neem	Honey light amber coloured and has good flavour.
Barringtonia spp.	Barringtonia-ceae	Small Indian oak	Common near coastal areas. Locally important. Honey slightly bitter.
Berberis spp.	Berberida-ceae	Barberry	Sub-Himalayan forests. Erratic sou-rce. Honey dark amber in colour.
Bombax ceiba L.	Bombacaceae	Red silk cotton	Wild in tropical dry forests, often cultivated. Nectar secreted profusely. Favourite source to all honey bees. Honey thin and light coloured.
Borassus flabellifer L.	Arecaceae	Palmyrah palm	Cultivated and wild in tropical humid climates, particularly along coastal districts. Locally important source of nectar. Honey dark amber and thick. In several localities where toddy is tapped in clay pots, bees in large numbers, get drowned in the sweet liquid, while foraging.
Brassica spp.	Brassicaceae	Mustards	Several species are very good sources. Of major importance in northern states. Honey granulates very quickly.
Cajanus cajan L.	Fabaceae	Pigion pea	Pulse crop. Important in Punjab, Bihar, Andhra Pradesh. More favoured by the European honey bee. Honey amber coloured, thick

Botanical Name	*Family*	*Common/Local Name*	*Importance to bee-keeping Characteristics*
Carvia callosa (Nees) Bremek.	Acanthaceae	Karvi	Pleitesial, endemic to Western Ghats. Honey thixotropic and has characteristic florescence.
Ceiba pentandra (L.) Gaertn.	Bombaca-ceae	White silk cotton	Cultivated and wild in tropical, usually dry areas. A favourite source. Honey thin and light coloured.
Citrullus lanatus (Thunb.) Mats. & Nakai	Cucurbi-taceae	Water melon	Cultivated, sometimes running wild. Honey wthin and light coloured.
Citrus spp.	Rutaceae	Acid lime orange, grape, fruit, etc.	Cultivated, rarely wild Favourite sources. Honey thick, light coloured, with fine flavour. Honey produced in Meghalaya, Himachal Pradesh, Punjab and in Nagpur area of Maharashtra. Some species are heavily sprayed with insecti-cides, which causes severe bee deaths.
Cocos nucifera L.	Arecaceae	Coco palm	Cultivated. A good source of nectar in several parts of India particularly in the coastal districts.
Coffea spp.	Rubiaceae	Coffee plant	Both the common species are good sources, but erratic due to dependence on atmospheric moisture for blooming and nectar sacretion. Honey thick and light coloured.
Coriandrum sativam L.	Apiaceae	Coriander	Cultivated. Seed crop constitutes a good source of thick and mild flavoured honey.
Delbergia latifolia Roxb.	Fabaceae	Rose-wood tree	Tropical forests. Honey light coloured and of very fine flavour. Locally important.
Diospyros spp.	Ebenaceae	Ebony	Several species occur in evergreen and semi-evergreen forests. Honey light coloured with fine flavour.
Eucalyptus spp.	Myrtaceae	Eucalypts	Several species are cultivated in plantations or on roadsides. Secrete nectar profusely. Erratic sources. Locally important. Honey often has a disagreeable smell, probably due to infestation of flowers by mites.

Botanical Name	*Family*	*Common/Local Name*	*Importance to bee-keeping Characteristics*
Gossypium spp.	Malvaceae	Cotton plant	Several species and varieties are good sources. Nectar from floral and extra floral nectaries. However, heavy insecticidal spraying causes serious losses to bee population.
Gmelina spp.	Verbena-ceae	Gum-har	Deciduous trees in several forests. Honey thin and light coloured. Nectar from the leaf nectaries is sometimes collected.
Grevillea robusta A. Cunn.	Proteaceae	Silver oak	Cultivated. Nectar very rich in sugars. Honey dark amber in colour.
Guizotia abyssinica Cass.	Asteraceae	Niger	Cultivated, but hardy crop in vast hilly tracts, particularly in Orissa, Madhya Pradesh, Maharashtra and Andhra Pradesh. Constitutes very important and reliable source. Honey amber coloured, and has a bitter after taste.
Helianthus annuus L.	Asteraceae	Sunflower	Cultivated as oilseed crop. Mainly favoured by the European honey bee. Unifloral honey obtained in Maharashtra.
Hevea brasi-liensis (HBK) Muell. Arg.	Euphor-biaceae	Rubber tree	Plantation crop in several states. A major source of honey in India. Nectar from extra-floral nectaries on petiolules of leaves. Honey light amber cloured.
Legerstroe-mia spp.	Lythra-ceae	Pride of the forest	Wild in tropical forests. Two species cultivated. Secrete nectar profusely. Honey thin and light coloured.
Lepeda-gathis cus-pidata Nees	Acantha-ceae	Akhara	Pleitesial undershrub in several parts of India. Honey light coloured and has good flavour.
Leucas aspera Spr.	Lamiaceae	Thumba	This and several species *Leucas* occur as forest undergrowth or in open forests. Honey light coloured and fine flavoured.
Litchi chinensis (Gaertn.) Sonner.	Sapind-aceae	Litchi	Orchard tree in several northen states. Honey very light coloured and has characteristic flavour and aroma.

Botanical Name	*Family*	*Common/Local Name*	*Importance to bee-keeping Characteristics*
Litsaea spp.	Lauraceae	Betel-nut Laurel	Evergreen forests. Honey thick and dark coloured.
Madhuca spp.	Sapotaceae	Mohua	Wild and cultivated, common in tropical deciduous forests. A very favourite source. Honey thin and light coloured.
Malus spp.	Rosaceae	Apple	Cultivated in temperate climates. Locally important.
Mangifera indica L.	Anacardi-aceae	Mango	Wild and cultivated, *the former* constituting good sources in some locations. Honey amber coloured and thick. Sweet exudations from young leaves and ternder shoots also collected by bees.
Medicago sativa L.	Fabaceae	Lucerne	Fodder legume, cultivated in several states. Important source, when allowed to flower and irrigated. Honey light coloured and thick.
Mimosa pudica L.	Mimosa-ceae	Touch-me-not	Ubiquitous as under-growth in several forest areas. A favourite source, available more or less through out the year. Honey light coloured and rich in pollen.
Moringa oleifera Lamk.	Moringa-ceae	Drum stick	Cultivated. When grown in large areas, constitutes an important source, particularly in Tamilnadu and Andhra Pradesh.
Ougeinia oojeinensis (Roxb.) Hoch.	Fabaceae	Sandan	Found in semi-evergreen and deciduous forests. Honey thin and light coloured.
Phlebophyllum kunthianum Nees	Acanthaceae	Kurinji	Pleitesial, gregarious in Nilgiris. Important source.
Phyla nodiflora (L) Greene	Verbena-ceae	Bokk-ena	Weed in cultivated and moist areas. Important source in Andhra Pradesh. Honey thick, light coloured and fine flavoured.
Plectranthus rugosus Wall.	Lamiaceae	Shain, Sula	Wild shrub in sub-Himalayan tracts. Very important autumn source. Honey of light colour and characteristic flavour.

Botanical Name	*Family*	*Common/Local Name*	*Importance to bee-keeping Characteristics*
Pongamia pinnata (L.) Pierre	Fabaceae	Indian Beech tree	Honey thick and has characteristic green florescence.
Premna tomentosa Willd.	Verbenaceae	Sanne anagalu	This and other species are good sources of light coloured honey. Important in Coorg, Karnataka.
Prosopis chilensis (Molina) Stuntz	Mimosaceae	Mesquite	Cultivated, but running wild, gregarious in several states. Favoured by the dwarf bee.
Prunus spp.	Rosaceae	Plum, peach	Cultivated and wild in temperate sub-tropical climates. Locally important.
Pterocarpus marsupium Roxb.	Fabaceae	Kino tree	Honey light coloured with good flavour.
Pterocarpus santalinus L.	Fabaceae	Red sanders	Honey light coloured with good flavour.
Pyrus spp.	Rosaceae	Pear, etc.	Cultivated in temperate climates. Locally important.
Rhizophora spp.	Rhizophoraceae	Kandal	Mangrove species. Locally important.
Robinia pseudo-acacia	Fabaceae	False acacia	Cultivated in north-western states. Excellent source.
Samanea saman (Jacq.) Merr.	Mimosaceae	Rain tree	Cultivated. Favoured by rockbees.
Sapindus spp.	Sapindaceae	Soap-nut	Although occuring in several states, very important in coastal districts. Honey available in winter, light coloured.
Schefflera venulosa (Wt. & Arn.) Harms.	Araliaceae	Anagalu	This and other species are common in evergreen and semi-evergreen forests. A major and important source in Coorg, Karnataka. Honey light coloured, thin and has very good flavour.
Sesamum indicum L.	Pedaliaceae	Sesame	Cultivated in dry areas. Honey thick, light coloured and has good flavour.
Sorghum bicolour (L.) Moench.	Poaceae	Pearl millet	Cultivated as grain orfodder crop. Local varieties are important as sources of nectar from sweet exudation from nodes and fungal infected leaves.

Botanical Name	*Family*	*Common/Local Name*	*Importance to bee-keeping Characteristics*
Spondias pinnata (L.f.) Kurz.	Anacardi-aceae	Indian hog plum	Honey amber coloured and thick.
Syzygium cumini skeels	Myrtaceae	Jamun	A major source in several parts of India. Honey has slightly bitter after-taste. Sweet exudations from young leaves also sometimes collected. Other species also locally important.
Tamarindus indica L.	Caesalpini-aceae	Tama-rind	Honey dark coloured.
Terminalia bellirica (Gaertn.) Roxb.	Combretaceae	Belleric myrabolan	Common in several forests. Honey thick and light coloured. Considered medicinal.
Terminalia chebula Retz.	Combretaceae	Chebulic	Common in several forests. Honey thick and myrabolan light coloured. Considered medicinal. Several species of *Terminalia* are useful sources and are locally important.
Thelapaepale ixiocephala (Benth.) Bremek.	Acanthaceae	Whyati	Pleitesial occurring as undergrowth in Western Ghat forests. Honey light coloured and has good flavour.
Thespesia populnea (L.) Soland. ex Corr.	Malvaceae	Indian tulip tree	Cultivated. Locally important in coastal districts.
Toona ciliata M.J. Roem.	Meliaceae	Red cedar	Important in North India.
Trifolium alexandrinum L.	Fabaceae	Berseem	Fodder legume, commonly cultivated in north-western states. Favoured by the European honey bee. Honey thick, light-coloured, but bland in taste.
Wendlandia spp.	Rubiaceae	*Bankat, thavasa* etc.	Wild shrubs or small trees, growing in open forests. Honey light coloured and mild flavoured.
Zizyphus mauritiana Lamk.	Rhamnaceae	Jujub tree	Wild and cultivated, hardy species. Source of fine flavoured and light coloured honey.

FORAGING BEHAVIOUR OF HONEY BEES

Unlike several anthophilous insects, which assimilate nectar as it is collected, honey bees collect the nectar, store it temporarily in their honey sac, carry it to their nest where it is regurgitated and is passed on to the house bees.

Most part of the nectar collected is stored for consumption later by other individuals in the hive. This difference in the nectar gathering and assimilation system, makes honey bees peculiar among plant visitors. The usual parameters adopted in the plant- pollinator studies, therefore, need to be modified when interpreting the honey bee foraging behaviour and its importance as a pollinator.

As stated earlier, honey bees need to collect massive quantities of food. The food habits are therefore modified and are different from those of other bees. They are highly evolved and show the most advanced features of anthophily; yet, they are polytropic and the food sources include even the anemophilous flowers like those of *Borassus, Cocos, Butea* and *Sorghum*. Nectaries outside the flowers or even on non-flowering plants are visited when they produce the required quality of nectar. The quality of nectar is decided by its component sugars, their proportion and concentration.

Communication among Bees

Honey bees have an efficient system of communication by which a successful forager can inform the potential foragers in the hive the direction, distance and quality of food. This system has long been identified as the bee dances. The dance of successful forager and the smell and taste of the food brought by it excite its comrades to fly out in search for the food (Ribbands, 1953; Frisch, 1967). In this search the bees are aided by the scent deposited by the earlier forager bee (Fergusson and Free, 1979; Free and Williams, 1983). Unrewarding sources are often marked with a repellent, so that other foragers are deterred from visiting them. In discriminating a food source honey bees use their highly developed optical, olfactory and gustatory senses. Differences in the concentration of sugars in nectar, their quality and quantity are communicated by vigour of the dances which changes proportionately. This communication system aided by the advanced sensory capabilities helps the bee colony to restrict its efforts to exploit only good and useful sources of food.

A vigorous dance excites several bees, while a slow dance attracts few bees. Thus an abundant source of nectar can be exploited efficiently by a large number of foragers and an insignificant source is visited by only one or two bees. As long as a food source is available, the foraging visits continue and as the crop wanes, the visits are reduced. Honey bees exhibit floral fidelity or constancy to the food source, while it exists.

Optical Sense

Honey bees have an ability to distinguish different flower shapes and figure-numbers (Leppik, 1955) like 2-, 3-, 4- and 5- merous flowers. Bees can perceive colours of flowers and other sources of food from great distances while in flight. They can distinguish shades of blue, purple, reddish purple, yellow and orange. They are blind to pure red. However, if ultraviolet is reflected in red flowers, such can be distinguished (Percival, 1965). Fluorescence of certain nectars observed in ultraviolet light can help bees reach the source of nectar (Thorp *et al.*, 1975, 1976).

Olfactory Sense

Honey bees have a highly developed olfactory sense. The usual fragrances that can be distinguished by humans can be distinguished by the bees. They can detect even a dilute fragrance with a very low odour intensity (Waddington, 1983). Lindauer (1949) found that addition of foul odours like skatol and cowparsnip to a sugar solution of the threshold concentration for dance activity, reduced dancing, but odours of peppermint oil, phlox, elder, rape, jasmine, or lime increased the proportions of dancing bees. In addition to these floral scents, bees use their own pheromones (e..g., Nassonov gland secretion) to mark good sources of nectar to attract other foragers, or to repel (2-heptanone) them from the flowers just exploited.

Time Sense

The sense of time in honey bees was recognised since 1900 when Buttel-Reepen observed bees foraging on buckwheat between early and late mornings each day (Ribbands, 1953). It has since been established that the honey bees have a 24-hour internal clock which they use to exploit freshly produced crops of nectar or pollen and thus can compete successfully with other visitors (Frisch, 1967).

Bees can use their sensory capabilities to recognise the different colours, shapes, and scents; associate these with the food source and remember this information for communication with other bees in the hive and for repetitive foraging trips.

Gustatory Sense

The sense of taste in bees was recognised quite early. Honey bees can distinguish sweet, salty and bitter tastes. They are very sensitive to salty and sour materials and reject sweet materials if mixed with them. Bitter substances are however not recognised in low concentrations (Frisch, 1950). Frisch studied the reaction of bees to thirty four sugars, or sugar-like substances, tasting sweet to human beings, and found that only nine of them were sweet to the bees : sucrose, maltose, glucose, fructose, trehalose, melesitose, fucose, alpha-methyl glucoside and inositol.

Bees can recognise a sweet substance when it reaches the sensory pits at the base of the tongue. They can discriminate approximately 5 per cent differences in sucrose concentration (Waddington, 1983). The decision to accept or reject a sweet liquid depends on the concentration of sugars in the liquid and the intensity of requirement of nectar in the bee colony. In times of scarcity of food, bees may accept a 1 - 4 per cent solution (Frisch, 1967), but when there is a choice of several nectar sources, normally the nectar with a high sugar content is preferred. The 'threshold of acceptance' was found to be between 30 per cent to about 5 per cent (about 1 to 1/8th molar solution). The higher the sugar content in the nectar, the better would be the energy economy for the bees. Pryce-Jones (1944) calculated that below 18 per cent of sugar in the nectar the honey bees 'work at a loss'.

Taste is probably the cue used in discriminating the different sugar concentrations; however, the viscosity of the solution may also be important (Waddington, 1983).

From the point of view of beekeeping or pollination biology, this is the most important factor. It has been observed that bees prefer nectars with higher sugar concentration to those having lower sugar content. Several authors investigated the sugar concentration of nectar of flowering plants (Vansell, 1939; Percival, 1965; Sharma, 1958; Shuel, 1970; see also Maurizio, 1975 for a review). The variation in sugar concentration in different species is very wide. The sugar content ranges from 5 per cent (in *Primulus* sp.) to 79 per cent in *Grevillea* (Deodikar *et al.*, 1957). Percival (1965) found in her study on some British and exotic species, that the bee flowers generally had nectars with 16-55 per cent sugar. Nectars with more than 50 per cent sugar are diluted before taken in by the bees (Simpson, 1964). Plants with concentrated nectars can compete successfully with the plants having low sugar nectar in attracting insect pollinators.

The sugar content of the nectar also varies greatly from hour to hour (Phadke, 1964; 1965), flower to flower and even from floret to floret in the same plant (Moffett, 1954). In Southern Arizona, Moffett *et al.* (1976) found that the genotypes of cotton with higher concentrations of sugar in their floral nectar attracted more honey bees than flowers with a lower percentage of sugar. When the differences in sugar concentration were more than 10 per cent, twice as many bees visited the flowers with the higher concentration. Among plums, the varieties Maynard, Eldorado and Milton have nectar containing 10.1, 14.9 and 28.4 per cent sugar, respectively (Percival, 1965). In a mixed orchard of these varieties, Milton was observed to attract most bees and was well pollinated. Satyanarayana (1975) found bees visiting *Syzygium cumini* Skeels in February when the sugar concentration in its nectar was about 28% but the same tree was ignored in March when the average sugar concentration was 25% and there were other competing nectar sources. In *Apis mellifera* the frequency of dancing by returning foragers was positively correlated with concentration of sugar solution they had collected (Waller and Bachman, 1981).

Where both floral and extrafloral nectaries exist on the same plant, the latter often produce more concentrated nectars. This may result in the bees ignoring the flowers, adversely affecting their pollination. However, in hybrid cotton, Eisikowitch and Loper (1984) found honey bees visiting the extrafloral nectaries in the early morning. When the flowers opened they visited floral nectaries and switched back to the extrafloral nectar when the secretion from floral nectaries began to dwindle in the afternoon. Some bees were observed to switch from one type to the other in the same trip.

The quantity of nectar produced in a flower varies from 0.3 mg in *Fagopyrum* to 1.6 g in *Liriodendron* (Pryce-Jones, 1944). *Protea mellifera* Thunb. in Africa secretes nectar in such large quantities that it can be collected by dipping a spoon into the flower. The energy spent on a foraging trip to collect a load of nectar is less when nectar is available in large amounts in a flower than when it is meagre. Ribbands (1953) reports of a nectar gatherer *Limnanthes* which made 1446 flower visits in a trip lasting for 106 minutes. On the other hand, a single flower of tulip can provide enough nectar for over 40 trips.

Sugars in Nectar

Among the common nectar sugars, Wykes (1952) found sucrose to be the most preferred by honey bees followed by glucose, maltose and fructose. However, Waller and Bachman (1981) found glucose to be least acceptable among the three nectar sugars. When a mixture of sugars is available, the sucrose-fructose-glucose (SFG) mixture was the most preferred. In a study of nectar sugars of 100 plant species from India, Bahadur *et al.* (1986) recorded 56 species with SFG type nectars. Although quantitative studies were not made, it is indicated that 32 of these had ± equal proportions of SFG. *Melilotus alba* Desr. (Furgala *et al.*, 1958) and other legume plants contain more or less equal proportions of the three sugars. However, the mixture of equal proportions of SFG is less attractive than sucrose or a mixture in which sucrose is dominant (Bachman and Waller, 1977). In an investigation on bee responses to different sugar solutions, Waller and Bachman (1981) found that sucrose resulted in more dances in the hive by the foragers than fructose, which in turn led to more dances than glucose.

Nectar of long tubed flowers is generally sucrose dominated while shallow flowers with more or less exposed nectaries have the preponderance of the two monosaccharides (Percival, 1965). There are several species of major importance to beekeeping in all the three types of nectars (eg., SFG ± equal : *Melilotus* ; S > F + G : *Robinia*, *Rhododendron*, Berberidaceae, Fumariaceae; F + G > S : *Rubia*, Brassicaceae, Caryophyllaceae, Scrophulariaceae). In the last type the bees have little to contribute in the inversion of sugars. Only the excess of water has to be removed before storage as honey. Interestingly, many of the advanced groups of plant families have this type of nectar and contain several species providing bee forage. Nectars of *Hevea* (Nair and Wakhle, 1983), *Grevillea* and *Schefflera* (Wakhle *et al.*, 1981) are F + G dominant, and are technically honeys. These are important honey plants, valuable to the bees, as they enable conservation of bees' energy (Suryanarayana, 1986).

Toxic Nectars

Nectars containing toxic constituents are troublesome in beekeeping, since the forager strength in the bee colony dwindles due to incapacitation or death of bees and in a few cases, rendering the honey unfit for human consumption (Deinzer *et al.*, 1977). Besides acetylandromedol (in several Ericaceae) and related compounds, scopolamine, atropine, jelsemine and other alkaloids, glucosides like arbutin have been reported in different honeys (see Maurizio, 1968). Although several of these compounds can be traced to the nectars, they are obviously not toxic to honey bees. Nectar from *Sophora microphylla* Ait. containing methylcytisine, matrine, cytisine and other alkaloids (Clinch *et al.*, 1972) is the only instance found in the literature, where bees were affected (mortality and narcosis). Several cases of poisoning of honey bees by certain sugars in nectar have, however, been reported. In the classic example of lime (*Tilia* spp.) nectar toxicity (Howes, 1945), mannose was found to be the culprit. Mannose was already known as strongly toxic to honey bees (Frisch, 1930). Sols *et al.*, (1960) explained the toxicity to be due to the disturbance in enzymes relating to carbohydrate metabolism in bees of various species. In *Tilia* species, the floral nectar and foliar exudate produce abnormally high amounts of mannose in dry years (Crane, 1977). Death or paralysis of honey bees foraging on *Tilia* flowers during exceptionally dry summers have been reported from several European countries. The bees are often found dead under the trees.

Galactose from the sweet exudates of Darwin tulip stigmas was found to be the cause of death of bees in the tulip flowers (Barker and Lehner, 1976). Besides mannose and galactose, arabinose, lactose, raffinose, stachyose, melizitose, melibiose and xylose are toxic to honey bees (Howes, 1945; Barker and Lehner, 1974; Crane, 1978).

Insecticides in Nectar

Poisoning of honey bees by nectar contaminated with systemic insecticides has been reported recently (Jaycox, 1964; Shuel, 1970; Rai *et al.*, 1977; Fielder and Drescher, 1984). Rai *et al.* (1977) found that monocrotophos, when injected into the trunks of coconut palms, was secreted in the flowers within 8 hours and *A. mellifera* foragers from two colonies kept near the palms, visiting the flowers for nectar, were poisoned. Citing the work of Lord *et al.* (1968) on the excretion of dimethoate and other systemic insecticides in the nectar of *Fuchsia, Tropaeolum* and *Vicia*, Shuel (1970) expressed concern that such contaminated nectars not only poison honey bees but also endanger human welfare because of the possible entry of insecticides into honey. Nectaries are probably unselective with respect to such substances and if they enter the plant and are not metabolised, they are likely to appear in the nectar. The very features of systemic insecticides that make them useful (transportability through the plant and resistance to breakdown in the soil and plant) make them hazardous in the context of beekeeping (Shuel, 1970). As the use of systemic insecticides is increasing in recent years, the problem assumes serious proportions. Revathi (1982) recorded presence of pesticides in samples of honey from India.

Potassium in Nectar

Although honey bees normally collect nectars containing salts of potassium, sodium, magnesium and calcium, a high potassium content seems to act as a deterrant. Waller *et al.* (1972) found that the levels of potassium in *Allium cepa* L. nectar varied from 3800 to 13000 ppm, about 19 times as high as that in nectar from competing flora tested. Honey bees avoided foraging on the onion nectar. However, an amphidiploid (*A.. cepa* X *A.. fistulosum*) where the nectar contained a low potassium level, was more attractive to bees than *A.. cepa*. Waller (1972) also found that bees preferred sucrose in concentrations from 30 to 50 per cent, but rejected the solution containing potassium citrate or ferricyanide.

FACTORS AFFECTING NECTAR FORAGING

Unlike in several other anthophilous insects, honey bee foragers gather food not exclusively for themselves but for their colony. Forager bees go out for nectar collection in response to one or more stimuli received within the hive. Outside the hive the foraging behaviour of the bees results from their innate responses to environmental stimuli (Doull, 1976). Thus nectar foraging is affected by factors within and outside the hive.

Nectar is collected primarily as a source of energy; when the nectar is available in nature, honey bees instinctively collect it and store it after processing it into honey. The need for energy/food is felt when the colony as a whole starts the process of growth at the beginning of the season (generally spring). When the temperature becomes ideal, the queen bee starts egg laying. This process is triggered by the worker bees which gather fresh pollen from the early flowers. This is eaten by the house bees to produce royal jelly, the special nutritious food to be fed to the queen bee and the young larvae. As the nectar flows into the hive, the house bees construct combs to make space for further brood rearing. Nectar gathering activity is found to be encouraged by the presence of empty combs within the hive (Rinderer and Baxter, 1978; Rinderer, 1982; Rinderer and Hagstad, 1984).

In temperate regions availability of nectar is generally low in early spring; then increases sharply to the annual maximum in late spring or early summer followed by a decline in both of species and abundance of nectar, by late summer, when usually only a few low quality sources exist. The growth pattern of the bee colony follows closely this seasonal pattern of floral resources (Rinderer *et al.*, 1984). Although detailed studies on tropical climates and the honey bees there are lacking, it is quite probable that a similar association of colony growth with the pattern of nectar secretion and availability exists (Thakar and Shende, 1962; Crane, 1975; Rinderer *et al.*, 1984).

The stimulus to forage for nectar is sustained further by the eagerness with which the house bees solicit nectar from the incoming nectar foragers.

Colony growth also involves collection of pollen. Pollen foragers need nectar/honey as a source of energy for their activity and as a binder for pollen collected in the trip. This and a series of other complex mechanisms within the hive make the house bees seek nectar from nectar foragers.

A growing colony requires water which is essential for the eggs to hatch, for the larvae to grow and for the nurse bees to dilute the honey which they mix with pollen and prepare larval food. Water is also needed to regulate the temperature within the hive. In an active growing season, such as spring and early summer, dilute nectar is collected in large quantities to meet the requirements of water. Under such conditions honey bees prefer nectars with low sugar.

Outside the hive the forager bees face the environmental factors directly, and indirectly through their effect on forage sources. Nectar foraging is also affected by other biological factors like competition between sources and competition with other flower visitors.

Apis and other large bodied eusocial bees like bumble bees, are known to forage under a wide and often less favourable metereological conditions than other bees found in the same area (Jaycox, 1970). Temperatures below 24°C are generally inimical to forage flights. However, honey bees have been observed to forage at lower temperatures in the sub-tropical regions. Abrol (1986) recorded 15°C as the minimum threshold temperature in such a region. On the other hand, foraging at temperatures above 40°C is often limited not as much by the bees' ability to withstand such high temperatures, as by the non-availability of suitable nectar in those conditions. At high atmospheric temperatures, a bee colony needs water to regulate the nest temperature. The foragers, therefore, seek water or very dilute nectars, which are difficult to get at high temperatures.

Honey bees likewise are capable of foraging under other inimical conditions like high wind velocity, high relative humidity or poor light intensity. However, these factors affect the plants and their nectar secretion activity. The quality of nectar is also affected. Bees may not forage on nectars of poor quality or those in inadequate quantity. There are thus complex interactions among factors such as temperature, light intensity, wind, rain, dew, time of day, colony size, stores of food in the colony, distance to food sources, ease of obtaining food, kind of food, concentration of sugars in the nectar, abundance of nectar, etc. (Michener, 1974). A hypothetical model involving some of these factors of the nectar foraging behaviour of honey bees is presented in the figure 1.

NECTAR GATHERING SYSTEM IN HONEY BEES

Nectar Collection

The mouth parts of the worker bees are different in structure and function from those of the queen or male bees (Snodgrass, 1956; Simpson, 1962) and are modified to help in the ingestion of nectar. The liquid food is sucked by the proboscis, formed by interlocking of the mouth parts. The glossa moves back and forth and pumps up the liquid into the oral cavity. The nectar then passes through the pharynx into the oesophagus and finally into its distal widened pear-shaped part called the honey sac (also called honey stomach or crop). The honey sac is a collecting and storage chamber used by the bees to receive and transport liquid food. At its distal end the honey sac is closed off from the midgut by the proventriculus. The proventriculus has a valve made up of four triangular flaps and a stem which connects it with the midgut. The valve is an important organ which filters and removes a significant part of the solid component of the liquid in the honey sac and passes it on to the midgut (Bailey, 1954). The solids consist mainly of pollen grains, which the bee collects incidentally through the nectar.

Normally an *A.mellifera* forager carries a load of about 25 mg of nectar in its honey sac (Park, 1922) although when filled to capacity the honey sac may hold 40 to 70 mg (Chauvin, 1968; Wells, and Giacchino, 1968)

Concentrated nectar is sometimes diluted by the salivary secretions of the glands situated in the head and thorax. They are also used to dissolve solid food like sugar crystals before it is ingested (Simpson, 1963, 1964). While in the pharynx the nectar is mixed with enzymatic secretions of the hypopharyngeal glands. This secretion is rich in diastase, invertase and glucose oxidase which act upon the sugars in the nectar and help in its conversion into honey. Rapid dilution of the nectar takes place in the honey sac (Oertel *et al.*, 1951).

Nectar Transport, Processing and Storage

After collecting a 'load' of nectar, the forager bee returns to the hive, where the house bees solicit the food from the forager. It then regurgitates the nectar into its oral cavity and by opening its mandibles, a drop of this liquid is got at the base of its glossa. The liquid is thence sucked by the house bee by its own proboscis. The house bee repeats this process when another house bee solicits the food from it. In the process, the nectar is mixed with the enzymatic secretions of the house bee. The food originally brought by a forager bee is thus enriched by digestive enzymes of the house bees and is passed on to others. The number of transitions from one be to the other may vary from a few, in the periods of a heavy nectar availability or 'flow', to many, when nectar is not so abundant. The enzyme-enriched nectar is ultimately deposited in the honey cells of the comb.

The transmission of nectar from the forager to the honey cell through several house bees within the hive marks an important stage of 'processing' or 'elaboration' of nectar into honey. The addition of salivary and hypo-pharyngeal gland secretions to the nectar increases the water and enzyme contents in it. In its dilute form the honey cannot be preserved for any length of time. Bees remove the excess water in a process known as 'ripening'.

The house bee, engaged in the ripening process, regurgitates the dilute honey from its honey sac, which is then spread out into a film below the folded proboscis. The film of honey is exposed to the warm and dry air of the hive. The honey is then sucked in and is regurgitated again. This process is repeated rapidly for 15-20 minutes. As the drop of honey is repeatedly exposed to the dry air, it loses some of its water. When the water content is about 40% the bee deposits the honey in small droplets on the cell walls or on the cell floor. In this condition some more water is evaporated due to air currents set inside the hive and over the open honey cells of the comb, by the fanning of wings by some bees at the entrance of the hive. The bees may finally remove this almost 'ripe' honey into other cells which are filled to 75 % of their capacity. The final ripening takes place here and the time taken for this may vary from one to a few days depending on the original water content in the nectar, the strength (number of bees) of the colony, the amount of air moved by fanning and the hive temperature, relative humidity and ventilation (Reinhardt, 1939; Park, 1932, 1949; Gontarski and Hoffman, 1963; Maurizio, 1975). When the honey is ripe or 'mature', containing 20% or less of water, the bees fill the cell completely and seal it by a cap of beeswax. In this sealed and airtight condition, honey can be stored for several years without spoilage.

Chemical Changes in the Nectar and its Conversion into Honey

Nectar contains sugars in varying proportions. Even as it is secreted by the nectary, the sugars undergo changes due to the action of the enzymes in it. The complex (di-or tri-saccharide) sugars are broken down into simpler sugars (hexoses) but at the same time, new sugars of high molecular weight may also be synthesized by transglucosidases and transfructosidases (Zimmermann, 1954; Shuel, 1955; Ziegler, 1968).

The chemical changes in the nectar become marked and rapid when the bee enzymes are added to it. The presence of invertase, diastase, glucose oxidase and catalase has been established (Schepartz and Subers, 1964, 1966a, b; White and Kushnir, 1967; Rinaudo *et al.*, 1973a, b; Wakhle, 1983). Giri (1938) demonstrated the presence of an acid phosphatase in some Indian honeys. The invertases (sucrase, saccharase) in the glandular secretions of bees act upon sucrose and other di- or tri-saccharides and glucose and fructose are produced. As in the case of plant enzymes, the bee enzymes too synthesize more complex molecules which are not originally present in the nectar (Duisberg, 1967).

The final composition of sugars in the mature honey depends on the original sugar spectrum in the nectar and action of all the plant and bee enzymes added to it. An important point to note is that honey is a supersaturated solution of mainly sucrose, fructose and glucose in the proportion of 0 – 5 : 35 – 45 : 35 – 40, respectively. This proportion is characteristic since it enables a maximum quantity of sugars to remain in solution, which prevents spoilage by yeasts or bacteria and other microbes and packs a maximum amount of energy per unit quantity of solution. Honey thus has a high caloric density (White, 1975a). On an average a gram of honey gives 3 calories of energy

Physical Properties and Composition of Honey

White (1975b) described honey, from the physical point of view, as an aqueous dispersion of material from inorganic ions and saccharides and other organic materials in fine solution, colloidally dispersed macro-molecules of protein and polysaccharides, spores of yeasts and moulds and pollen grains. It is a syrup of mainly glucose and fructose, their content making up about 80 %, most of the remaining being water. Honeys having 80 per cent solids have a refractive index of 1.4865 and a specific gravity of 1.4027 at 20°C (Wedmore, 1955) It is a viscous fluid, the viscosity varying significantly depending upon its solid content and temperature. Honey has the property of rotating the plane of polarized light. Many floral honeys are laevorotatory, since fructose content is generally more than that of glucose. Honeys produced by *Apis florea* Fab. (the little honey bee) and *Trigona iridipennis* Smith (the stingless bee) contain a high proportion of dextrins, causing a positive polarization (Phadke, 1968). Glucose in honey, when in excess, compared to the fructose component, tends to granulate, leaving the liquid portion with lower sugar concentration.

In this context, the presence of glucose (and not fructose) in nectars of 96 out of 100 plant species in India studied by Bahadur *et al.* (1986) is interesting, since granulation and consequent partial dilution resulting in fermentation and spoilage of honey is common in India and other tropics and subtropics.

Honeys show a range of colours starting from very pale yellow to dark amber, looking black. Honeys produced from exposed nectaries and exudations on leaves and other parts of plants are darker in colour, due to infestation by sooty moulds and other fungi (Howes, 1945). A few honeys show fluorescence (Suryanarayana, 1978).

Chemically honey contains besides sugars and water, organic acids, proteins, amino acids, vitamins, enzymes, minerals, colouring materials (carotene and polyphenols) and aromatic compounds (carbonyls, alcohols and esters). Table 2 gives the gross chemical composition and physical properties of honey.

TABLE 2 : Chemical composition and physical properties of honeys from different species of *Apis*.

	A.dorsata	*A.florea*	*A. cerana*	*A. mellifera*[1]	
				U.S.S.R.	U.S.A
Specific Gravity at 27 °C	1.387	1.445	1.390		
Direct Polarization	–2° 21′	+1° 18	–2° 20′		
Water %	20.89	16.5	20.89	19.3	17.2
Total Dissolved Solids %	75.22	83.5	77.57		
Non-reducing Sugars %	3.20	1.83	3.37	5.75	8.6
Fructose %	37.43	38.94	36.48	34.9	38.2
Glucose %	32.13	32.34	33.39	32.5	31.3
Dextrins %	1.569	8.66	1.966	1.26	1.53[3]
Acidity (as formic acid) %	0.251	0.268	0.188		0.57[4]
Ash %	0.388	0.728	0.187	0.20	0.169
Proteins %	1.070	1.138	0.556	0.066[2]	0.041[2]
Undetermind %	2.141	3.187	2.184		

Data on honeys form *Apis dorsata, A..florea* and *A..cerana* from Phadke (1967, 1968).

1. From White 1975a; 2. as Nitrogen; 3. Higher sugars;
4. Calculated as gluconic acid.

A few toxins have been reported in honeys from Ericaceae (*Rhododendron, Azalea, Andromeda, Kalmia*), *Datura, Gelsemium, Euphorbia, Melaleuca, Ligustrum, Coriaria, Lasiosiphon* and *Lobelia* (Chaubal and Deodikar, 1963; White, 1975a). Such toxic honeys are however very rare.

All honeys contain osmophilic (sugar tolerant) yeasts. Species of *Nematospora, Saccharomyces, Schizosaccharomyces, Torula* and *Zygosaccharomyces* have been reported. *Madhupriya kamatii* Kumbh. *Saccharomyces mellis* Fab. et Quin., *S.rouxii* Bout. *Schizosaccharomyces slooffiae* Kumbh, *Torulopsis lodderiae* Kumbh. and *Torulopsis etchelsii* Lod. et Rij have been recorded in Indian honeys (Kumbhojkar, 1969, 1986). Yeasts in honey cause its fermentation, when the water content is more than 20 per cent. Honey is hygroscopic and when exposed to humid atmosphere, can absorb atmospheric moisture which increases the water content.

NECTAR STUDIES AND PROSPECTS FOR BEEKEEPING

Modern beekeeping is still in its infancy in India and several countries. Large areas with untapped floral resources exist in the world. Considering the present area under rubber tree plantations alone, 125 000 metric tonnes of honey can be produced every year, in India if the potential is fully exploited (Suryanarayana, 1983). The significance of this figure will be obvious when the world honey production is kept in view (630430 tonnes, Crane, 1975). An understanding of the nectaries and their biology helps not only the complex plant-pollinator relationships, but also, more importantly, from the standpoint of economic application of this knowledge in the improvement of crop production using bees and in the improvement of honey production and beekeeping.

Figure 1 : A hypothetical model of nectar foraging behaviour in honey bees

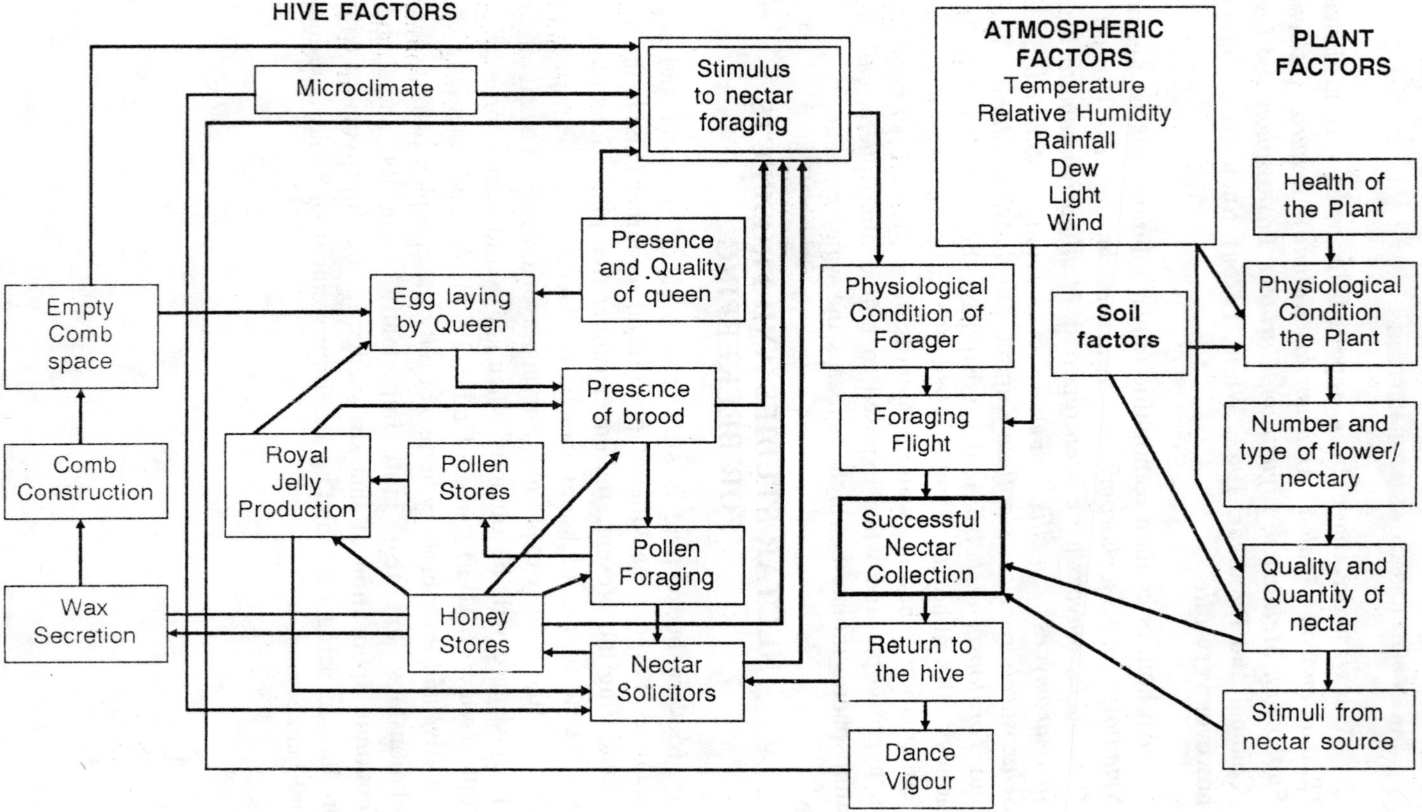

Literature Cited

Abrol, D.P. 1986. Eco-physiological adaptations between pollinating bees and their flowers. *Environ. Ecol,, 4* : 161-162.

Bachman, W.W. and Waller, G.D. 1977. Honey bee responses to sugar solutions of different compositions. *J. apic. Res., 16*: : 165-169.

Bahadur, B., Chaturvedi, Arthi and Ramaswamy, N. 1982. Nectar types in Indian plants. *Proc. Indian Acad. Sci. (Plant Sci.), 96* : 41-48.

Bailey, L. 1954. The filtration of particles by the proventriculi of various aculeate Hymenoptera. *Proc. R. ent. Soc. Lond. (A), 29* : 119-123.

Barker, R.L. and Lehner, Y. 1974. Acceptance and sustenance value of naturally occurring sugars fed to newly emerged adult workers of honey bees (*Apis mellifera* L.). *J. exp. Zool., 187* : 277-285.

Barker, R.J. and Lehner, Y. 1976. Galactose, a sugar toxic to honey bees, found in exudate of tulip flowers. *Apidologie, 7* : 109-111.

Butler, R. 1953. Nectar. *Bee Wld, 34* : 106-116.

Chaubal, Pushpa D. and Deodikar, G.B. 1963. Pollen grains of poisonous plants 1. Poisonous pollen in honey samples from Western Ghats (India). *Grana Palynol., 4* : 393-397.

Chauvin, R. (ed..) 1968. *Traité de biologie de l'abeille.* Vol. I to V. Masson et Cie., Paris.

Clinch, P.G.. Palmer-Jones, T. and Forster, I.W. 1972. Effect on honey bees of nectar from the yellow kowhai (*Sophora microphylla* Ait.). *N. Z. J. Agric. Res., 15* : 194-201.

Crane, Eva. 1977. Dead bees under lime trees. *Bee Wld, 58* : 129-130.

Crane, Eva. 1978. Sugars poisonous to bees. *Bee Wld, 59* : 37-38.

Deinzer, M.L., Thomson, P.A., Burgett, D.M. and Isaacson, D.L. 1977. Pyrro-lizidine alkaloids : their occurrence in honey from tansy ragwort (*Senecio jacobaea* L.). *Scie,, 195* : 497-499.

Deodikar, G.B. 1961. Some aspects of bee botany. In: *Prof. S..P. Agharkar Commemoration Volume*, MACS Res. Inst., Pune. pp.61-78.

Deodikar, G.B., Thakar, C.V. and Phadke, R.P. 1957. High nectar concentration in floral nectaries of Silver Oak, *Grevillea robusta. Indian Bee J., 19* : 84-85.

Doull, K.M. 1970. An analysis of bee behaviour as it relates to pollination, in *The Indispensable Pollinators.* Rep. IX Polln. Conf., Hot Springs, Arkansas, 5-18.

Duisberg, E.B. 1967. Honig und Kunsthonig. *Handb. Lebensmittelchemie, 5* : 491-559.

Eisikowitch, D. and Loper, G.M. 1984. Some aspects of flower biology and bee activity on hybrid cotton in Arizona, USA. *J. apic. Res., 23* : 243-248.

Fergusson, A.W. and Free, J.B. 1979. Production of a forage-marking pheromone by the honeybee. *J. apic. Res., 18* : 128-135.

Fielder, L. and Drescher, W. 1984. Residue analysis of insecticides in nectar : possible contamination after pre-blossom treatment. *Proc. 5th Symp. Polln. Versailles,* 27-30 Sept. 1983, 209-213.

Free, J.B. and Williams, Ingrid, H. 1983. Scent-marking of flowers by honey bees. *J. apic. Res., 22* : 86-90.

Frisch, K. von 1930. Versuche ueber den Geschmackssinn der Bienen. *Naturwissenschaften, 18* : 169-174.

Frisch, K. von 1950. *Bees.* Cornell University press, Ithaca.

Frisch, K. von 1967. *The Dance Language and Orientation of Bees.* Harvard Univ Press, Cambridge, Mass.

Furgala, B., Gochnauer, T.A. and Holdaway, F.G. 1958. Constituent sugars of some northern legume nectars. *Bee Wld, 39* : 203-205.

Giri, K.V. 1938. Chemical compostion and enzyme content of Indian honey. *Madras agric. J., 26* : 68-72.

Gontarski, H. and Hoffmann, I. 1963. Ueber Aufnahme und Verarbeitung der zuckerhaltigen Nahrung bei der Hongbiene. *Z. Bienenforsch., 6* : 184-198.

Howes, F.N. 1945. *Plants and Beekeeping.* Faber & Faber, London (Rev. Edn. 1977).

Jaycox, E.R. 1964. Effect on honey bees of nectar from systemic insecticide-treated plants. *J. econ. Ent., 57* : 31-35.

Jaycox, E.R. 1970. Honey bee foraging behaviour : Responses to queens, larvae, and extracts of larvae. *Ann. Entomol. Soc. Amer., 63* : 1689-1694.

Kevan, P.G. and baker, H.G. 1983. Insects as flower visitors and pollinators, *Annu. Rev. Entomol, 28* : 407-453.

Kumbhojkar, M.S. 1969. Osmophilic yeasts in Indian honeys. *Curr. Sci., 38* : 347-348.

Kumbhojkar, M.S. 1986. Prof. Deodikar's Contribution to the studies on osmophilic yeasts in Indian honeys. *Indian Bee J., 48* : 37-38.

Leppik, E.E. 1955. How bees recognise numbers. *Amer. Bee J., 95* : 472-473.

Leppik, E.E. 1977. *Floral Evolution in Relation to Pollination Ecology.* Today & Tomorrow's Printers and Publishers, New Delhi.

Lindauer, M. 1949. Ueber die Einwirkung von Duft-und Geschmacksstoffen sowie anderer Faktoren auf die Tanze der Bienen. *Z. vergl. Physiol., 31* : 348-412 (*Apic. Abs.* 200/51).

Lord, K.A., May, M.A. and Stevensen, J.H. 1968. The secretion of the systemic insecticides dimethoate and phorate into nectar. *Ann. appl. Biol., 61* : 19-27.

Maurizio, Anna. 1962. From the raw material to the finished product : honey. *Bee Wld, 43* : 66-81.

Maurizio, Anna. 1968. Les plantes toxiques. In *Traite de biologies de l'abeille*, Vol. IV. (ed.) R. Chauvin, Masson et Cie., Paris.

Maurizio, Anna. 1975. How bees make honey. In: (ed.) Crane, Eva. *Honey. A Comprehensive Survey* ed. Crane, Eva, Heinemann, London.

Michener, C.D. 1974. *The Social Behaviour of the Bees*. Harvard Univ. Press, Cambridge, Mass.

Moffett, J.O. 1954. Nectar secretion. in *Report of the State Apiarist*, Iowa State, 36-42.

Moffett, J.O., Stith, L.S., Buckhardt, C.C. and Shipman, C.W. 1976. Nectar secretion in cotton flowers and its relation to floral visits by honey bees. *Amer. Bee J., 116* : 32, 34 and 36.

Nair, K. Shakuntala and Wakhle, D.M. 1983. A qualitative and quantitative study of foliar nectar of rubber tree. *Indian Bee J., 45* : 113-114.

Oertel. E., Fieger, E.A., Williams, V.R. and Andrews, E.A. 1951. Inversion of cane sugar in the honey stomach of the bee. *J. econ. Ent., 44* : 487-492.

Park. O.W. 1922. Time and labour factors involved in gathering pollen and nectar. *Amer. Bee J., 62* : 254-255.

Park, O.W. 1932. Studies on the changes in nectar concentration produced by the honeybees, *Apis mellifera*. Part 1. Changes which occur between the flower and the hive. *Res. Bull. 151, Agric. Expt. Sta.*, Iowa St. Coll. Agric. and Mech. Arts, Entom. Sec. Iowa.

Park, O.W. 1949. How bees make honey. In: (ed.) R.A. Grout. *The Hive and the Honeybee*. Dadant & Sons, Hamilton, Ill.

Percival, Mary S. 1965. *Floral Biology*. Pergamon Press, Oxford.

Phadke, R.P. 1964. Nectar concentration in *Carvia callosa* Bremk. *Indian Bee J., 26* : 22-25.

Phadke, R.P. 1965. Nectar concentration in *Thelapaepale ixiocephala* Bremk. *Indian Bee J., 27* : 73-76.

Phadke, R.P. 1967. Studies on Indian honeys. 1. Proximate composition and physico-chemical characteristics of Indian multifloral apiary honeys from *Apis indica* bees. *Indian Bee J., 29* : 14-26.

Phadke, R.P. 1968. Studies on Indian honeys. 3. proximate compostion and physico-chemical characterisation of honeys from the wild honey bees *Apis dorsata, Apis florea* and *Trigona*. *Indian Bee J., 30* : 3-8.

Pryce-Jones, J. 1944. Some problems associated with nectar, pollen and honey. *Proc. Linn. Soc. Lond., 155* : 129-174.

Rai, B.K., Allicock, P. and Delph, G. 1977. Honeybee and injection of monocrotophos into coconut palm. *Indian Bee J., 39* : 13-14.

Reinhardt, J.F. 1939. Ventilating the bee colony to facilitate the honey ripening process. *J. econ. Ent., 32* : 654-660.

Revathi, Venkatraman. 1982. *Some Biochemical Evaluations of Indian Honeys*. Unpublished M.Sc. thesis. Bombay University, Bombay.

Ribbands, C.R. 1953. *The Behaviour and Social Life of Honeybees*. Bee Res. Assn., London.

Rinaudo, M.T., Ponzetto, C., Vidano, C. and Marletto, F. 1973a. The origin of honey saccharase. *Comp. Biochem. Physiol., 46B* : 245-251.

Renaudo, M.T., Ponzetto, C., Vidano, C. and Marletto, F. 1973b. The origin of honey amylase. *Comp. Biochem. Physiol., 46B* : 253-256.

Rinderer, T.E. 1982. Regulated nectar harvesting of the honeybee. *J. apic. Res., 21* : 74-87.

Rinderer, T.E. and Baxter, J.R. 1978. Effect of empty comb on hoarding behaviour and honey production of the honeybee. *J. econ. Ent., 71* : 757-759.

Rinderer, T.E. and Hagstad, W.A. 1984. The effect of empty comb on the proportion of foraging honeybees collecting nectar. *J. apic. Res., 23* : 80-81.

Rinderer, T.E., Bolten, A.B., Collins Anita M. and Harbo, J.R. 1984. Nectar foraging characteristics of Africanised and European honeybees in the neotropics. *J. apic. Res., 23* : 70-79.

Satyanarayana, I. 1975. Sugar concentration in nectar from *Syzygium cumini* Skeels. *Indian Bee J., 37* : 21-24.

Schepartz, A.I. and Subers, M.H. 1964. The glucose oxidase of honey. 1. Purification and some general properties of the enzyme. *Biochem. Biophys. Acta*, 85 : 228-237.

Schepartz, A.I. and Subers, M.H. 1966a. Catalase in honey. *J. apic. Res., 5* : 37-43.

Schepartz, A.I. and Subers, M.H. 1966b. Observations on honey diastase. *J. apic. Res., 5* : 45-48.

Sharma, P.L. 1958. Sugar concentration of nectar of some Punjab honey plants. *Indian Bee J., 20* : 86-91.

Shuel, R.W. 1955. Nectar secretion. *Amer. Bee J., 95* : 229-234.

Shuel, R.W. 1970. Current research on nectar. *Bee Wld, 51* : 63-69.

Simpson, J. 1962. The salivary glands of *Apis mellifera* and their significance in caste determination. *IV Congr. U.I.E.I.S. Pavia,* 173-188.

Simpson, J. 1963. The source of the saliva honey bees use to moisten materials they chew with their mandibles. *J. apic. Res., 2* : 115-116.

Simpson, J. 1964. Dilution by honeybees of solid and liquid food containing sugar. *J. apic. Res., 3* : 37-40.

Snodgrass, R.E. 1956. *Anatomy of the Honeybee*. Comstock Publ. Associates, Cornell Univ. Press, Ithaca, N.Y.

Sols, A., Cadenas, E. and Alvarado, F. 1960. Enzymatic basis of mannose toxicity in honey bees. *Science N.Y., 131* (3396) : 297-298.

Suryanarayana, M.C. 1978. Bee plants of India 1. *Carvia callosa* (Nees) Brem. *Indian Bee J., 40* : 7-10.

Suryanarayana, M.C. 1983. The rubber tree (*Hevea brasiliensis*) — an important nectar source in the tropics. *Proc. 2nd Int. Conf. Apic. Trop. Climates* I.A.R.I., New Delhi, 656-658.

Suryanarayana, M.C. 1986. Honey bee — flower relationship. (Abstract). *Bot. Surv. India, 28* : 55-62.

Thakar, C.V. and Shende, S.G. 1962. Management pattern for experimental apiaries. *Indian Bee J., 24* : 91-101.

Thorp, R.W. Briggs, D.L., Estes, J.R. and Erickson, E.H. 1975. Fluorescent nectar. *Science, 189* : 476.

Thorp, R.W., Briggs, D.L., Estes, J.R. and Erickson, E.H. 1976. Fluorescent nectar. *Science, 194* : 342.

Vansell, G.H. 1939. Sugar concentration of Western nectars. *J. econ. Ent., 32* : 666.

Waddington, K.D. 1983. Foraging behaviour of pollinators. In: *Pollination Biology*, (ed.) Leslie Real, Academic Press Inc., Orlando, U.S.A.

Wakhle, D.M. 1983. Enzymes in Indian honeys. *Proc. 2nd Int. Conf. Apic. Trop. Climates*, I.A.R.I., New Delhi, 703-710.

Wakhle, D.M., Nair, K. Shakuntala and Ramesh, B. 1981. Sugar compostion in nectars of certain plants. *Indian Bee J., 43* : 6-7.

Waller, G.D. and Bachman, W.W. 1981. Use of honeysac load and dance characteristics of worker honeybees to determine their sugar preferences. *J. apic. Res., 20* : 23-27.

Waller, G.D., Carpenter, E.W. and Ziehl, O.A. 1972. Potassium in onion nectar and its probable effect on attractiveness of onion flowers to honey bees. *J. Amer. Soc. Hort. Soc., 97* : 535-539.

Wedmore, E.B. 1955. The accurate determination of the water content of honeys. 1. Introduction and results. *Bee Wl,, 36* : 197-206.

Wells, P.H. and Giacchino, J. jr. 1968. Relationship between the volume and the sugar concentration of loads carried by honeybees. *J. apic. Res., 7* : 77-82.

White, J.W.jr. 1975a. Compostion of honey. In: (ed.) Eva Crane. *Honey : A Comprehensive Survey*. Heinemann, London, 157-206.

White, J.W.jr. 1975b. Physical characteristics of honey. In: (ed.) Eva Crane. *Honey : A Comprehensive Survey* Heinemann, London, 207-239.

White, J.W.jr. and Kushnir, I. 1967. The enzymes of honey : examination by ion-exchange chromatography, gel filtration and starch-gel electrophoresis. *J. apic. Res., 6* : 69-89.

Wykes, G.R. 1952. The preferences of honeybees for solution of various sugars which occur in nectar. *J. expt. Biol., 29* : 511-518.

Ziegler, H. 1968. La sécrétion du nectar. In : *Traité biologie de l'abeille*, vol. III. ed. R. Chauvin, Massonet Cie, Paris, 218-224.

Zimmermann, M. 1954. Ueber die sekretion saccharose-spaltender Transglukosidasen im pflanzlichen Nektar. *Experientia, 10* : 145-146.

FLORAL NECTARIES SERVING POLLINATION OF CULTIVATED PLANTS OF HUNGARY

S. GULYAS
Institutum Botanicum Et Hortus Botanicus
Universitatis De Jozef Attila Nominate Szeged, Hungary.

ABSTRACT

The aim of this review is to examine and emphasise the role of floral nectaries serving pollination of cultivated plants of Hungry. Most cultivated plants are allogamous and are dependent on honey bees for their pollination which in turn are dependent on nectar produced by floral nectaries. With new varieties released year after (peach, sunflower etc.) it is essential that their nectaries are given due attention in relation to productivity. In Szeged, Hungary, many hybrids/genotypes of *Robinia pseudo-acacia*, a multipurpose tree and *Helianthus annus* for its edible oil, in relation to melliflory has been discussed vis-a-vis the role of floral nectaries in relation to higher yield. Accordingly, nectaries and nectar rich hybrids/genotypes has led to establishment of *Acacia* forests for country's economy. It is opined that nectary characters are hereditary and therefore, its role in agriculture be exbloited particularly in wood, fruits, oil yielding and medicinal plants (Editor).

Key words : Floral nectaries; Pollination; cultivated plants; Hungary.

The structure of floral nectaries have been studied for over a century; that is why the nectaries of our more important nectar producing fruits, of agricultural, horticultural and wild plants are fairly

---

This paper has been written in essay format and has been included in view of its originality and thought provoking ideas for the benefit of agriculture and national economy (*Editor*)

well known. [Fahn (1951), Frei (1955), Gulyàs (1968), Gulyàs & Kincsek (1982), Kirchoff (1985)]. Some of the characteristics of nectaries are shown in Plates I and II.

Relying upon scanning electron micrographs several ideas have been described of how nectar migrates from cell to cell finally, appearing on the surface. One of these is shown in Plate III. (Eymé (1967), Schnepf (1969), Rachmilevitz & Fahn (1973), Kàlmàn & Gulyàs (1975), Fahn, (1979)).

Measuring the amount of nectar taken from the flowers by glass capillaries — or by some other method — with corresponding calculations, it is possible to predict the amount of nectar and honey, respectively, expected on an area of 1 Ha during the flowering of sunflower (Kulijev (1952), Halmàgyi & Keresztesi (1975), Herrera (1985)).

The chemical analysis of nectar revealed the occurence of sugar, poisonous substances etc. (Percival (1961), Pate et al. (1985)). All this knowledge, however, have proved to be insufficient in today's growing of cultivated plant with high productivity. In a number of countries applying modern (chemical) technologies resulted in exterminating wild, useful pollinating insects and thus honey bee (*Apis mellifica*) remained the main go-between of pollination.

Year after year cultivators are producing new varieties since higher productivity or oil content etc. have become a basic interest of national economy. With varieties of self pollination this has not been a problem. The majority of our cultivated plants, sometimes their 70 per cent however, is in need of allogamous pollination. Unfortunately, we know very little, sometimes nothing at all; of the structure and nectar production of floral nectaries of new hybrids.

A better knowledge would be even more important because honey bee; if it can; favours this or that allogamous floral nectaries. Flowers of varieties producing much and dense (sugary) nectar are more frequently visited and pollinated, while those producing less dense nectar are neglected. For example, of the two sunflower varieties growing side by side; one area is perfectly pollinated by honey bees (even more if their number is not too great) thus yielding a fair harvest, while the others lag behind. The case is similar in spring with nepe and flower varieties, or in summer with the pollination of sunflower and medicinal plants.

Quite reasonable that the study of nectaries have come in the forefront. Nowadays more than 500 peach varieties, at least 80 mast-types or e.g. more than 100 sunflower varieties, hybrids, genotypes have been produced.

And there is not a single floral biologist of flowers, anatomist of nectaries who would be able to tell us what kind of basic differences are there between the nectaries and nectar production of the so many variations, which of them has nectary assuring a fruitful pollination. Nectar production of certain subspecies is even less known.

Researches of this kind are of economic importance; therefore to study the structure and production of nectaries is necessary in and for the work of biologist. Because of the secure pollination varieties with high nectar production have become plants with double and many fold. Of our own researches with the above purposes we report on a series of studies of different hybrids, genotypes of a tree (*Robinia pseudo-acacia*) and of an agricultural/industrial plant with soft stem (*Helianthus annuus*). *Robinia pseudo-acacia* is regarded as one of the best melliferous trees in Eurasia.

In Gödöllő (Hungary) more than 60 cultivars and selected varieties of *Robinia* have been gathered from all over the world. (Halmàgyi — Keresztesi, 1975). On the basis of comparative (complex) studies carried out for several years the best varieties for forestry have successfully been found. Eg. R.p.var. rectissima hybrids and those from the USA with masttype stem and some with pink/?/ flowers have proved to be the best. In Szeged (Hungary), the Botany Department of the University have studied the structure of floral nectaries of the same hybrids from the point of view of apiary.

For comparative anatomy studies nectaries were preserved in 40% ethyl alcohol, then dehydrated with ascending series of alcohol and put in a 1-1 mixture of absolute alcohol and ether. Following this glands were soaked with 2-4-8% celloidine. Of the glands embedded in celloidine sections of 15-20 μm thickness were cut by microtome. These sections — after extracting celloidine — were purified in 10% Na-hypochlorite and 5% acetic acid and stained with haematoxylin-chrisoidin double staining. The structure of the stained preparations was studied and measured with Nu-2 microscope.

The structure of nectaries is shown in plate IV. The results show that in the flowers the glandural tissue of nectaries between the ovary and androeceum is of different thickness. Some examples are given in pictures 1,3,5,7 (Plate IV). Table 1 shows that the thickness of the glandular tissue varies from 6 to 16 cell rows, thus differences of 2,5 magnitude can be observed in the nectaries of hybrids and species of *Robinia*. Nectar production results were similar to differences in the structure of glands (Table 1).

TABLE 1 : Summary of differences between the nectaries of *Robinia pseudo-acacia,* selected, endemic species and hybrids

Regional types, hybrids and cultivars	*Thickness of glandular tissue cells*			*Volatile cells*
	6—9	*9—11*	*11—16*	
R.P. "egylevelü/monophylla/	+			+
R.P "Gödöllói"/Hung/	+			+
R.P "Ricsikai"/Hung./	+			
R.P. "Nyirségi"/Hung./	+			+
R.P. "Zalai"/Hung./	+			
R.P. "Jàszkiséri"/Hung./	+			
R.P. "Pénzesdombi"/Rom./	+			+
R.P. "Gori"/Hung./	+			
R.P. "Ullói"/Hung./		+		
R.P. "Szajki"/Hung./		+		+
R.P. "Csàszàrtöltési"/Hung./		+		+
R.P. "ERTI"/Hung./		+		+
R.P. "Arbóc"/USA/		+		+
R.P. "HC-4138"/USA/		+		+
R.P. "HC-4149"/USA/		+		
R.P. "R-42 Kv."		+		
R.P. "R/43 Kv."		+		
R.P. "Rózsaszinviràgu"			+	+
R.P. "HC-4146"/USA/			+	+
and *Robinia dubia*			+	
Nectar-Production :	0,5–2 mg good	2–3 mg better	3–5 mg best	×

NOTE : R.P. = *Robinia pseudo-acacia*, Rom. = Romanian, HC = Hybrid
Kv. = Cultivar, R = rose colour, Àrbóc = mast-type,
Ró = zsaszinviràgu/R/ = Cultivar

Anatomical studies of nectaries of forest trees were compared and it was found that there are several hybrids *Robinia pseudo-acacia* which are equally excellent for forestry and apiary, having double wood and nectar production. The Robinias therefore the typical of double use-and best from economic viewpoint. Presently in Hungary new *Acacia* forests could be established only because of these.

We looked among the best from the point of view of apiary hybrids of *Robinia* for characteristics which are the most attractive for apiarists. Such are eg. cells containing volatile oils in nectaries making, both the flower and nectar more sweet smelling and pleasant (Table 1).

Growing sunflower is widespread in the agriculture all over the world. It is grown on a very wide area amounting to several millions of hectares. At present the work of breeders is double. Among the aims we find eg. high oil content, higher productivity, swift flowering, etc. in Szeged (Hungary) on the experimental plant of the Grain Research Institute 110 sunflower cultivars, hybrids, etc. are grown under the guidance of Dr. Joseph Frank. Sunflowers differing in various characters are grown here from different countries of the world.

At the Botany Department we studied how floral nectaries of various sunflower cultivars, hybrids, etc. differ from each other. Previous measurement data of 20 cultivars show considerable differences in floral nectaries surrounding the style. There are three fold diferences in magnitude (Plate VI). Differences in nectar production were similarly significant.

Glands are full of glandular tissue. Differing from other plants in some hybrids there are phloem elements in this tissue. Such a sunflowr produces va riety/hybrid nectar rich in sugar thus markedly attracts bees (Table 2).

Studies are now being carried out but the data obtained so far called our attention to hybrids producing more and sugary nectar.

Thus, if from among hybrids with high oil content and productivity, resistance, etc. we select those having the best developed nectary, we find sunflowers are of really many fold use.

TABLE 2 : The size of nectaries of *Helianthus annus* hybrids, cultivars and genotypes /μm^2.

Hybrids, cultivars and genotypes	*Surface of longsection of floral nectaries* μm^2	*Phloem elements*
Helianthus annuus "Citosol-2"	11336	+
Helianthus annuus "HRO-fertil"	11194	++
Helianthus annuus "HRO-steril"	10912	+
Helianthus annuus "Koflor-2"	10127	+
Helianthus annuus "Rodeo"	10012	+
Helianthus annuus "GH-7"	5839	+
Helianthus annuus "Marianne"	5712	+

Producing sunflowers with good nectaries — supposing perfect insect pollination, gives us certainty of nectar production. Finally, I should like to emphasize that in a given plant the comparison of cultivars and hybrids, if the flower pollèns are otherwise fertile, namely the flower is allogamous is reasonable for pollination only on the basis of the magnitude and structure of floral nectaries.

The nectar production of flowers, depending on environmental factors, often changes, while their structure does not or does only slightly.

Regarding the hereditary character of the structure of the nectaries, glands are of considerable importance and with good structure and function hold promise for the effective pollination of sunflowers and other plants.

Explanation to Figures

PLATE I : Outlines of various types of stomata on the surface of nectaries.

FIGS. 1-8 : 1. *Perowskia*, 2-3. *Robinia*, 4. *Monarda*

5. Double stomata in *Stachys, Mentha, Lycopus.*
6. Compound stomata of three as in *Lamium*

7—8. Compound stomata of four and five or stomata groups' on the surface of the nectary of *Salvia*.

(First of all there are isolated stomatas at small nectaris /0-0, 8 mm/, double stomatas at medium size /0,8-3 mm/ and stomata groups at the biggest ones.)

9. Cross-section of nectary and petal /*Monarda didyma*, 200x/

10. Cross-section of nectary /*Phlomis tuberosa*/ with stomata. /500x/

11. Cross-section of nectary /*Lamium amplexi-caule*/ with phloem elements. /500x/

12. Surface view of extrafloral leaf-nectary /*Ailanthus glandulosa*/ with outlet for nectar. /120x/

PLATE II : Scanning electron micrographs of the surface of floral nectaris of different fruit-trees.

1. *Padus avium* c.v. ''Majusi ropogós'' looox.
2. *Prunus domenstica* c.v. ''Ringló'' 5oox.
   Note one-celled trichome on the surface of nectary.
3. *Prunus cerasus* c.v. ''Érdi bótermó'' 3ooox.
4. *Prunus armeniaca* c.v. ''Kecskeméti mammut''
   f, the nectar gets across the sunken stomata to the surface.

   The epidermis of the nectary is covered by numerous sunken stomata. Each stoma is surrounded by a ring of several epidermal cells with conspicuous cuticular folds.

NOTE : ''Màjusi ropogós'', ''Ringló'', ''Érdi bótermó'', ''Kecskeméti mammut'' are hungarian cultivars.

PLATE III : Ultrastructure of the extrafloral nectary of *Ricinus communis* as seen in electron micrographs.

1. Glandular tissue cell in period following secretion. (40000x)
   G = Golgi bodies, N = Nucleus, ER = Endoplasmatic reticulum,
   C = Chloroplast, W = Wall.
2. The vesicles of the nectar-transporting lomasomes cross the plasmalemma. (8oooox.)

PLATE IV : Floral nectaries of *Robinia pseudo-acacia* hybrids and selected endemic species.

1. *Robinia pseudo-acacia* ''Gödöllói'' nectary (500x.)
2. *Robinia pseudo-acacia* ''HC-4146 nectary with stomata (500x.)
3. *Robinina pseudo-acacia* ''R-44-Kv'' nectary (500x.)
4. *Robinia pseudo-acacia* ''ERTI'' surface of nectary with stomata (500x.)
5. *Robinia pseudo-acacia* ''Árbóc, USA'' nectary (500x.)
6. *Robinia pseudo-acacia* ''ERTI'' nectary with volatile cells (500x.)
7. *Robinia pseudo-acacia* ''HC-4146'' nectary with volatile cells (500x.)

NOTE : HC = Hybrid, R = rose colo, Árbóc = mst-type, Gödölloi,
ERTI, = regional types.

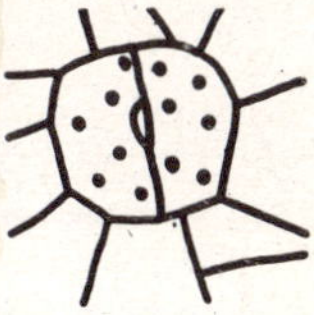
1

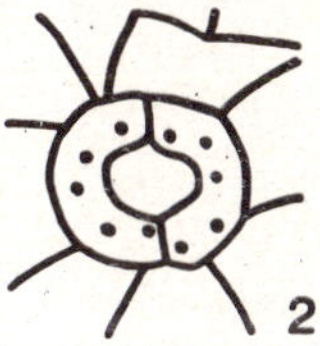
2

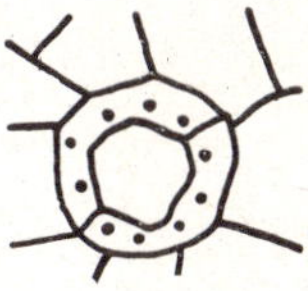
3

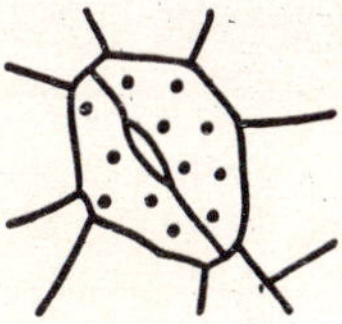
4

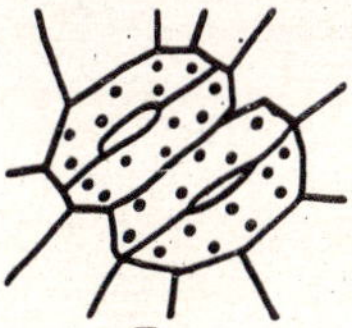
5

6

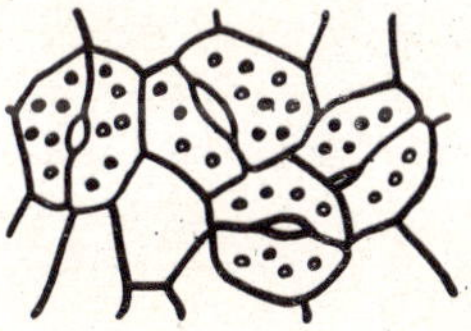
7

8

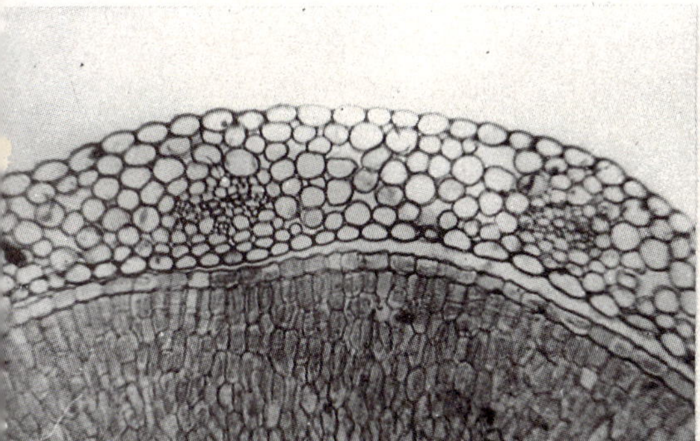
9

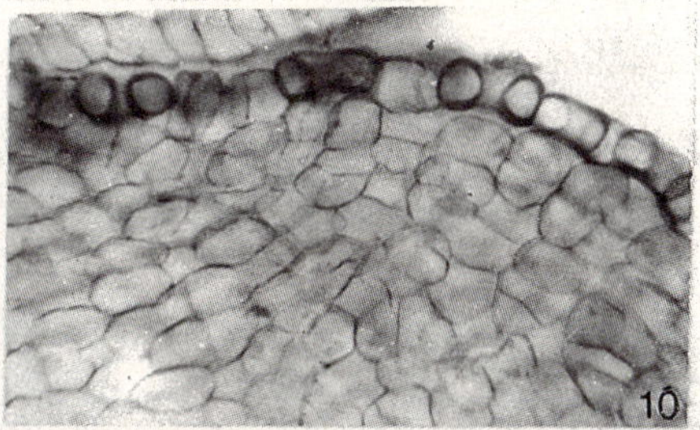
10

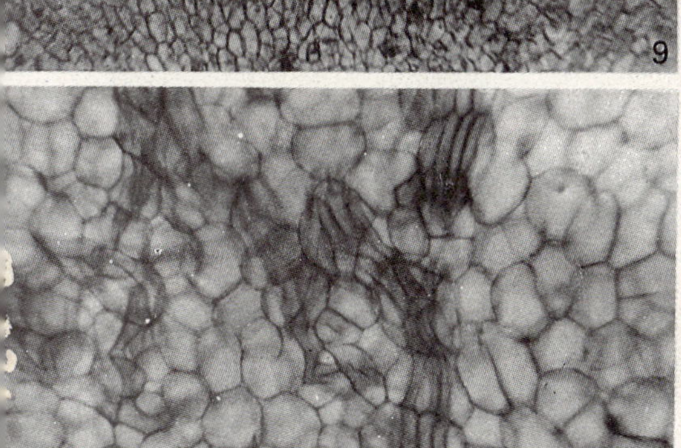
11

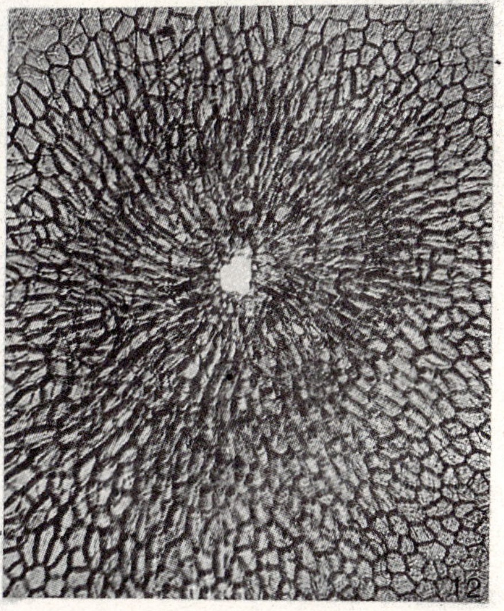
12

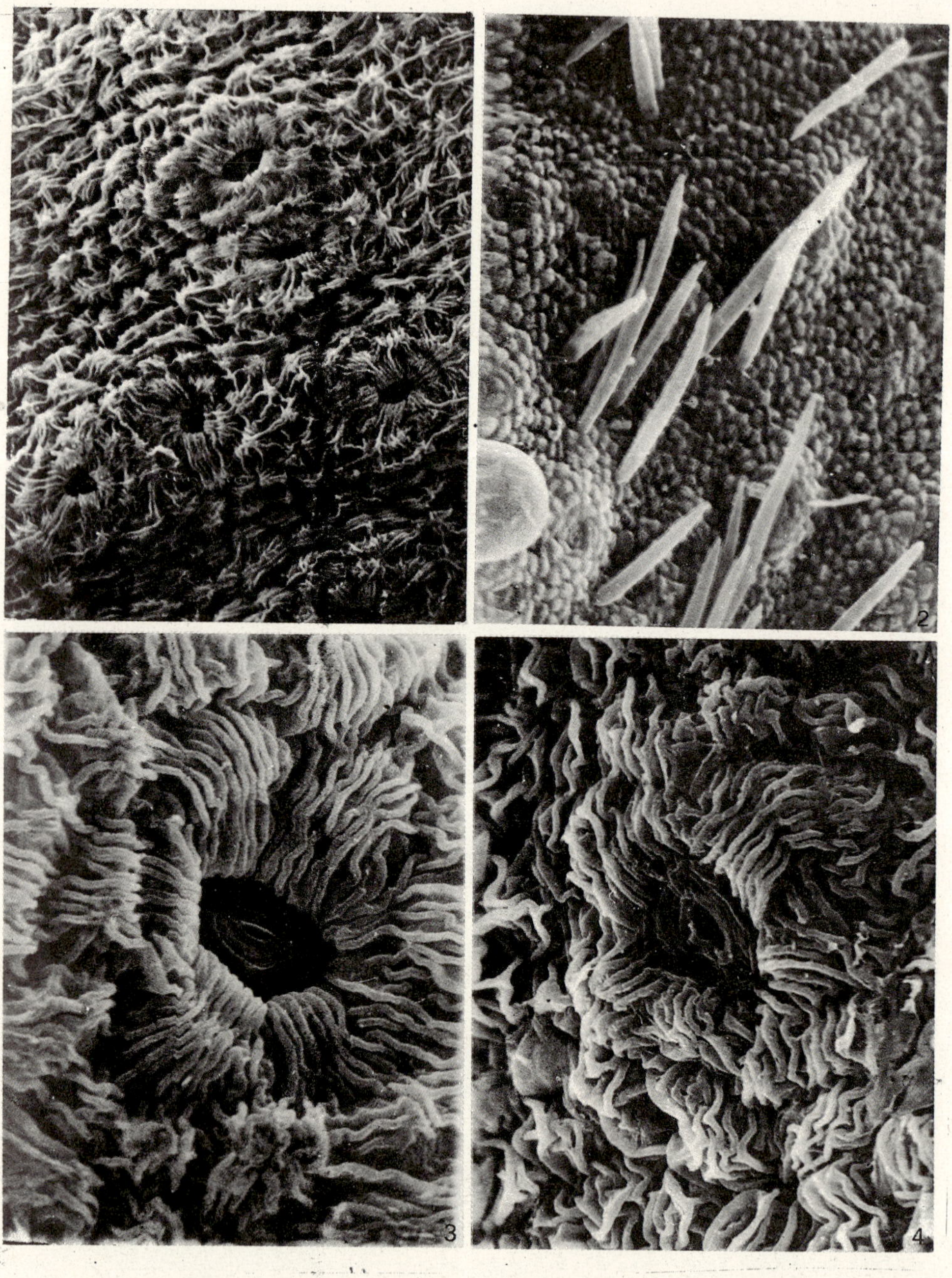
2
3
4

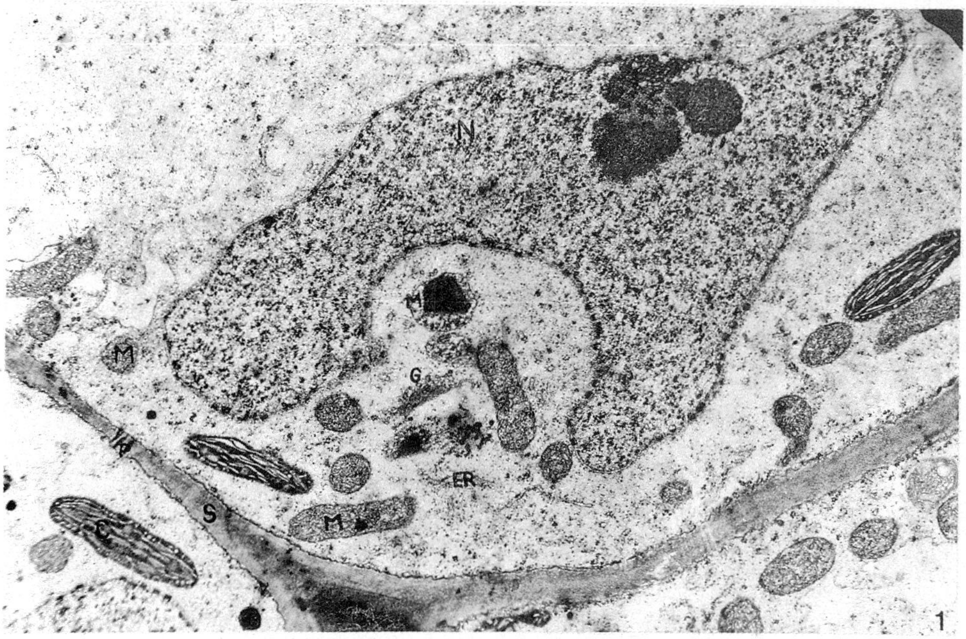
N
M
M
G
W
ER
S
M
C
1

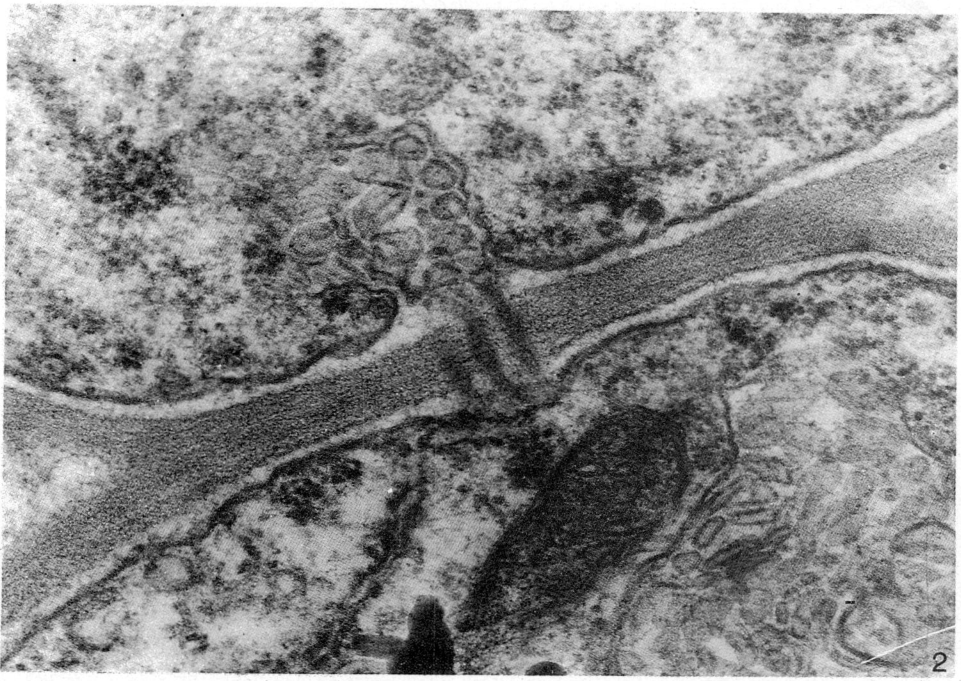
2

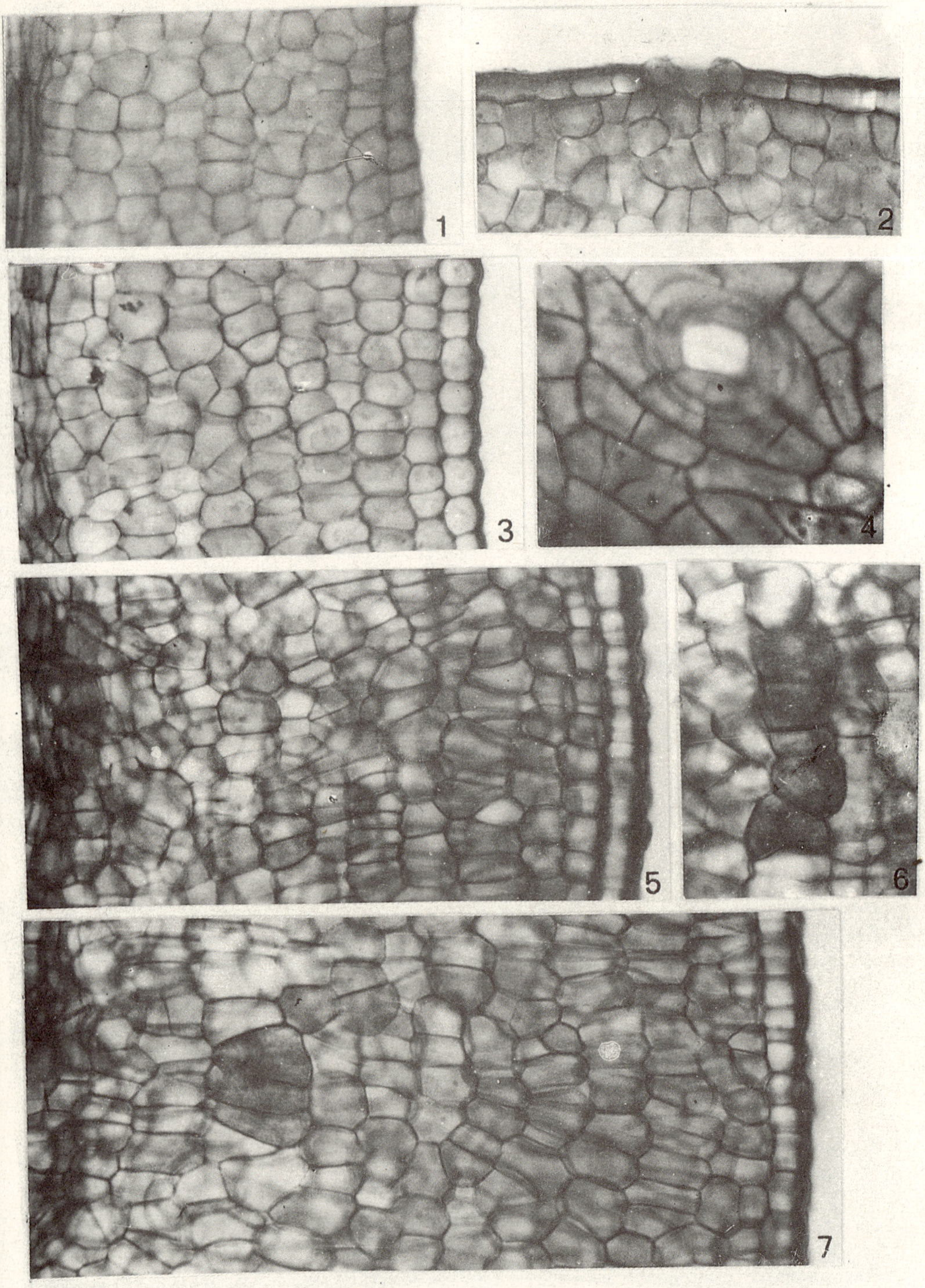
1
2
3
4
5
6
7

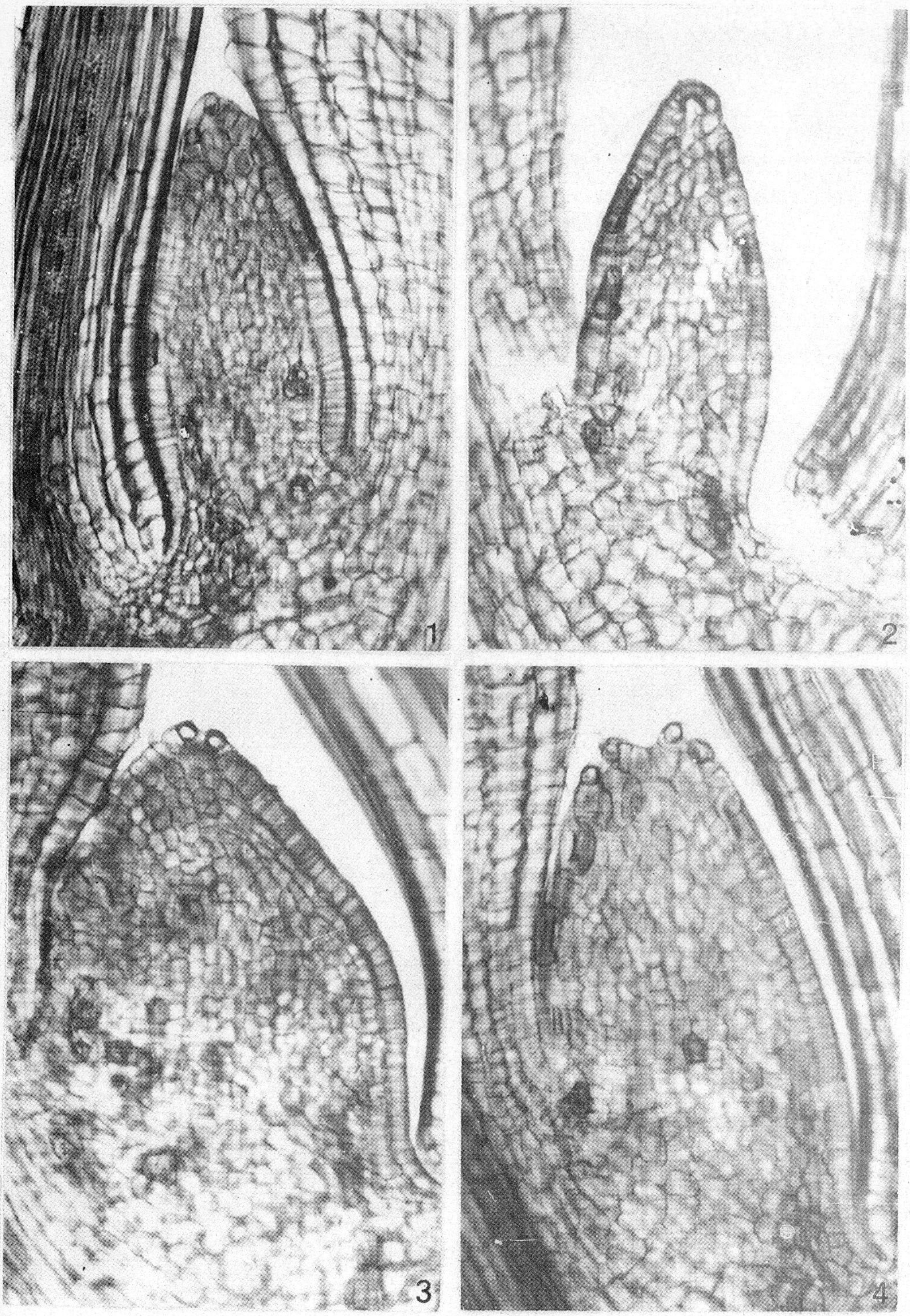
1
2
3
4

PLATE VI : Anatomical differences as seen in longisections in nectaris of *Helianthus* hybrids.

1. *Helianthus annuus* "G-98" 280x.
2. *Helianthus annuus* "CR-3" 280x.
3. *Helianthus annuus* "HRO-fertil" 280x.
4. *Helianthus annuus* "Citosol-2" 230x.

Literature Cited

Eymé, J. 1967. Nouvelles observations sur l'infrastructure des tissues nectarigenes floraux. *Botaniste.* 1-6. 169-184.

Fahn. A. 1951. On the structure of floral nectaris *Bot. Gaz., 113* : 464-470.

Fahn, A. 1979. *Secretary Tissues in Plants.* Academic. Press. London.

Frei, E. 1955. Die Innervierung der floralen Nektarien dikotyler Pflanzenfamilien. *Schwiz. Bot. Ges., 65* : 60-114.

Gulyàs, S. 1968. Szerkezet és produkció kapcsolate Labiatae nektàriumokban. (Correlation between struçture and production of the nectaries of Labiatae). C.Sc. Dissertation, Szeged (Hungarian).

Gulyàs, S., Kincsek, I. 1982. Floral nectaries of species of Papilionaceae. *Acta Biol. Szeged., 28* : 1-4. 53-63.

Humàgyi, L., Keresztesi, B. 1975. A méhlegelo. (Bee pasture, in Hungarian). Budapest.

Herrera, J. 1985. Nectar secretion patterns in Southern Spanish mediterranean scrublands.

Kàlmàn, F., Gulyàs, S. 1975. Ultrastructure and mechanism of secretion in extrafloral nectaries of *Ricinus communis. Acta. Biol. Szeged., 20* : 1-4. 57-67.

Kirchof, K.B. 1985. Foliar, nonstructural nectaries in the Marantaceae. *Can. J. Bot., 63* : 1785-1788.

Kulijev, A.M. 1952. Zadacsi izucsenija medonosznüh i perganosznüh rasztenij Moszkva-Leningràd.

Pate, J.S., Peoples, M.B., Storer, P.J. and Atkins, C.A. 1985. II. Nectar composition, origin of nectar solutes, and nectary functioning. *Planta., 166* : 28-38.

Percival, M.S. 1961. Types of nectar in Angiosperms. *New Phytol., 60* : 235-281.

Rachmilevitz, T. and Fahn, A. 1973. Ultrastructure of Nectaries of *Vinca rosea* L., *Vinca major* L., and *Citrus sinensis* Osbeck cv. *Valencia* and its Relation to the Mechanism of Nectar Secretion. *Ann. Bot., 37* : 1-9.

Schnepf, E. 1969. Sekretion und exkretion bei Pflanzen. Springer-Verlag. Wien-New York.

THE ROLE OF NECTARIES IN AGRICULTURE

P.D. CHAUBAL[1], J.S. ALURI RAJU[2] and C. SUBBA REDDI[2]
[1]Department of Botany, Shivaji University
Kolhapur 416 004, India.
[2]Department of Environmental Sciences
Andhra University, Visakhapatnam 530 003, India

ABSTRACT

Nectar is a primary floral reward offered to the pollinator, and nectar production is a function of nectaries at the base of the flowers. It provides instant energy for the pollinator because it contains sugars, aminoacids, proteins and other micronutrients. The blossoms of both wild and agricultural crop plants are visited and pollinated by insects. Insect species are many and show differences in size and pollination efficiency with regard to the flower types. In agriculture, floral nectar plays an important role for the production of enhanced yields. Because, nectar is very abundant and the insects visit the flowers very regularly and frequently; the foraging results in self-and/or cross-pollinated crops, insect visits enhance the yield and quality by cross-pollinating the flowers. The nectar concentration is also equally important. Because, different groups or even species of insects tend to have a preference for a particular range of nectar concentration.

The pollinator of crop plants includes different groups of insects, but honeybees are more dominant. A list of common foragers of crop plants has been provided. The nectar foragers-cum-pollinators for different crops such as pulse, vegetables, fruit, oil, condiments, medicinal, perfume, forage legumes, etc. have also been provided separately.

Key words : Nectaries, relationship; role in Agriculture.

INTRODUCTION

Modern agriculture has achieved significant increase in the crop yield per hectare and is able to support a much greater population than was possible during the past. The overall increase in crop production is due to the consideration of pollination aspects, in addition to the various scientific and technological progress made in various other approaches as plant breeding, biotechnology, irrigation, fertilizers, weed and pest control management.

Pollination of flowers is effected by wind, water, insects, birds and mammals. Majority of the crops are pollinated by insects and birds, though in general, Poaceae crops are wind-pollinated. the Poaceae members produce large amount of dry and light pollen which is easily transported by wind. The insect-pollinated crops on the other hand, produce comparatively less, sticky, heavy pollen but produce nectar in high quantity and/or quality. The nectar plays an important role in pollination, and occupies a vital position in agriculture.

The insect-pollinated flowers usually contain one or more nectaries of various shapes and sizes and produce nectar. The nectar is an instant source of energy for the insects. Therefore, the insects probe the flowers for nectar and such probing results in pollination.

Nectaries Versus Pollinators

Zavrashvili (1972) reported that Charles Darwin, while observing the importance of nectar secretion in flowers, noted that the floral nectar serves as the most valuable measure of adaptation for attracting various nectar foraging insects. In course of time, this character became more and more adaptive and perfectly affective in majority of the entomophilous species. The evolution of the flowering plants, their varied types of flowers along with their pollinating insects, took place long before the appearance of human beings on this planet. The floral types have evolved adaptations to their typical pollinating agents. Indications of such direct natural adaptations between many plants and insects have been recorded in the literature. It shows that the origin of a plant species can best be located and determined by the origin of its adapted insect species (Crane and Walker, 1983).

There are over 20,000 species of insects (Adey *et al.*, 1986; Crane and Walker, 1983) which show differences in their size, nesting habit and pollination efficiency with regard to the flower types of different crop plants. Among these, various species of bees are the most important pollinators. The best known and usually the prominent pollinators are the honey hive bees, which can be suitably reared and easily transported in large numbers from place to place for crop pollination on a large scale. Wasps are effective pollinators for some floral types and so do the flies, hover-flies, butterflies, moths and midges to a certain extent (Crane and Walker, 1983). In general, ants, aphids, bees (honey bees, other gregarious and colonial bees and solitary bees), beetles, butterflies, flies, midges, mosquitoes, moths, thrips, wasps, etc., are involved in the pollination of commercial crops, though bees dominate (McGregor, 1976). Usually, insects other than bees are beneficial to a lesser degree and important at specific times for specific crops only as in the case of *Theobroma cacao* which is pollinated by flies, thrips and ants, *Ficus carica* pollinated only by fig wasps and *Hevea brasiliensis* by midges and thrips. This may be due to their habit, morphology and mode of reproduction. Ants, being closely related to bees and wasps, are morphologically, physiologically, and socially advanced. Yet, their role as pollinators is considered negligible. The following characters are proposed for the rarity of ant pollination systems. 1. Ants are smooth, small, and flightless; little pollen can adhere to them (Kevan and Baker, 1983). 2. Floral nectars or floral parts are repellent to ant (van der Pijl, 1954; Janzen, 1977; Stephenson, 1981). 3. Ants are lured away from flowers by means of extrafloral nectaries (Bentley, 1977; Elias, 1983). 4. Pollen transfer by ants between plants does not occur because inter- plant distances are relatively large. 5. The ants do not forage as widely as winged pollinators. 6. Pollen exposed to the ant integument for brief periods exhibits reduced viability and germination. However, there have been some amply documented ant pollination systems from various studies (see Subba Reddi and Aluri, 1993).

Aphids feed on plant sap and nectar, but rarely contact with pollen. They have little role in pollination. Beetles feed upon pollen and other flower parts and may effect pollination in certain crops.

However, pollen in enough quantity is unlikely to stick to the slick chitinous body of beetle for transfer to other flowers. Some times, they show destructive effects and their presence on the floral parts often repels other beneficial pollinators.

Butterflies are covered with scales, to which very few pollen grains may adhere. Further, their proboscis is relatively long and delicate and is unlikely to carry and transfer much pollen. Frequently, while obtaining nectar, their body does not come in contact with the pollen. Therefore, the butterflies appear to have little value as pollinating agents (McGregor, 1976). Recent studies, however, show that there are quite a few species specifically adapted to butterfly-pollination (Subba Reddi and Meera Bai, 1984).

Flies are of considerable importance as pollinators of some crops, especially the Apiaceae, some Brassicaceae and specific onion plants, as also mango, apple, avacado, pear, berries, cherries, strawberries and others.

Midges and thrips are seldom recognised as pollinators. Thrips have been recognised as main pollinators for some members of Asteraceae, Solanaceae, Fabaceae, Verbenaceae (Mathur and Mohan Ram, 1978; Ananthakrishnan, 1993). Wasps are sparsely covered with coarse spines and not suitable for pollen transfer as are the hairs of bees. Therefore, wasps are considered to be of little significance as pollinators. However, Scoliidae wasps are excellent pollinators for alfalfa and cotton blossoms and the tiny fig wasp (*Blastophaga*) for the figs.

Insects belonging to the order Hymenoptera, Diptera, Lepidoptera, Coleoptera, Neuroptera, Homoptera, Hemiptera, Orthoptera, etc., visit the flowers. Some of the different orders, families and genera of insects usually involved in the crop pollination are represented in table 1.

A survey of blossoms of various plant species revealed that the honey bees constituted the major component of the insect fauna visiting them for nectar (Sharma, 1983). Although ants, beetles, butterflies, moths and many other groups of insects are involved in the pollination

TABLE 1 : Some common nectar foragers of crop plants

Order	*Family*	*Genus*	*Common name*
COLEOPTERA	Chrysomelidae	*Halictus*	Spinach beetles
		Luperomorpha	Leaf beetles
		Phyllotreta	Flea beetles
	Coccinellidae	*Coccinella*	Lady bird beetles
		Sumnius	Lady beetles
DIPTERA	Sacrophagidae	*Sacrophaga*	Flesh flies
	Syrphidae	*Eristalis*	Flower flies
	Tabanidae	*Chrysops*	Horse flies
HEMIPTERA	Aphididae	*Brevicoryne*	Cabbage aphid
	Lygaeidae	*Nysins*	Lygaeid bugs
	Miridae	*Creontiades*	Mirid bugs
		Nesidiocoris	Mirid bugs
	Pentatomidae	*Bagrada*	Painted bugs
HYMENOPTERA	Andrenidae	*Andrena*	Mining bees
	Anthophoridae	*Anthophora*	
		Braunsapis	
		Ceratina	Carpenter bees
		Melissodes	Melissode bees
		Peponapis	
		Xenoglossa	
		Xylocopa	Carpenter bees
	Apidae	*Apis*	Honey bees
		Melipona	Stingless bees
		Trigona	
	Bombidae	*Bombus*	Bumble bees
	Eumenidae	*Ancistrocerus*	Solitary wasps
	Halictidae	*Halictus*	Sweat bees
		Lasioglossum	True sweat bees
		Nomia	Alkali bees
		Rophitoides	
	Megachilidae	*Anthidium*	
		Chalicodoma	
		Luthurgus	
		Megachile	Leaf cutting bees
		Osmia	
	Melittidae	*Melitta*	Melitta bees
	Xylocopidae	*Xylocopa*	Carpenter bees
LEPIDOPTERA	Hesperiidae	*Potanthus*	Dart butterflies
	Lycaenidae	*Chaeroprocta*	Walnut blue butterflies
		Cosmolyce	Pea blue butterflies
	Noctuidae	*Heliothis*	Gram caterpillars
		Plusia	Cabbage semiloopers
	Nymphalidae	*Venessea*	Painted lady
	Pieridae	*Anaphaeis*	Bagnai butterflies
		Pieris	Cabbage butterflies

of crop plant species, members of Apidae, Andrenidae, Anthophoridae, Halictidae, Megachilidae, Bombidae, and Melittidae commonly contribute to their pollination at large. Among these, however, Apidae are of greatest interest and by far the most important as pollinators, in both tropical and temperate regions. Honey bees have been noted to be the most efficient pollinators due to their field behaviour, frequency of visits and ability to pollinate flowers per unit time.

Unlike other insects, the bees present longer working hours and high population density when compared to other insects throughout flowering period. Moreover, most of the other insects have been observed to be harmful pests of the crop plants and lack the necessary morphological and behavioural characteristics required for pollination (Kaker, 1980).

The pollination status of most of the tropical, subtropical and temperate crops is known. Certain important crop plants grown in the tropics and subtropics are autogamous or anemophilous and do not require bee and insect pollination. These include potato, cassava, hemp, jute, filbert, walnut, sugarcane, forage grasses, and cereals (barley, wheat, rice, maize, oats, rye and soghum). Nesterov (1972) noted that some crops are normally self-pollinated, but natural cross-pollination has been observed in them as in some apple varieties. Moreover, flowers visited by insects set more fruits and seeds than those not visited and the crop is therefore, benefited due to cross-pollination. He further reported that self-fertile crop species also give a good yield only after cross-pollination. Thus, many self-fertile crop plants, viz., beans, cotton, flax, rape, tobacco, tomatoes, etc., produce better and larger fruits and seeds when cross-pollinated. Sugar beet is pollinated both by wind and insects. For the crops such as brassica, vegetables, kenaf, onion, pasture legumes, rubber, tea and tobacco, pollination is required only if the plant is needed to set seeds either for propagation or breeding. Some crops depend entirely upon insects for pollination and production of fruits and seeds. Different insects that visit the flowers of such crops for nectar and may take part in pollination are enumerated in the tables 2-8. These tables are based on the literature by McGregor (1976).

TABLE 2 : Pulse crop species and their nectar foragers

Crop species	*Common name*	*Nectar forager*	*Status as pollinator*
Cajanus cajan	Pigeon pea	*Apis cerana indica*	B
		Megachile anthracine	B
		M. bicolor	B
		M. cephalatus	B
		M. femorata	B
		M. flavipes	B
		M. lanata	B
Canavalia ensiformis	Jack bean	*Apis cerana indica*	B
C. gladiata	Sword bean	,,	B
Dolichos biflorus	Horse bean	,,	B
Dipteryx odorata	Tonka bean	,,	E
Glycine max	Soya bean	,,	LI
		Nomia cognata	LI
Lablab niger	Lablab bean	*Apis cerana indica*	E
Macrotyloma uniflorum var. *uniflorum*	Horse gram	,,	MB
Phaseolus aureus	Green gram	,,	B
P. coccineus	Scarlet-runner bean	,,	I
		Bombus sp.	LI
P. lunatus	Lima bean	*Apis cerana indica*	I
		Bombus sp.	LI
		Thrips	LI
P. vulgaris	Haricot bean	*Apis cerana indica*	B
		Bombus sp.	LI
		Trigona sp.	LI
Pisum sativum	Garden pea	*Apis cerana indica*	B
		Osmia submicans	B
Vicia faba	Broad bean	*Apis cerana indica*	B
		Anthophora parientina	B
		Bombus sp.	B
		Cataglyphis bicolor	LI
		Xylocopa aestuans	LI
Vigna sinensis	Cow pea	*Apis cerana indica*	I
		Bombus sp.	LI

B = Beneficial; I = Important; LI = Less important; E = Essential;
MB = May be beneficial; MI = Most important; V = Visitor.
The same expanded words are used for the abbreviations for all the other tables 3-8.

TABLE 3 : Vegetable crop species and their nectar foragers

Family	*Crop species*	*Nectar forager*	*Status as pollinator*
Apiaceae	*Daucus carota*	*Andrena* spp.	I
		Apis cerana indica	MI
		Colletes spp.	V
		Chloralictus spp.	V
	Pastinaca sativa	*Apis cerana indica*	I
Asteraceae	*Cichorium endivia*	,,	I
	C. intybus	*Andrena* spp.	I
		Anthidium spp.	I
		Apis cerana indica	MI
		Halictus spp.	I
		Osmia spp.	I
		Prosopis spp.	LI
	Cynara scolymus	*Apis cerana indica*	B
	Lactuca sativa	,,	B
		Agapostemon spp.	V
		Butterflies	V
		Flies	V
		Wild bees	V
		Halictus spp.	B
Brassicaceae	*Brassica oleraceae* var. *botrytis*	*Ancistrocerus* spp.	LI
		Andrena spp.	I
		Apis cerana indica	MI
		Bombus spp.	LI
		Ceratina spp.	LI
		Eristalis spp.	V
		Halictus spp.	I
		Lasioglossum spp.	I
		Megachile spp.	V
		Melitta spp.	LI
		Sarcophaga spp.	V
		Xylocopa spp.	V
	B. pekinensis	*Apis cerana indica*	I
	B. napobrassica	,,	I
	B. rapa	,,	I
	Raphanus sativus	*Anthophora* spp.	I
		Apis spp.	MI
		Nomia spp.	I
Chenopodiaceae	*Beta vulgaris*	*Andrena* spp.	I
		Anthophora spp.	I
		Apis spp.	MI
		Halictus spp.	I
		Megachile spp.	LI

Convolvulaceae	*Ipomoea batata*	*Apis cerana indica*	MI
		Melissodes rufodentacta	V
Cucurbitaceae	*Benincasa hispida*	*Apis cerana indica*	B
	Citrullus lanatus	,,	I
	C. vulgaris	,,	I
	Cucumis melo	*Andrena* spp.	I
		Apis cerana indica	MI
		Halictus spp.	I
		Megachile rotundata	V
		Nomia spp.	I
		Nomiodea variegata	V
		Pithitis samaragdina	V
	C. sativus	*Apis cerana indica*	MI
	Cucurbita maxima	,,	MI
	C. mixta and *C. moschata*	*Ceratina binghami*	I
		Diabrotica spp.	V
		Halictus spp.	I
		Nomiodes spp.	V
		Peponapsis pruinosa	I
		Xenoglossa spp.	V
		Xylocopa spp.	V
	C. pepo	*Apis cerana indica*	MI
		Trigona ruficrus	I
		Xylocopa fenestrata	I
	Lagenaria siceraria	*Apis cerana indica*	MI
		Bombus spp.	V
		Crepuscular insects	I
		Hummingbirds	V
		Nectar collecting bats.	V
	Luffa aegyptiaca	*Apis cerana indica*	MI
		Megachile rotundata	LI
		Pithitis smaragdina	V
		Xylocopa pubescens	LI
	Momordica charantia	*Apis cerana indica*	MI
	Sechium edule	,,	MI
Malvaceae	*Abelmoschus esculentus*	,,	I
		Bombus spp.	LI
Moraceae	*Artocarpus heterophyllus*	*Apis cerana indica*	I

Solanaceae	*Lycopersicon esculentum*	,,	B
		Augochloropsis ignita	V
		Bombus spp.	V
		Exomalopsis glubosa	V
		Halictus spp.	B
	Solanum melongena	*Apis cerana indica*	B
		Bombus spp.	MB
		Xylocopa spp.	MB
Liliaceae	*Allium cepa* and *A. fistulosum*	*Apis cerana indica*	MI
		Andrena candida	I
		Halictus spp.	I
		Nomioides spp.	LI
	Asparagus officinalis	*Apis cerana indica*	B

TABLE 4 : Fruit crop species their nectar foragers

Family	*Fruit crop species*	*Nectar forager*	*Status as pollinator*
Anacardiaceae	*Mangifera indica*	Ants	V
		Trigona spp.	I
		Flies	LI
		Apis cerana indica	MI
	Spondias cythera, S. mombin,	,,	MI
	S. purpurea	*Trigonella* spp.	I
Annonaceae	*Annona cherimola, A. montana,*	Ants	MB
	A. diversifolia, A. muricata,	*Apis cerana indica*	MB
	A. reticulata,	*Coccinella* spp.	MB
	A. squamosa	*Scymnus* spp.	MB
	Asimina triloba	*Apis cerana indica*	MB
Apocynaceae	*Carissa carandus, C. grandiflora*	,,	MB
Caricaceae	*Carica papaya*	,,	MI
		Hummingbird	V
		Moth	V
		Trigona spp.	I
		Xylocopa spp.	V
Cucurbitaceae	*Citrullus lanatus*	*Agapostemon splendense*	V
		Apis cerana indica	MI

		Augochlorella gratiosa	V
		A. caerula	V
		Halictus spp.	I
	Cucumis anjuria, C. melo	*Apis cerana indica*	MI
Ebenaceae	*Diospyros discolor*	,,	E
	D. ebenaster, D. kaki	,,	
	Durio zibethinus	,,	B
	Eleagnus philippinensis	,,	B
	E. latifolia		
Ericaceae	*Vaccinium macrocarpon*	,,	E
		Bombus spp.	E
Euphorbiaceae	*Antidesma bunius, A. dallachyanum*	*Apis cerana indica*	MB
	Phyllanthus acidus, P. emblica	,,	MB
Fabaceae	*Tamarindus indica*	,,	MI
Flacourtiaceae	*Dovualis abyssinica, D. caffra,*	,,	E
	D. hebecarpa	*Bombus* spp.	MB
	Flacourtia cataphracta, F. indica, F. rukam	*Apis cerana indica*	E
Guttiferae	*Garcinia livingstonei, G. mangostana*	,,	B
	Mammea americana	,,	B
Lauraceae	*Persea americana*	,,	MI
		Flies	LI
		Wasp	LI
		Wild bees	LI
Malphigiaceae	*Malphigia glabra,*	*Apis cerana indica*	E
	M. punicifolia	*Eristalis agorum*	I
Moraceae	*Artocarpus altilis, A. heterophyllus, A. hypargyra*	*Apis cerana indica*	MB
	Ficus carica	*Blastophaga psenes*	E
Musaceae	*Musa* spp.	*Apis cerana indica*	I

Myrtaceae	*Eugenia aggregata, E. dombeyi, E. luschnathiana, E. uniflora*	,,	MB
	Feijoa sellowiana	,,	I
	Myricaria cauliflora	,,	B
	Psidium cattleianum, P. guajava	,,	I
	Syzygium cumini, S. jambos	,,	B
Oxalidaceae	*Averrhoa bilimbi, A. carambola*	,,	MI
Passifloraceae	*Passiflora edulis, P. flavicarpa,*	,,	MI
	P. quadrangularis	*Epicharis* spp.	LI
		Trigona spp.	I
		Xylocopa spp.	V
Punicaceae	*Punica granatum*	*Apis cerana indica*	E
		Ceratina spp.	MB
		Trichodes pp.	MB
Rhamnaceae	*Ziziphus jujuba, Z. mauritiana*	*Apis cerana indica*	B
Rosaceae	*Cydonia oblonga*	,,	MI
	Eriobotrya japonica	,,	B
	Fragaria xananassa	,,	MI
		Beetles, butterflies,	LI
		Flies, thrips	LI
		Halictus spp.	I
	Malus spp.	*Apis cerana indica*	MI
	Prunus armenica	,,	I
	P. persica	,,	MI
		Megachile spp.	V
		Osmia cornifrons	LI
	P. persica var. *nectarina,*	*Apis cerana indica*	I
	Prunus spp.	,,	MI
		Bombus spp.	I
		Megachile spp.	V
		Osmia lignaria	V
	Pyrus communis, P. malus	*Andrena* spp.	MB
		Apis cerana indica	MI
		Bombus spp.	I
		Halictus spp.	I
		Megachile spp.	V
		Osmia cornifrons	V

	Rubus idaeus, R. occidentalis, R. strigossus	*Andrena* spp.	I
		Apis cerana indica	I
		Bombus spp.	I
		Colletes spp.	V
		Halicts spp.	B
		Nomia spp.	B
Rutaceae	*Casimiroa edulis*	*Apis cerana indica*	B
	Citrus spp.	*Andrena crinica*	I
	Euphorbia longan	*Apis cerana indica*	MI
	Euphorbiaceae	*Xylocopa* spp.	V
		Apis cerana indica	E
Sapindaceae	*Litchi chinensis*	,,	I
		Calliphorid spp.	LI
		Melipona qadrifasciata	LI
		Trigona spp.	I
		Ants, flies, wasps	V
	Melicocca bijuga	*Apis cerana indica*	E
Sapotaceae	*Calocarpum sapota C. viridis*	,,	B
	Chrysophyllum cainito	,,	B
	Manilkara achras	,,	MB
	Pouteria campechiana	,,	MB
Saxifragaceae	*Ribes hirtellum*	,,	B
	R. grossularia	,,	B
Sterculiaceae	*Grewia asiatica*	,,	B
Tiliaceae	*Muntungia calabora*	,,	B
Vitaceae	*Vitis* spp.	,,	B
		Halictus spp.	B
		Scaeva pyrastri	V
		Syrphid fly	V

TABLE 5 : Oil crop species and their nectar foragers

Family	*Crop Species*	*Nectar forager*	*Status as pollinator*
Asteraceae	*Carthamus tinctorius*	*Apis cerana indica*	MI
		Halictus spp.	I
		Lasioglossum spp.	V
		Megachile spp.	MB
		Melissodes spp.	MB

	Guizotia abyssinica	*Apis cerana indica*	MI
	Helianthus annus	,,	MI
		Bombus haemorrhoidalis	MB
		Braunapsis spp.	V
		Diadasia enavata	V
		Dianthidium curvatum	V
		Dufourea marginata	LI
		Halictus spp.	LI
		Megachile lanata	V
		Melissodes agilis	B
		Svastra obliqua expergata	V
		Xylocopa spp.	V
	Vernonia anthelmintica	*Apis cerana indica*	I
Brassicaceae	*Brassica* alba	,,	MI
		Syrphid flies	LI
	B. capestris	*Andrena* spp.	I
		Apis cerana indica	MI
		Halictus spp.	I
		Megachile spp.	LI
		Nomioides spp.	V
	B. campestris	*Apis cerana indica*	MI
	var. *sarson*	,,	MI
	var. *toria*		
	B. hirta	,,	MI
		Ceratina binghami	B
	B. juncea	*Apis cerana indica*	MI
		Andrena spp.	I
	B. napus	*Andrena ilerda*	I
		Apis cerana indica	MI
		Eristalis tenax	LI
		Halictus spp.	I
	B. nigra	*Agapostemon* spp.	V
		Apis cerana indica	MI
	Eruca sativa	,,	MI
		Andrena spp.	I
		Colletes spp.	V
		Halictus spp.	LI
Euphorbiaceae	*Aleurites fordii*	*Apis cerana indica*	MI
	Ricinus communis		MB
Linaceae	*Linum usitatissimum*	,,	MI
		Bombus spp.	LI
		Thrips spp.	V
Pedaliaceae	*Sesamum indicum*	*Apis cerana indica*	B

TABLE 6 : Condiment, medicinal and perfume crop species and their nectar foragers

Family	*Crop species*	*Nectar forager*	*Status as pollinator*
DICOTYLEDONS			
Apiaceae	*Anthemum graveolens*	*Apis cerana indica*	MI
	Apium graveolens var. *rapaceum*	,,	I
	Carum carvi	,,	MI
	Coriandrum sativum	,,	B
	Foeniculum vulgare	,,	I
	Pimpinella anisum	,,	E
Asteraceae	*Chrysanthemum cinerariifolium*	,,	B
		Beetles, flies	V
Brassicaceae	*Brassica juncea*	*Apis cerana indica*	MI
		Agapostemon sp.	V
	B. nigra	*Andrena* sp.	I
Lamiaceae	*Lavendula* spp.	*Apis cerana indica*	B
Lauraceae	*Cinnamomum zeylanicum*	,,	E
Myristicaceae	*Myristica fragrans*	,,	MI
		Beetles	V
Myrtaceae	*Eucalyptus* spp.	*Apis cerana indica*	MI
	Pimenta dioica	,,	E
		Ceratina spp.	I
		Exomalopsis spp.	V
		Halictus spp.	I
	Syzygium aromaticum	*Apis cerana indica*	MI
Papavaraceae	*Papaver somniferum*	,,	B
Piperaceae	*Piper nigrum*	Ants	E
Rubiaceae	*Cinchona* spp.	*Apis cerana indica*	E
Solanaceae	*Capsicum annum*	Ants	V
	C. frutescens	*Apis cerana indica*	B
		Exomalopsis pulchella	V
Sterculiaceae	*Cola acuminata*	*Apis cerana indica*	B
		Flies	LI
MONOCOTYLEDONS			
Orchidaceae	*Vanilla* spp.	*Apis cerana indica*	MI
		Melipona spp.	I
Zingiberaceae	*Elettaria cardamomum*	*Apis cerana indica*	B
		Trigona spp.	LI

TABLE 7 : Miscellaneous crop species and their nectar foragers

Family	*Crop species*	*Nectar forager*	*Status as pollinator*
NUTS			
Anacardiaceae	*Anacardium occidentale*	*Apis cerana indica*	MI
		Black and red ants	B
Fabaceae	*Arachis hypogea*	*Anthidium* spp.	LI
	A. voandzeia	*Apis cerana indica*	MI
		Bombus spp.	I
		Halictus spp.	I
		Lasioglossum spp.	B
		Megachile spp.	V
		Melissodes spp.	B
Fagaceae	*Castanea* spp.	*Apis cerana indica*	MI
Proteaceae	*Macadamia* spp.	,,	MI
Rosaceae	*Prunus amygdalus*	,,	MI
Arecaceae	*Cocos nucifera*	,,	I
BEVERAGES AND STIMULANTS			
Rubiaceae	*Coffea arabica*	*Apis cerana indica*	MI
		Lasioglossum spp.	LI
		Melipona spp.	I
Solanaceae	*Nicotiana* spp.	*Apis cerana indica*	B
Sterculiaceae	*Cola nitida*	,,	B
		Flies	LI
	Theobroma cacao	Ants	B
		Aphids	V
		Ceratopogomid spp.	V
		Midges	MB
		Thrips	V
		Trigonella jaty	I
		Apis cerana indica	MI
Theaceae	*Camellia sinensis*	,,	B
TEXTILE AND FIBRES			
Bombacaceae	*Ceiba pentandra*	,,	MI
Fabaceae	*Crotalaria juncea*	,,	E
		Megachile spp.	V
		Xylocopa spp.	V

Malvaceae	*Gossypium* spp.	*Anthophora confusa*	LI
		Halictus spp.	I
		Lithurgus atratus	MB
		Megachile spp.	MB
		Melissodes agilis	MB
		Melitoma euglossoides	MB
		Nomia spp.	LI
		Apis cerana indica	MI
	Hibiscus cannabinus	,,	B

TABLE 8 : Forage legume crops and their nectar foragers

Family	*Crop species*	*Nectar forager*	*Status as pollinator*
Fabaceae	*Anthyllis vulneraria*	*Apis* spp.	I
	Astragalus giger	,,	B
	Lespedeza sp.	,,	B
		Bombus spp.	MЬ
	Lotus corniculatus	*Apis* sp.	MI
	L. tenuis	*Anthidium* spp.	I
		Megachile spp.	MB
	L. uliginosus	*Osmia* spp.	I
	Lupinus anguistifolius	*Andrena* spp.	I
		Anthophora ursina	I
		Apis spp.	MI
		Bombus spp.	I
		Lasioglossum spp.	LI
		Tetralonia dubita	LI
		Xylocopa virginia	V
	Medicago sativa,	*Andrena* spp.	I
	M. lupina	*Anthidium florentinum*	V
		Anthophora parietina	I
		Apis spp.	MI
		Bombus spp.	I
		Braunsapis spp.	B
		Ceratina binghami	LI
		Chalicodoma flavipes	V
		Eucera spp.	V
		Halictus spp.	V
		Megachile spp.	V
		Melissodes spp.	V
		Melitta leporina	V
		Melitturga clavicornis	V
		Nomia melanderi,	
		N. unidentate	B
		Osmia seculsa	V
		Pithitis smaragdina	V

		Pseudomegachile flavipes	V
		Rophitoides canus	B
	Melilotus alba	*Apis* spp.	B
	M. alba annua	*Magachile rotundata*	B
	M. officinalis	,,	B
	Onobrychis vicifolia	*Apis* spp.	B
	Pueraria thunbergiana	*Anthophora parietina*	I
		Apis spp.	MI
		Megachile rufipes	V
	Trifolium alexandrinum	*Andrena*	I
	T. hirtum,	*Anthidium* spp.	I
	T. hybridum,		
	T. incarnatum.	*Anthophora parietina*	LI
	T. medium,		
	T. pratense,	*Apis* spp.	MI
	T. repens,		
	T. resupinatum,	*Bombus* spp.	I
	T. subterraneum,		
	T. vesiculosum.	*Halictus* spp.	B
		Eucera spp.	V
		Megachile rufipes	
		Nomia unidentata	V
		Osmia spp.	B
	Vicia sp.	*Apis* spp.	MI
		Andrena spp.	I
		Anthophora parietina	B

Nectaries and their potential in Agriculture

The data presented in the tables 1 and 8 reveal that the various insects differ greatly in their pollination efficiency. Different species of bees are the primary pollinators and usually the only ones. Certain wasps are effective in the case of some crop species. Limited pollination is effected by flies and hover flies, butterflies, moths and midges. But honey bees are the principal pollinators. Usually the only ones that are widely useful as pollinators are the bees of *Apis cerana indica.*

It is to be noted that various insects visit different crop flowers for deriving the necessary néctar and casually effect pollination. It shows that the nectaries have a very important place in agriculture. As per the estimate of Crane and Walker (1983) and Adey *et al.*

(1986) there are about 85 to 105 crop species pollinated mostly by bees. No wonder, much of our food supply is derived directly or indirectly from insect- pollinated plants (Townsend, 1974), which results in quality crops, higher yield and therefore, a profitable harvest. In this connection, Mel'nichenko (1972) remarks that scientific experiments and practical experience have proved that insect-pollination of entomophilous crop plants is the most effective and cheapest method of increasing yield by 25 to 100% which otherwise is not possible with manuring, irrigation or other agronomical practices. Moreover, he states that the yield of the crop plants depends upon their nectar production and the quantity of nectar produced. It regulates bee visits to the flowers and subsequent occurrence of cross-pollination and the crop yield. In consequence, certain measures have been developed and put to effective use for the cross-pollination of agricultural crops and one such measure is to increase the nectar productivity of entomophilous crop species through a compound of chemical fertilizers and organic manures, as well as developing varieties of nectariferous plants.

Nectar studies of 23 different plants revealed varying sugar concentrations from 14% in *Tecoma grandiflora* 70% in peach and pear (Sharma, 1983) and silver oak (*Grevillea robusta*) with highest record of 79% (Deodikar, 1962). The average sugar concentration of some major nectar plants has been found to vary from 35-52% (Anonymous, 1946-1956).

The availability of nectar and pollen attracts the pollinators. Bees have a sharp instinct for locating nectar and evaluating its quality (Bogoyavlenskii, 1972). Rymashevskii (1972) reported that honey bees prefer to visit flowers with a high sugar content, rather than those secreting more nectar, which thus affects the number of bees visiting different plots in the field. Therefore, to intensify the floral visits of bees, it is important to increase the quality than the quantity of the nectar. However, in contrast to honeybees and bumblebees, the wild solitary bees do not show such a response to the quality or quantity of nectar produced by the flowers they visit.

Sharma (1983) reported that the dominant factors affecting bee visits appear to be nectar abundance, sugar concentration and pollen. Majority of flowers offer nourishment in the form of nectar (carbohydrate) and pollen (protein) and the blossoms achieve the objective of being visited and then fertilized by means of mechanisms ranging from very simple to the highest degree of refinement. In addition, close adaptation between flowers and bees exists with respect to nectar and proboscis. She suggested that for higher crop yield, plant breeders should prefer crop species which attract insects more in competition with other species flowering simultaneously in the vicinity, as honey bees and other insects show a predilection for nectar of higher concentration. Bentley (1983) noted that most work on nectaries in agriculture has been done in the temperate zone on pollination and honey production and tropics are regarded as the last unexploited lands where a very large proportion of the natural vegetation and cultivated crops including the major plantation cash crops as cacao, coffee, etc., as well as the farm crops as pulses, vegetables, fruits, nuts, etc., are pollinated by insects. She further suggested that close attention must be provided to the characteristics of the nectar as also to the biology of the pollinating species and to the effect of pesticide applications. In this respect, extrafloral nectaries can play a role in biological control of crop pests. Ants and other hymenopterans are attracted to extrafloral nectaries and the presence of such predaceous, parasitic or territorial insects can reduce the effects of herbivores on crop species with extrafloral nectaries as in *Gossypium, Passiflora*, etc. (Bentley, 1976; 1977).

It is thus evident that though nectaries play a vital role in relation to agriculture, yet a much wider field remains unexplored, especially in the tropics, with respect to nectar characteristics, biology of pollinators and extrafloral nectaries in relation to biological control of crop pests.

Literature Cited

Adey, M., Walker, P. and Walker, P.T. 1986. *Pest control safe for bees*. International Bee Research Association, U.K. pp.1-149.

Ananthakrishnan, T.N. 1993. The role of thrips in pollination. *Curr. Sci., 65* : 262-264.

Anonymous, 1946-1954. Annual Reports of the Central Bee Keeping Research Station, Punjab and Final Report. ICAR, New Delhi.

Bentley, B.L. 1976. Plants bearing extrafloral nectaries and the associated ant community : Interhabitant differences in the reduction of herbivore damage. *Ecology, 54* : 815-820.

Bentley, B.L. 1977. The protective function of ants visiting the extrafloral nectaries of *Bixa orellana* L. (Bixaceae). *J. Ecol., 65* : 27-38.

Bentley, B.L. 1983. Nectaries in Agriculture with an emphasis on the tropics. In: (eds.) B.L Bentley and T. Elias.*The Biology of Nectaries Columbia University Press, New York. pp. 204-222.*

Bogoyavlenskii, S.G. 1972. Effect of nectar productivity of plants on yield. In: (eds.) Kozin R.B. *Pollination of Entomophilous agricultural crops by bees.* Amerind Publishing Company, New Delhi. pp. 118-124.

Crane, E. and Walker, P. 1983. The impact of pest management on bees and pollination. International Bee Research association, U.K. pp. 1-129.

Deodikar, G.B. 1962. Some aspects of Bee Botany. *Indian bee J., 24* : 3-22.

Elias, T.S. 1983. Extrafloral nectaries : Their structure and distribution. In: (eds.) B.L. Bentley and T. Elias. *The Biology of Nectaries.* Columbia University Press, New York, pp. 174-203.

Janzen, D.H. 1977. Why don't ants visit flowers. *Biotropica, 9* : 251.

Kaker, K.L. 1983. Prospects of bees as pollinating agents of cauliflowers. Proc. 2nd Int. Conf. Apiculture in tropical climates. IARI, New Delhi. pp. 545-556.

Kevan, P.G. and Baker, H.G. 1983. Insects as flower visitors and pollinators. Annu *Rev. Entomol., 28* : 407- 453.

Mathur, G. and Mohan Ram, H.Y. 1978. significance of petal colour in thrips-pollinated *Lantana camara* L.; *Ann. Bot., 42* : 1473-1476.

McGregor, S.E. 1976. *Insect Pollination of Cultivated Crop Plants.* US Govt. Printing Press, Washington, pp. 1-411.

Mel'nichenko, A.N. 1972. Role of insect pollinators in increasing yields of agricultural plants. In : eds. Kozin, R.B. *Pollination of entomophilous agricultural crops by bees.* Amerind Publishing Company, New Delhi. pp. 1-14.

Nesterov, Y.S. 1972. Role of honey bees as pollinators of apple orchards. In: (eds.) R.B. Kozin. *Pollination of entomophilous agricultural crops by bees.* Amerind Publishing Company, New Delhi. pp. 15-18.

Rymashevskii, V.K. 1972. Nectar productivity and plant visitation by bees. In: (eds.) R.B. Kozin *Pollination of entomophilous agricultural crops by bees.* Amerind Publishing Company, New Delhi. pp.114-117.

Sharma, K.K. 1983. Bee Keeping — An aid to productive agriculture. Proc. *2nd Int. Conf. Apiculture in Tropical Climates.* IARI, New Delhi. pp. 622-639.

Stephenson, A.G. 1981. Iridoids deter nectar thieves from the flowers of *Catalpa speciosa. Bull. Ecol. Soc. Amer., 62* : 165.

Subba Reddi, C. and Aluri, R.J.S. 1993. Chemical Ecology of Insect Pollination — An Overview. In: (eds.) T.N. Ananthakrishnan and A. Raman, *Chemical Ecology of Phytophagous Insects.* Oxford & IBH Publishing Co. Pvt. Ltd. New Delhi. pp. 211-225.

Subba Reddi, C. and Meera Bai, G. 1984. Butterflies and pollination biology. *Proc. Indian Acad. Sci., 93* : 391-396.

Townsend, G.F. 1974. Beekeeping and agricultural development. *Wild. Anim. Rev., 12* : 36-40.

Van der Pijl, L. 1954. *Xylocopa* and flowers of the tropics. I. *The bees as pollinators.* Lists of flowers visited. *Proc. Koninkl. Nederl. Akad. van. Wetenschappen (Amsterdam) Series, C 57* : 413-423.

Zavrashvili, R.M. 1972. Role of honeybees as pollinators of citrus flowers. In: (eds.) R.B. Kozin, *Pollination of Entomophilous Agricultural Crops by Bees.* Amerind publishing Company, New Delhi. pp. 86-89.

INDEX